Historically Black Colleges and Universities

Wintergreen/Orchard House, Inc.

New Orleans, Louisiana • Brunswick, Maine

MACMILLAN • USA

Data for this guide was collected by Wintergreen/Orchard House, Inc. of New Orleans, Louisiana, and Brunswick, Maine, a major research and database publishing organization specializing in the field of higher education for over fifty years.

Macmillan General Reference
A Simon & Schuster Macmillan Company
1633 Broadway
New York, NY 10019-6785

Library of Congress Cataloging-in-Publication Data

Historically black colleges and universities / Wintergreen/Orchard
    House, Inc.
        p.   cm.
    Includes index.
    ISBN 0-02-860584-5
    1. Afro-American universities and colleges--Directories. 2. Afro-
    American universities and collegs--Admission.
    I. Wintergreen/Orchard House, Inc.
    L901.H556   1995
    378.73'08996073--dc20
                                                        95-41496
                                                            CIP

Manufactured in the United States of America

10 9 8 7 6 5 4 3 2 1

Contents

Foreword

*by H. Patrick Swygert, J.D.,
President,
Howard University*

The existence of Historically Black Colleges and Universities (HBCUs) is more critical today than in the past, for it is at these institutions that our identity as a people and our ancestors' achievements are illumined, where we explore the "self" and the "other," where, for a brief moment in our lives, we begin the arduous journey in preparing ourselves for survival in a society which is "ours" and, yet, not "ours," where we impart to students the moral imperatives which will sustain and guide them in times of despair and reflection, where we prepare students not only for professions and careers, but to be caring and informed men and women. The time is now for the HBCUs to sustain and, yes, maintain academic programs that foster the development of African-American men and women who are familiar with the world that was and is, and who can discern what their relation to it is.

It is this common thread which courses through the curriculum of the HBCUs, for the curriculum demands and compels the development of men and women who can look at Western civilization, its principles of justice, liberty, government with the consent of the governed, and equality under the law through the critically focused lenses and prisms of the singular African-American experience. This common thread is evident in how we articulate and implement our missions, how we conduct the business of our universities in support of the academic program. HBCUs demand that their students study both the intellectual legacy of the West, the source of the most powerful and pervasive influences on America and all of its people as well as their own legacy as it is refracted through the lenses of the

West, while they examine the legacy of the West as it is refracted through their own cultural identity.

It is a curriculum that ensures that a graduate with a bachelor's degree will be conversant with the best; a curriculum which, expanding on a phrase from Matthew Arnold, has been thought, written, and otherwise expressed about the human condition. In HBCUs, this curriculum reflects what an educated African-American must know.

H. Patrick Swygert, J.D., was recently named president of Howard University in Washington, D.C. Previously, he served as president of SUNY at Albany in Albany, N.Y. Prior to that, he held several positions at Temple University in Philadelphia, Pa., including Executive Vice President, Vice President of University Administration, Special Counsel to the President, Professor of Law, and Acting Dean of the Law School.

A 1965 graduate of Howard University with an A.B. in History, he is also a 1968 graduate of Howard University School of Law.

His many awards and citations include: Outstanding Educator, N.Y. State Black and Puerto Rican Legislative Caucus, 1994; Outstanding Achievement Award, N.Y. State African-American Research Foundation, 1994; Frederick Douglass Society Freedom Fighter Award, Philadelphia, Pa., 1993; Black Law Students of Temple University Appreciation Award, 1988; Howard University Alumni Club of Greater Philadelphia, Outstanding Alumnus Award, 1985.

He has also served as a board member at numerous colleges, commissions, and public service and charitable organizations.

Preface

by Norman C. Francis, LL.D.,
President,
Xavier University of Louisiana

and Antoine Garibaldi, Ph.D.,
Vice President for Academic Affairs,
Xavier University of Louisiana

For more than 135 years, historically Black colleges and universities have quietly but effectively gone about the business of providing quality postsecondary education to all of their students, the majority of whom have been and are African-American. Never discouraged by the less-than-adequate financial and physical resources in their early years, the faculty and staff of our 100+ institutions devoted their untiring efforts to the intellectual and social development of eager, highly able and ambitious students. Thus, the majority of African-American educators, scientists, lawyers, physicians, businesspeople, and many other professionals were trained by this small group of institutions.

That original mission of HBCUs continues today as we graduate 30% of all bachelor's and 15% of all master's degrees awarded to African-American students. Because HBCUs represent only three percent of the nation's 3,600 colleges and universities (and enroll 28% of all African-Americans who attend four-year institutions), our retention and graduation rates, as well as our success in motivating students for future opportunities, are outstanding, though often unheralded. A perfect example of that preparation is demonstrated by the numbers of HBCU graduates who obtain advanced degrees. Approximately one-fourth (23%)—1,069—of the 4,679 African-American doctoral degree recipients between 1989 and 1993 received their undergraduate degrees at HBCUs, and 17 of the top 21 institutions which awarded baccalaureate degrees to those doctoral recipients were also HBCUs.

Still characterized by small classes, enrollments between one and five thousand students, extraordinarily talented African-American students from all across the nation (and the world), high expectations, regular advising by faculty and staff, high standards of academic quality, diverse faculty and staff, and a sense of purpose, historically and traditionally Black colleges and universities are ideal environments for learning, for growing, for sharing, and for achieving. It is for that reason that publications of this kind are so important, as they provide comprehensive information to aspiring students—and to the general public—on the wealth, diversity, and contributions of our institutions to higher education in America. We demonstrate our worth each day as we contribute substantially to the preparation of the 21st Century's corps of leaders and professionals.

Norman C. Francis, LL.D., has been the president of Xavier University of Louisiana for 28 years. Previously, he held a variety of administrative positions at the university, including executive vice president and assistant to the president in charge of development.

Throughout his career, Dr. Francis has served on the board of many educational and business organizations. He is currently the Chairman of the Board for Southern Education in Atlanta and was formerly the chairman of the Member President's Council for the United Negro College Fund.

He earned his undergraduate degree from Xavier in 1952 and a law degree from Loyola University of the South in 1955.

Dr. Antoine Garibaldi is Vice President for Academic Affairs and Professor of Education at Xavier University of Louisiana. He has served as Dean of the College of Arts and Sciences and as Chairman of the Department of Education.

He is the author of ten books and monographs and more than 60 research articles and chapters in scholarly journals and books.

He has been a teacher and administrator in elementary and secondary schools, as well as a researcher at the U.S. Department of Education. He currently serves on more than 20 local, state, and national committees.

He earned his undergraduate degree from Howard University in 1973 and his Ph.D. in Educational and Social Psychology from the University of Minnesota in 1976.

The Role of Historically Black Colleges and Universities

The National Association for Equal Opportunity in Higher Education

The colleges and universities listed in this book are all members of NAFEO, the organization overseeing schools, both public and private, that were founded as Black institutions as well as others whose student population is predominantly Black.

The 1954 Supreme Court decision of <u>Brown v. Board of Education</u> and its progeny focussed the national attention on the dual and unequal primary and secondary education systems nationwide, and spurred two decades of litigation designed to redress the inequalities. The inital debate paid little attention to the inequalities in higher education, nor did it focus on the nation's historically Black colleges and universities as the nation's true equal educational opportunity institutions. In the wake of Brown, NAFEO was founded to provide an international voice for the nation's historically and predominantly Black colleges and universities and to place the issue of equal educational opportunity in higher education and economic equity on the national agenda. Since its inception, NAFEO has effectively done this. It has also served as a clearinghouse for information on Black colleges; as a coordinator of Black higher education; and as a resource for the presidents of the nation's historically and predominantly Black colleges—large and small, public and private, urban and rural, liberal arts, scientific and technological.

Today, NAFEO represents 117 historically and predominantly Black public and private colleges and universities. Most of the NAFEO institutions emerged as the result of the ignominious history of selective exclusion of African-Americans from other higher education institutions and the maintenance of segregated systems of higher education. Unlike white majority institutions, from their inception, HBCUs have been open to people of all races, ethnicities, colors, and religions. They serve a legitimate and unique role in educating racial and ethnic minorities and others who because of socio-economic status might not otherwise get an education. Like the Brandeis, Catholic, Bryn Mawr, Gallaudet, and Brigham Young universities, to name a few, HBCUs serve particular segments of our diverse population.

HBCUs have recruited and enrolled, nurtured and developed the progeny of slaves, and others who might otherwise have been excluded from higher education in other institutions. When predominantly white institutions were admitting students based only on test scores, familial financial largesse, or membership in the right closed fraternity or club, HBCUs were taking, and continue to take, affirmative steps to provide equal educational opportunities to all. NAFEO institutions enroll almost 300,000 students, a disproportionate number of whom come from low-income families. This figure represents less than 20% of African-American students enrolled in higher education institutions. However, NAFEO institutions graduate roughly 30,000 students annually, reflecting in excess of 30% of the total number of African-American students who receive baccalaureate degrees each year; and NAFEO institutions graduate 35% of all African-Americans receiving postsecondary degrees.

Because of the historical and contemporary mission of NAFEO institutions, these institutions have an enhanced role to play in assuring that viable educational opportunities are available to disadvantaged citizens. Toward this end, tuition and fees at HBCUs are generally lower than those of the larger, more affluent institutions. In addition to attracting the best and brightest students—increasingly because HBCUs with their high quality and low tuitions now represent a "best buy" in higher education—HBCUs are by-and-large located in distressed neighborhoods and are accessible to many who are targeted for job training and retooling in the national effort to transition some recipients of public assistance from welfare to work. Most important, perhaps, HBCUs offer a personalized, welcoming, nurturing environment to those whom learning may be a forgotten experience, and a challenging environment to those who are ready to excel.

The recent Supreme Court decision that overturned the University of Maryland's Banneker Scholarship program and the decision of the Regents of the University of California to rescind its equal educational and affirmative action programs signal a new day for NAFEO and a new battle for the believers and protectors of equal educational opportunity and educational equity in America. Both decisions portend the increased need to preserve, enhance, and expand HBCUs so that these institutions can absorb the students of fewer means, racial and ethnic minorities, women, older Americans, veterans, persons with disabilities, socially and economically disadvantaged persons, and others, though protected under the nation's affirmative action laws, who may be turned away from majority higher education institutions in greater number, as retrenchment in educational opportunity and affirmative action enforcement by those institutions proliferates.

Reprinted with permission from NAFEO from "A Celebration of Historically Black Colleges and Universities."

Applying to College

by Karen Clagett, College Guidance Counselor, Winnacunnet High School, Hampton, New Hampshire

A Plan for Applying to College

Freshman and sophomore years (and beyond)

1. Begin by getting to know your teachers and counselors well.

You needn't be teacher's pet or loiter around the Guidance Office, but, let's face it, teachers and counselors are busy people. You need to make the effort so that communication is easier, so you'll be able to ask for help easily. The better others know you, the more they can help you, and, it must be remembered, the more fully they can write about you on recommendation forms. Always ask questions about anything that confuses you in the process of applying to college and try to anticipate problems. For example, an important question would be "Can I take every subject test every time the tests are offered?" The answer is "No." If you want to take an achievement test in German or Hebrew or in a number of other subjects, you need to know on which of the testing dates it will be offered.

2. Be a collector of all information about colleges.

Talk with relatives, friends, alums of your school. Attend college nights and college fairs. Use football games or art shows or plays as an excuse to get on local campuses. Even if you want to attend college far away from home, a visit to a nearby campus can bring such issues as the best campus size, location, and curriculum offerings into perspective for you. Always keep in mind the source of your information; not everyone is objective or shares your concerns. Read newspaper and magazine articles on issues of higher education. Look at campus publications. Learn what resources your guidance office offers—computer software, catalogues, videos, viewbooks. Begin flipping through the pages on specific colleges and universities in this or other guides.

Junior year

If you're reading this as a junior, you just have to work a little harder and more quickly. Don't neglect the suggestions made for the freshman and sophomore years.

1. Make an appointment with your guidance counselor for your parents and you.

You will want to discuss what you must do to improve your preparation for both college and college selection.

2. Get a social security number.

You'll need it to apply for college, financial aid, and jobs.

3. Work conscientiously on your self-assessment.

4. List the college features you value. Consider:

    A. Do you want to go to an historically Black college or university? Most probably, since you have picked up this guide, you are considering an HBCU. This book is designed to illustrate what this small group of schools has to offer and to give prospective students a chance to compare them, one to another.

    B. In what kind of *environment* are you comfortable, challenged?

      • *Size* (small – under 2,500; medium – 2,500 to 8,000; large – 8,000 to 15,000). Do you value individual attention or do you want a vast menu of course offerings? How important is it to you to know many of your fellow students? to have access to faculty? to have a sense of control over your environment? Do you enjoy working with vastly different kinds of people? Is it important to keep an almost family-like atmosphere in your dorm or do you long for autonomy?

- What about *location*? Is this your chance for the big city? Big cities mean excitement, lots of cultural and sports events, job opportunities. They also mean distractions from study and campus life (if indeed there is a campus), noise, and dirt. Do you long for green pastures? Rural environments make outing clubs, ski trips, agricultural study easier. It may also be a long drive to another college for a date. Does suburbia appeal to you? Does being just outside a big city offer the best of both urban and rural environments or not enough of either for you? How close do you want to be to home?

C. Do you want to attend a liberal arts college, a business college, a university, a college for the performing arts, etc.? Might a two-year college be a good match for you? (About half of all entering freshmen begin with this choice.) Have you chosen what you wish to study or do you need the more exploratory approach of liberal arts colleges? Does a core curriculum with course requirements make sense to you or do you want free choice of all classes?

D. Will you consider a *single-sex institution*? What are the advantages and disadvantages of such schools? Because not every student will consider a single-sex college and because about 50% of the student population is ineligible, you may find that you can be a successful applicant at a college with high selectivity. (You might wish to talk with alumni/ae here.)

E. What *sports and other extracurricular activities* do you want to find? At what competitive level are various sports played? Will you be able to compete successfully? Will you be so outstanding that your skills will help your admission's chances? What special programs (such as junior year abroad) are attractive? Do you wish to participate in co-op education where you work and study at the same time? Do internships in government or business interest you?

F. How important is *financial aid*? Are the colleges you are interested in "need-blind"? In other words, can they fund the students they want? How many students receive some kind of aid? Would you like to be involved in a Cooperative Education program that would allow you to work while you attend college? Do the institutions you are considering have such co-op programs in your field of interest?

5. *Make a note of the tests you should take (PSAT [Preliminary SAT I], SAT I, SAT II, ACT, etc.). Note when they will be given so family activities may be planned accordingly.*

Your counselor may have this information and registration details and deadlines already gathered together for you. Be certain to find out from teachers and counselors when it would be best for you to take specific achievement tests. Remember that if you are considering applying for Early Decision or Early Action, you will need to take tests early. Fill out the Student Descriptive Questionnaire on the SAT I form so that you'll be able to receive information from colleges and so that searches by colleges interested in you will find you.

6. *Write away for college catalogues and viewbooks when you become interested in an institution.*

A simple postcard is fine. This is the time to ask for specifics on financial aid or on majors and programs that are of interest to you. Clear out a box or a drawer of your desk and buy file folders for it. Use a folder for each college and for special topics such as "Deadlines" or "Financial Aid."

7. *In the spring, develop a preliminary list of colleges.*

Write or call for information from any that are new to your list. *Think about visiting colleges for viewing and interviewing in the summer*—especially if you are considering colleges that are far from home. Write ahead to schedule interviews—popular colleges become booked early. You won't have much time to spare next year and high schools frown on absences due to college visiting. Visit and interview during the summer between your junior and senior year even if you later decide not to apply.

8. *Consider participation in one of the many summer study programs and locate a summer job if you need to make money to help with college costs.*

Try to make the most of your summer through an interesting job, travel with an academic program, or summer study. This is a chance for you to do something that will distinguish you from the rest.

9. *If you think you may be an Early Decision or Early Action candidate, or if you are graduating early, you must have all required tests completed by the July following your junior year.*

10. *Know your grade point average and class rank.*

Try to get a realistic picture of yourself as a candidate. Have a good talk about this with your college counselor.

Senior year

Let's assume you've followed the calendar to this point. (If not, you need to review the suggestions for earlier years and do some *quick* catching up.)

1. Remember that the first semester of your senior year is seen by many colleges as the most current and best indicator of the type of student you will be in college. You will be busy this semester, *but do not neglect your school work.*

2. In early fall, narrow your list of colleges to between five and ten. Your counselor can help here. Be sure you have application forms and all other materials for each. If you have not visited colleges on the list and it is at all possible to do so without missing too much school, call and make appointments. Call early.

3. Familiarize yourself with all applications and forms. Make a note of all important deadlines (for tests, registrations, applications, interviews, etc.). You will probably have to write at least one essay for each application. Jot down topics and begin to think about ideas. Separate school report forms and teacher recommendation forms from the pile of material you will keep. Give school report forms to your counselor when you have your final list. (Occasionally a university may ask for the whole application to be submitted together, and you will need to take your part to school to be sent with your transcript and recommendations.) Select those teachers who know you and your work best and for whom you have done well, and ask them to complete teacher recommendation forms. Supply teachers with a list of your interests, activities, and accomplishments. Give teachers addressed, stamped envelopes for recommendations. Keep track of who is writing where, and be sure to note deadlines on the recommendations. Send thank-you notes to teachers.

4. Keep track of which colleges will be sending representatives to your school and make arrangements to meet with those from institutions in which you are interested.

5. Through your own thoughts, and discussion with counselors, parents, and others, get your list into final form and begin filling out applications.

How to Complete the Application Process

Standardized Tests You Will Take

The words "SAT scores" loom large in the world of high school juniors and seniors. To a student, the idea of being compared with thousands of others, ranked, and "quantified" is more than scary. The scores sometimes seem a measure of personal worth. Parents can do a great deal to alleviate the counterproductive anxiety that surrounds these tests by understanding this and by refraining from adding, however subtly, to the already considerable pressure.

It may help to know that while standardized tests are taken into account by most admissions offices, they can be low on the list of factors that determine admission. What they do is provide a measure of a student's ability and achievement, but that reading must be given greater dimension by a knowledge of the student's environment and school record. Usually tests are used in conjunction with a student's transcript to determine whether he is an overachiever (low scores, high grades—often good) or an underachiever (high scores, low grades—generally bad). An 800 score on a math SAT I can be damning if you are receiving a D in mathematics. A 500 in the verbal SAT I coupled with a teacher recommendation that points to significant accomplishment and improvement can demonstrate your motivation and grit. This does not mean that a student should not try to do his very best on the exam, for it should be obvious that the best combination is high scores *and* high grades!

You do need to know what tests you will take, when you will take them, and how to prepare for them.

Students are given standardized tests throughout their school careers, but the following tests are specifically related to the college admissions process. For all tests mentioned below, registration materials and sample test questions are available through high school counselors. The tests are listed in the order in which most students will take them.

1. PSAT/NMSQT (Preliminary SAT I/National Merit Scholarship Qualifying Test). This test is given in October of each year. Some students take the test only as juniors. Other students take the test for practice as sophomores. The test functions as a trial run for the SAT I, and junior-year PSAT scores are used as qualification for National Merit Scholarships. Black and Hispanic students can use the test to qualify for other scholarships. The test has verbal and mathematical sections and is largely multiple-choice. There are a few questions in the math section that require students to grid in their own answers. A score page that gives test results helps students interpret their scores and plan for the SAT I.

2. SAT I: The PSAT and SAT I are tests which measure verbal and mathematical reasoning. Comparisons of several selected reading passages will be required. The math sections of the tests will have a few questions that do not offer multiple-choice answers but instead require students to grid in their own answers. You should be sure to carefully read the PSAT and SAT I information booklets that you receive when you register so that you are familiar with the format of the questions.

Beginning with the SAT I given in the spring of 1995, the College Board implemented a new "recentering" policy which has affected SAT I scoring. Test scores reported in this directory pertain to students who took the SAT I in spring 1994 or earlier, and entered college in fall 1994, before "recentered" scores were in effect. If an applicant's test score is critical to his/her qualifying for admission to a particular college or university, he or she should contact the school directly concerning its current admissions requirements.

You will be given an opportunity to fill out the Student Descriptive Questionnaire when you take the SAT I. Completing this will ensure that you receive mail from colleges.

The SAT I. This is given a number of times throughout the year. Your counselor will let you know the dates it will be given at your school or in your area. Most students take the examination in late spring of their junior year and in autumn of their senior year. Some students also take the test early in the junior year for additional preparation. The SAT I is a two-and-one-half-hour, largely multiple-choice exam measuring verbal and mathematical reasoning abilities. Students have to grid in their own answers to a few of the questions in the math section. Vocabulary, verbal reasoning, and comprehension of reading material are tested in the English sections; arithmetic, elementary algebra, and geometry are covered in the math sections. The test is scored on a scale of 200 to 800, and a booklet useful in score interpretation accompanies the results.

3. *The ACT.* This test combines the ability orientation of the SAT I with the accomplishment orientation of the SAT II (formerly called ACH, or achievement test). The ACT measures educational development in English and mathematics. The ACT tests a student's ability to reason and solve problems. It is a multiple-choice examination, and scores are reported on a scale of 1 to 36, 36 being the highest.

4. *SAT II.* If you take the SAT I, you will probably have to take several SAT II subject tests. SAT II tests are given in many disciplines. Some achievement tests evaluate disciplines not generally taught in high schools, e.g., Hebrew. If you have a special area of academic achievement, check for an examination covering it. The tests are one-hour, multiple-choice exams that measure knowledge in such areas as English, foreign languages, the sciences, history, and mathematics. A new opportunity is an SAT II foreign language test given in the fall only. To determine which and how many tests to take, you should consult the catalogues of the colleges in which you are interested for their specific requirements. You should also check with your subject teachers, especially in foreign languages and mathematics, to be certain you are making the best decision. You will need, for example, to decide whether to take Mathematics Level One or Level Two and whether the number of years you have studied a foreign language makes the SAT II test in that discipline a good choice for you. Your guidance or college counselor can also help here. SAT II tests are given more than once a year, and your counselor can advise you as to the appropriate date. However, some tests on certain subject areas are given only *once* a year. Plan ahead. You may wish to take a test in one discipline twice for practice. Often a series of SAT II tests are taken twice. *If you complete a course for which there is an SAT II test—say biology in the 10th grade—you should arrange to take the test as near as possible to the date you completed the course.*

Scores for these tests are reported on the same 200 to 800 scale as the SAT I.

5. *AP* (Advanced Placement). The AP examinations given each year in May allow able students who do well on the tests to receive college credit and/or advanced standing for work done while in high school. The examinations are given in many fields, and a student's school does not have to have an established AP course for students to take the test. While the exams vary from discipline to discipline, most involve both objective and essay sections and are several hours long. The test is scored from 1 to 5, with 5 the highest. Each institution treats the examinations differently, but many will grant college credit for scores from 3 to 5.

6. *TOEFL* (Test of English as a Foreign Language). You will need to take this test if you have been in the U.S. only a few years and if English is not your native language. Consult your counselor for dates and information about this test.

7. *CLEP* (College-Level Exam Program). This series of examinations is designed to test knowledge gained by students through life experience as well as academic study. It involves a series of five examinations on general topics and several on specific subjects. Students and nonstudents interested in finding out more about these tests which allow college credit to those with demonstrated competency should check with the counselor at the nearest high school.

Students are given sample test questions with registration for all of these tests. Don't forget to read through them carefully.

"Can I Prepare for Standardized Tests?"

A conscientious, sustained effort through your school years supplemented by extensive reading is the most effective preparation for a test designed, like the SAT I, to gauge general abilities. Many evaluators of the scores of standardized tests say that the test separates readers from nonreaders, with the scores of readers *significantly* higher.

There are many prep courses for takers of the SAT I. These courses can alleviate anxiety and uncertainty about the test. By introducing you to the format of the test, giving you the basic strategies involved in analyzing and answering the different types of questions, they help to allay fears of the unknown. The drill offered in such courses can increase your speed and facility in dealing with the test through creating a familiarity with its structure and limits.

You can also improve your own skills by a self-directed program of drill, study, and practice testing. The College Board publishes *Taking the SAT I*, given to you when you register for the test. Arco's Test Preparation books provide a complete course of review and reinforcement for all facets of standardized test taking. Learning analytical and study techniques may sharpen your awareness and understanding of the nature and structure of the tests. Sample exams allow you to develop reflexive, automatic skills through repetition and to analyze your strengths and weaknesses through explained answers. See reading list below for relevant titles.

Whether to take a preparation course is a purely personal decision. Do *not*, however, take an SAT I course in place of a school English or other academic course. College admissions officers frown on such tactics.

For the SAT II tests, the ACT, the AP, and the CLEP (all of which examine knowledge rather than ability), methodical, structured review will be very helpful. You will do best by planning out your review over a period of time. This will permit you to cover each phase of the material in some depth. For help in implementing your own study program, see the list below, and don't forget to use the samples given out when you register for the tests.

Reading List:

Following are a number of books published by Arco that cover all facets of the standardized tests taken by college-bound students. They may be ordered from Simon & Schuster, Inc., 201 West 103rd Street, Indianapolis, IN 46290.

Preparation for the SAT—Scholastic Assessment Test, Eleventh Edition, Deptula. *Verbal Workbook for the SAT*, Miller, Morse-Cluley, Freedman, Haller. *Mathematics Workbook for* the *ACT*, Saunders, et al. *American College Testing Program (ACT)*, Twelfth Edition, Levy & Levy. *Verbal Workbook for the ACT*, Lakritz. *Mathematics Workbook for the ACT*, Saunders, et al. *CLEP College-Level Examination Program*, Third Edition, Lieberman, Ph.D., et al, Third Edition. *Advanced Placement Examination in English: Composition and Literature*, Second Edition, Rozakis. *Advanced Placement Examination in Biology*, Heller. *Advanced Placement Examination in Mathematics*, Smith, Griffin. *Advanced Placement Examination in American History*, Second Edition, Crum. *Advanced Placement Examination in Computer Science*, Schulman, Austin, Page. *Advanced Placement Examination in European History*, Levy & Levy.

The Campus Visit and Personal Interview

The interview seems like one of the scariest aspects of the college process. Many students feel shy speaking about themselves or unsure about what questions they should ask. The interview may even come relatively early in the selection process, before you are really set to think about college. It doesn't have to be horrific, however, and may be useful and fun if you follow a few suggestions.

As is said about so much in the college selection process, start early. Otherwise, if you are interested in highly competitive colleges, you may not even obtain an interview. Whenever possible, make arrangements by letter or phone *several months* before you plan to visit. Ask for written confirmation of the arrangements you make. Many colleges will arrange for you to spend a night in the dorms and attend classes if you ask well ahead of your visit. You might wish to ask to speak with a professor in your field of interest or with a coach. Try to get as much as possible of your campus visiting and interviewing done in the summer between junior and senior year. Senior year is a hectic round of academic responsibilities, extracurricular activities, and college application duties. It is hard to do much traveling then. You must also learn your school's policy about absence from classes for visiting colleges. Many schools discourage such absences during the fall of your important senior year. Abide by the rules; adhering to policy will save you and everyone else a lot of hassle. If you visit in the summer and a campus doesn't seem very lively or if you simply want to check it out again, there is the possibility of a return visit. Get started early.

Some colleges seem too far away for a visit. This may be true, but there are a few points you should consider before you give up the idea of a campus visit. First, would you buy a $80,000 car without a test drive? That's what many four-year colleges will cost. Maybe you should get to that campus, somehow. It is extremely difficult to discover the character and personality of an institution without a visit. Second, if it really is impossible to visit, at least arrange for an alumni/ae interview. Most colleges and universities have alums in all areas of the country and will set up an interview for you. Second-hand information is better than none, but do consider whether the alumnus attended the institution recently or is up-to-date about it.

When you make your appointment, find out if the interview will be *evaluative* or *informative*. The first is a part of the admissions selection process and will be used to help determine how good a candidate you are. The second provides an opportunity for you to learn about the institution and is *not* a part of the selection process. You should know how the interview will be used before it begins.

How important is the interview? Well, as you can see, interviews are used differently by different colleges. In general, however, an evaluative interview that goes well will help keep you in the mind of the interviewer when decisions are made in the spring. Often interviews that do not go well are not held against students. Admissions officers are aware of the pressures involved and the natural tendency to be nervous. Still, it is obviously to your advantage to do as well as you can.

How can you have a good interview? Know something about yourself and about the institution before you arrive. Think about your strengths and weaknesses, your accomplishments and interests. Try to present yourself as confident, but not overly aggressive. Ask interesting questions (questions that do not cover material answered in the college's catalogue!). Dress neatly, but don't overdress. Sit up, show you are interested and interesting, and look your interviewer in the eye. This is not the time to hold back; you want to show who you are. Take some initiative. Be sure you mention aspects of yourself and your life you wish to emphasize. Do not try to "psych out" the interviewer and give him what he wants to hear. He is a professional who interviews many students a day during the interview season. He will quickly see through any facade you present. Instead, try to encourage a real conversation. Colleges are looking for students who have a sense of themselves and where they may be heading. Through their selections, college admissions officers must create the community for the college. They need to feel you will contribute to and benefit from their institution so you should consider what makes each college and university you visit unique.

Questions you may encounter at an interview. You might like to practice answering some of these in a mock interview with a friend or parent who can offer an evaluation of the clarity, enthusiasm, and substance of your response.

1. Describe yourself. Do you think others see you as different from the way you see yourself? Why?

2. If you could change something about yourself, what would you change? Why?

3. How would you like to be remembered after you leave your college campus? at the end of your life?

4. What is your most important characteristic? Why?

5. Tell about a book, movie, television program, experience you have read, seen, had recently. Why did it have an impact on you?

6. Whom do you admire? Why?

7. Tell about your family and describe your relationships with family members.

8. What new areas of interest do you want to explore in college?

9. Why do you want to attend an HBCU? What especially attracts you to this institution?

10. What will you miss most when you leave your home and community?

When you go for your visit—Take a tour *before* your interview so that you'll be in a better position to ask questions and understand your interviewer's comments. Try to see as much as possible. Check out student facilities such as sports arenas, dining halls, bookstores, and pubs. Can you imagine yourself in these places? Does the size of the campus seem comfortable? Are the facilities appropriate for pursuing your major interests? Eavesdrop on student conversations, and don't be shy about asking students questions. Most students will be flattered to be asked their opinions. They've been through the visiting process, too. Visit classes if possible. Try to evaluate the atmosphere of the campus. Friendly? Sophisticated? Hard-working? Fun-loving? Use your notebook or folders on colleges in which to record impressions. If your parents and friends are along, discuss impressions but try to do so after you have formed your own.

Other considerations in evaluating a college or university include the availability of internships, foreign study, intercampus exchanges, and independent study. How many students opt for these and how difficult are they to incorporate into a required program? How much flexibility is there in your choice of curriculum? Will you be required to take core courses or are you free to elect all courses? When do you need to decide on a major? Are double majors possible? Interdisciplinary, self-constructed majors? How many classes are you likely to have with under 20 students? over 50 or 75? What is the mix of commuter and residential students? Is the academic year based on semesters? trimesters? What is the geographical and socioeconomic diversity of the student body? What kind of access will you have to computers? labs? studios? Many of these questions will be answered in catalogues. If they are not, they are good questions to ask during your visit.

Arrive on time for your interview and take, if possible, a copy of your school transcript, or at least a record of the courses you have taken. You may also want to provide a list of your activities and interests. While colleges and universities are academic institutions, don't think everything you say has to involve school, reading, or academic achievements. Try to leave a sense of the total you. Record the name of your interviewer. You may wish to follow up with a thank-you note. And, if you have any questions later, or if something special, such as an award, happens to you between application time and when you are notified of the admissions decision, you may want to contact him. Your interviewer of the summer may also arrive at your high school in the fall as the visiting representative from his college, and it would be nice to remember who he is!

Near the end of your interview, it is entirely appropriate for you to ask the interviewer how he sees you as a candidate for admission to his institution. His answer will help you plan more successfully as you make the many decisions ahead.

The Application

Although applications differ from college to college, most consist of: 1) your part (data to be supplied, a personal essay, and the application fee); 2) your high school's part (a secondary report form for grades and information about the school and a mid-year report form to keep you honest and keep you from coasting); 3) a part for teachers' recommendations.

The first section of your part of the application usually asks for specific information on your personal and school life. You may need to include your social security number, your class rank, and your school's College Board code number. Often you must state whether you plan to live on campus, whether you are applying for financial aid, and what your tentative plans for a major and an occupation are. (Colleges don't require you to have your life completely planned, but want to have a sense of how many English majors or pre-med students they may have on campus. Don't feel you have to commit yourself to an area but do indicate any genuine interests.) There is a place to list the names of your parents and siblings. A request is often made for the names of colleges and universities they have attended.

Colleges want the names of all the schools you have attended during your high school years, including summer school. Besides providing a place for the schools' names and addresses, colleges may want you to arrange for a copy of your transcript from *each* institution to be forwarded. Colleges often ask for the names of the teachers who will submit a teacher's recommendation for you, so that if a recommendation is delayed, you and the teacher can be easily notified. There is usually a place for SAT I, ACT, SAT II tests, Advanced Placement Tests, and the Test of English as a Foreign Language (TOEFL) scores. Some colleges will ask whether you have ever been suspended or expelled and provide an opportunity for you to explain the circumstances.

You may often have a chance to list academic and nonacademic honors and to record extracurricular, summer, and employment experiences in this part of the application. The application may ask questions about community service, your travel experience, and your foreign language abilities. Remember, when you have been given the opportunity to include lists of honors, sports teams, or countries visited, do not repeat your lists as part of your essay. Instead, treat one experience or activity in detail.

Institutions are, of course, interested in what you have learned. You may be asked to list books you have read, or to comment on your reading, and/or to evaluate an important educational experience. Colleges want to see that you are an interested and receptive student. Take care with such questions. Think and plan before you answer them.

Finally, you may be asked whether you wish to waive your right under the Family Educational Rights and Privacy Act of 1974 to see interview notes and recommendations should you matriculate.

Each application is somewhat different from all others. The information above should, however, give you an idea of an application's basic elements and prepare the way for the first time you stare at that formal application. The second part of the application you must complete is the personal essay. Not all institutions require an essay, but most do, and it is a very important way of presenting yourself. Because it is so important and because it is often the most intimidating task for students, there is a special article devoted to suggestions on how to write it. See page *xxii*.

A few simple suggestions concerning the whole application procedure are in order here:

1. Apply early. Many colleges and universities make their decisions as student applications are received. You don't want to risk having the freshman class filled when your application is received. Even at institutions that do not use a kind of rolling admission, applications are often read in the order in which they are completed. It is better to be early than late or even just on time!

2. Write your application yourself or type it yourself. Do *not* have it professionally typed. Colleges want to feel that students are willing to take the time and care to do their own applications. The typing skills of your father's secretary do not impress them. Your application should present *you* as clearly and as *personally* as possible. Be certain, of course, that all information is clear, accurate, and complete.

3. Keep standardized test scores. These are often requested. It is also your responsibility to have official scores sent to each college. You can do this when you take the tests or later. It is best to use the spaces provided on the tests and to obtain Additional Report Forms from your counselor only when needed. Remember, you must write your name and address exactly the same way each time you take a test, or your scores will not be combined.

4. Ask teachers well in advance for recommendations. They are time-consuming and a labor of love. Appreciate the work done. Teachers may certainly write one letter of recommendation that is appropriate for a number of colleges and that can be copied and sent to each. It is better to ask the one teacher who knows you best to send off six copies than to ask six different teachers. Supply stamped, addressed envelopes for each recommendation. A list of your activities, accomplishments, and interests is often helpful to the teacher. Be sure to underline or point out the deadline for the submission of each recommendation. Keep a record of who writes which recommendations and send thank-you notes to teachers.

5. You may want to send supporting material—photographs, drawings, tapes—if you are especially talented in one area. Be honest, but not too critical when you assess how helpful these materials may be.

6. Additional recommendations from others, outside of school, who know *you* (not your mom or dad) well may be included, but don't overload.

7. You may be able to use your essay for several applications, but be certain that it is well-suited to each.

8. There is a Common Application that many colleges accept that allows you to take a shortcut and avoid so many different applications. If the colleges to which you are applying also have their own applications, you may want, however, to use the individual applications which are tailored to the institution.

9. If a college to which you are applying does not provide a school report form, you should ask your counselor to send a transcript, school profile, and school letter of recommendation anyway. If a college does not require a teacher recommendation, but you feel that you will have a good one, arrange for a copy to be sent to the college.

A short glossary of terms that pertain to the applications process follows. There is a more extensive glossary for other college terms located on page *xxxix* of this book.

Application Glossary

Deferred Admission. This is a term used to indicate that many colleges will allow an admitted student to postpone matriculation for a year for a number of reasons (financial, to be a foreign exchange student, etc.).

Early Action, Early Notification. The name of an admissions program that allows a candidate who applies by a certain date, usually in the autumn, to receive early notification of the admissions decision. If a student is accepted under an Early Action Program, the student *is not obligated* to attend that institution.

Early Admission. A policy that allows extremely well-qualified students to enter college before graduation from high school.

Early Decision. The name of an admissions program that allows a candidate who applies by a certain date, no later than November 15, to receive notification of the admissions decision soon after December 15. Unlike Early Action, acceptance under Early Decision obligates a student to attend only that institution. Colleges may offer either of two plans: 1) Early Decision, First Choice (EDP–F). Students must withdraw applications from all other colleges as soon as they receive acceptance. 2) Early Decision, Single Choice Plan (EDP–S). Students may not apply to other colleges unless they are rejected.

Early Entrance. This is similar to Early Admission. A student matriculates at an institution before having graduated from high school. This type of admission is reserved for very few, extremely well-qualified students.

Early Evaluation. This provides an opportunity for students who apply by a specified date to be told whether their admission to a particular college is "likely," "not likely," or "possible." Knowing your chances helps in planning whether you will apply to other colleges, to how many others you will apply, and of what degree of selectivity they should be.

Rolling Admission. Under this type of admissions system, colleges and universities admit students at various times in the year depending on the date of application and the qualifications of the student. *When the upcoming freshman class is filled, admissions close.* It is naturally to your advantage to apply early to such institutions.

The Essay

Just how do you show your talent, intelligence, humor, creativity, and writing ability in one short essay? Well, no one will say that it's easy. But college isn't easy either and that is where a good essay will get you. The answer, though not easy, is simple: *You must be courageous enough to be you.*

Why courageous? Most of us feel our lives are too insignificant to appeal to someone else without window dressing. We're tempted to incorporate the thoughts of others, to take on earth-shattering issues—to do anything in short to make us seem better than we think we are. Unfortunately (fortunately?) a college admissions officer isn't interested in the ideas of your parents, counselors, or friends. Nor is he interested in what you think he will want to hear; don't second-guess. He does not need to read another seventeen-year-old's solution to nuclear war. *He wants to get to know the student whose essay is in front of him—you.*

Everyone has in his life the stuff of excellent college essays; the trick is to find it. And, how do you locate this "stuff" and use it to show your best self? By thinking about the specific essay questions posed, by studying all other directions carefully, by reflecting on your own experiences, and by responding in clear, honest, and direct prose.

Essays too often sound exactly the same. Think of your reader. An admissions officer may be faced with fifty application folders to read in a day; certainly he will read thousands before the end of the admissions season. Stay away from traditional treatments of traditional topics; it's hard to grab an admissions officer's attention and interest with the twentieth travelogue of his day, a biography that begins, "I was born . . .," or the hundredth piece he has read in a week on "Why I would like to attend your college."

Instead of listing the countries you visited on a trip abroad or the pavilions at the World's Fair, select one experience that really had an impact on you and explore that experience in depth. Explain how it changed you and why. Don't try to impress, but do try to interest. And one of the best ways of interesting someone else is to be interested in what you are writing yourself.

Your essay is your chance to show who you are. Try to be spontaneous and imaginative. Look for original approaches or viewpoints. For example, a failure that is well-described, has clearly shown your ability to cope, and pinpoints what you have learned from it is really more impressive than a list of ten accomplishments. In fact, problems, difficulties, or fears can often lead to interesting discussions. Think about all that has happened to you in your family, with friends, at school, in activities. Locate turning points in your life, analyze important relationships, consider family crises. Remember your subject should be a vehicle for showing your values and beliefs. Don't be afraid to be personal—that's what it's all about. You want to remain in the mind of your reader as a distinctive individual.

To find the best topic for you, and to write well about it, you will need time. Some can be gained by planning ahead. Some by disciplining yourself to cut out the agony; many students spend hours on the telephone commiserating with friends who are also struggling. This is counterproductive; it wastes valuable time and postpones your thinking about your purpose. To keep the bother to a minimum, start small. Jot down a few possible topics. Try to develop each. Look for the connections and conclusions that can be made. Try out a few paragraphs on what seem the likeliest topics. Remember, with enough time you can scrap one idea for another. Explore. When you are satisfied that your topic is personal, character-revealing, and interesting, write your rough draft. Let it sit for awhile and then try to revise it objectively, but don't water it down to rob it of spontaneity. Be sure to check for spelling errors and other problems with "mechanics." Colleges are not interested in sloppy efforts. Be certain you have followed all directions.

Here is a checklist that you can use to evaluate your essay. You may also want to ask someone else to check your essay against it after reading what you have written.

1. Is this interesting? *Will it stand out because it shows who I really am?* Is it about something that is important to me?

2. Do I analyze, conclude, offer observations, present theories? In other words, *do I show I can think?* Do I get every bit that is possible out of my issue, experience, story?

3. Is my presentation logical? Do I support my contentions?

4. Is there good transition between ideas?

5. Do I have a conclusion rather than a summary at the end?

6. Is all the information relevant? Is everything stated as clearly and effectively as possible?

If you ask for the opinions of others, be certain it is you who do the rewriting and devise solutions to problems. You are ultimately responsible for your essay's vision and revision. Decide whether you will type or write out the final copy. Be as neat as possible. Mail your essay off on time. Take a deep breath and give yourself a hand.

Applying for Financial Aid

When financial aid is an important consideration in your acceptance of a college—and these days it is for just about everyone—please remember to consider that the "award package" (which consists of loans, student work, and scholarships) can vary greatly from college to college. This means that you must consider the award in relation to the cost of each college. You may find that the small expensive college you thought you could never afford is well endowed and can offer you far more aid than a state university, making the smaller college actually cheaper! This is one of the reasons why, though aid or the lack of it may determine your final college decision, you shouldn't allow concerns over money issues to keep you from considering colleges in the beginning. You just have no way of knowing what may happen; hence, work to keep money worries apart from the initial decisions.

Federal Financial Aid—Most federal financial aid is based on your financial need as determined by subtracting what you (and your parents, if you are dependent) can reasonably be expected to contribute toward your educational costs (known as the Expected Family Contribution, or EFC) from the cost of attendance at a specific school. Probably the most important part of this simple-looking formula is the calculation of your EFC. This is done by completing one of several need-analysis forms. The most common is the Free Application for Federal Student Aid (FAFSA), and some colleges may require the supplemental Financial Aid Form (FAF). To find out which form or forms you should use, contact the financial aid office at the school or schools you are considering attending. A college may ask for both the FAFSA and the FAF, and may also ask for its own form to be completed as well.

(The FAFSA and FAF forms are available at your high school.) Once you have the right form(s), fill it (them) out completely and carefully. Errors can cause delays in the financial aid process.

Although these forms ask many different questions, the most important ones relate to income, and require specific information directly from your or your parents' federal tax returns. After you have completed the form, mail it as soon as possible—deadlines are important throughout the entire financial aid process! You should try to apply for financial aid in January or February preceding the academic year you plan to enter college, but you may apply at any time. Be sure to make a photocopy of your application and have copies ready of any of the documents you used to complete your application, in the event your financial aid administrator requests them. Do *not* send them with your application.

If you or your family have special circumstances that are not covered by the questions on the form, be sure to explain those circumstances fully and clearly in the appropriate section and provide a separate statement directly to the financial aid administrator of each college. He or she will then be able to make a much more accurate assessment of your need for financial aid. Note that all information used in determining need will be kept confidential by the financial aid office.

While all the details of applying for student financial aid seem to be a bother, the rewards—in terms of the assistance you receive—can be great. If you read and follow all application instructions, meet deadlines, and provide additional documentation when necessary, the application process is easier than it may first appear. However, don't get lazy and assume that your financial aid is taking care of itself. The result can be disastrous. When you have any doubts or questions, contact a professional financial aid administrator at any college for assistance. He or she will be happy to help you.

If you do not think you will be eligible for aid, you might still want to fill out the FAFSA. Now there are federal, low-interest loans available to *all* families *regardless* of income.

State Financial Aid—After federal aid, the second most commonly known type of assistance comes from your state. Generally, you must be a resident of the state in which you are enrolled in school to qualify for these funds; however, some states have reciprocal agreements which allow you to use the funds outside your home state. To inquire about this, as well as how to apply, you need to contact the appropriate agency for your state.

Merit Scholarships—While many colleges do earmark the largest percentage of scholarship money to needy students, merit scholarships are having a resurgence. Greater competition among colleges means that some are trying to attract good candidates through financial incentives. If you are a good student, be sure to inquire about the possibility of merit scholarships at each of the institutions to which you apply.

Co-op Education—Check out the possibility of entering a co-op (cooperative education) program. Schools that have such programs, and there are many, allow you to work while you study. The financial and career benefits are great, though you may need some extra time to earn your degree. Read the section on Cooperative Education below.

Local and Employment-Related Awards—Almost every community, service organization, and large company has special scholarships available. Check with your school counselor, employers (yours, your parents'), personnel offices, churches, etc. Look in your local newspapers for announcements of application dates for community scholarships and competitions.

Minority Scholarships—In addition to the above-mentioned awards, available to qualified applicants regardless of ethnicity, many states, schools, and local organizations have funds earmarked for members of minority groups. There are also many professional societies offering aid to Black students in a particular area of study. Two broader scholarship programs do deserve mention here:

- The United Negro College Fund (UNCF) provides financial assistance to students enrolled at its member institutions—40 private HBCUs included in this book, as well as the Interdenominational Theological Center in Atlanta, Georgia. See page *xxxi* for complete listing of UNCF member institutions. For more information, contact:

  The College Fund/UNCF
  500 East 62nd Street
  New York, NY 10021
  (212) 326-1100

- The National Association for the Advancement of Colored People (NAACP) offers scholarships to members studying in a variety of disciplines. For more information about individual scholarships and eligibility, contact:

  NAACP
  4805 Mount Hope Drive
  Baltimore, MD 21215-3297
  (410) 358-8900

Private Sources of Financial Aid—The merit, local, and employment-related awards mentioned above are really a part of this broader category of student financial aid. Because individual programs are too numerous to mention, we will simply point you in the right direction so that you may research these alternative sources of assistance if you wish. While there are firms that will do this type of research for you (for a fee), you will generally have as great a success or better by going to the public library and doing the work yourself. You will find many reference books that list these private sources. You need to determine the specific programs for which you may qualify, request any application materials, and complete them accurately within required deadlines. Funds from these sources may generally be used in combination with any aid you receive from state or federal sources, or may be an alternative if you do not qualify for need-based financial aid. Like any research project, searching for these funds is time-consuming, but the payoff can be just what it takes to cover any remaining need you have that is not met by aid from another source.

While financial aid is intended to help you cover your educational costs, remember that the government still maintains that the primary responsibility to pay for an education lies with the student and family. If you find that all of your need has not been met, review what you feel you and your family can contribute to be certain you have planned to contribute your full share. Check with banks and other financial institutions to see if they offer plans for borrowing for college. If a gap still exists, contact the college of your choice. Some help may be available. Once you matriculate, changing financial situations can usually be accommodated; once an institution has invested time and money in you, it wants to keep you. Help may involve a regular payment plan, or counseling to take fewer courses to reduce your costs. After all, "sticking it out" is better than wasting the time you've already invested. So, be a good student aid consumer, seek help when you have problems, and financial aid will help you achieve your educational goals.

Additional Reading: *College Scholarships and Financial Aid*, John Schwartz and Wintergreen/Orchard House Inc., (ARCO).

Cooperative Education: Financial Aid Alternative

When financial aid is not enough to pay spiraling college costs, an important option you should consider is using a cooperative education program. In fact, because the advantages of "co-op education" go well beyond allowing you to finance your college education while receiving it, students for whom financial considerations are not a factor might also do well to participate in a co-op.

Cooperative education is the name given to a variety of plans in 900 colleges and universities in the United States and Canada which allow students to integrate academic study with work experience. Students have the opportunity while still in college to earn money, test career options, gain work experience, and participate fully in the "working world." Institutions offering co-op plans vary in admissions selectivity and include both four-year and two-year colleges. Cooperative programs can be found in the fields of agriculture, arts, business, computer sciences, education, engineering, health professions, home economics, humanities, natural sciences, social and behavioral sciences, technologies, and vocational arts. Not all participating colleges and universities offer co-op in all fields, however, so you should ask about the possibility of combining work and study in your areas of interest when you make preliminary inquiries.

Some institutions offer parallel study and work programs while others alternate several months of classes with work opportunities. Student commitments to athletics and other interests can often be accommodated by local placements. There is usually a chance for several different placements during your college career should you wish to experiment with career possibilities. Campus Cooperative Education Coordinators help locate positions, provide counseling, and monitor student performance.

The National Commission for Cooperative Education offers a sampling of previous co-op assignments: library assistant at the Library of Congress, copy person at the *New York Times*, shuttle resources assistant for NASA, physical therapy aide at a Denver hospital, assistant to the General Director of Banque Franco-Portugaise in Paris, accounting assistant for Arthur Andersen & Company, traffic analyst for Continental Forest Industries, programmer for an observatory in Northern Ireland, nursing assistant at Johns Hopkins, and industrial engineering analyst. Even such a short list suggests the great variety of opportunities, here and abroad, and the potential for valuable entrees into professional fields.

Some 200,000 students are now a part of cooperative education programs with a combined wage of one billion dollars a year. Statistics on career decisions and job placement for co-op students are impressive. According to the Commission for Co-op Education, 40 percent of students continue to work for their co-op employers after graduation, 40 percent upon graduation find work in their field of interest, and 15 percent decide to remain in school to earn professional degrees.

For free information concerning co-op education and a comprehensive list of participating colleges and universities including the areas in which each institution participates in co-op, write The National Commission for Cooperative Education, 360 Huntington Avenue, Boston, Massachusetts 02115.

After Acceptance

Notices of acceptance may arrive as early as the autumn of your senior year if you apply to some colleges with rolling admissions, or as late as the summer after graduation if you are admitted from a college's wait list. A few extremely well-qualified and mature students may even be admitted a year early (Early Acceptance). In general, however, here's what to expect.

If you are an Early Decision (E.D.) candidate or an Early Action (E.A.) candidate who has submitted an application by December 1, you should hear from the college in the third or fourth week of December. (A few colleges have a second, slightly later E.D. date. If you apply later, of course, you will be notified of the admissions decision later.) If you are admitted as an E.D. candidate, you are obligated to attend that college unless financial aid is insufficient, and you may wish to send your deposit as soon as possible so you can sit back and relax (about admission, not about school, for your record throughout your senior year will be reported to the college and should be consistent with your earlier record). If you are accepted as an E.A. candidate, you are free to apply to other colleges and are under no obligation to make an immediate response in order to save your place. You may find that your application has been deferred for consideration with the regular admissions pool later in the spring. While this is disappointing, be assured that your desire to attend that college has been made clear by your choice to apply E.D. or E.A., and that knowledge of this desire will certainly not hurt you.

A rolling admissions candidate may hear almost anytime during the senior year, depending on the date of the submission of the application. A few colleges even offer the option of immediate acceptance based on interview or audition. Most candidates for regular admissions, however, will receive notification from colleges in March and April.

Whenever you are accepted, you need to know that *colleges have agreed to abide by the Candidate's Reply Date of May 1*. This means that you should not have to respond to an offer of admission until you have heard from all colleges or universities to which you have applied or by May 1, whichever comes earlier. *Important*: If you receive pressure from colleges for a decision before you have heard from all of those to which you applied, tactfully remind them of this policy. Athletes and other students whose abilities and talents make them prime candidates may receive this kind of pressure from coaches or admissions offices. If the college or university is unwilling to cooperate, contact your school counselor for help and ask him to notify the president of your state or regional Association of College Admission Counselors.

Wait lists. You may find that a college is not able immediately to offer you a place, but puts your name on a "wait list." These lists are used when students who have received an offer of admission decline that offer and a position in the freshman class is thus open. If you are "wait listed" and do not hear from that college by May 1, you must accept another offer and send a deposit. If you are then notified of an opening from the wait list, you may change your mind, but will have to forfeit your deposit.

Be considerate. Once you have made your decision, notify all colleges and universities *immediately*. If you accept one offer and turn down four, four places at colleges will be available to others. If someone else is considerate, you may get a place from a wait list even before May 1.

Visits. In the period between mailing out decisions and May 1, many colleges sponsor days on campus to bring students to the college for one final look. If you are at all undecided, take advantage of this opportunity, and if no formal visiting day exists, ask to visit on your own. Making your final decision is obviously important; go about it wisely.

Financial aid. Occasionally you will be notified of acceptance before the financial aid packages are finished. If you do not have all the financial aid information that you need in order to make a decision, notify those colleges in which you are most interested that you need more time. Getting more time is usually not a problem. If the financial aid offer from the college you are most interested in is not what you feel you need, it might be worth asking for a reconsideration. You may not get it, but if you do and it enables you to attend that college, the letter will be worth it.

All acceptances are conditional. They depend on your continuing to produce the work and show the maturity that earned you that acceptance. Your high school will be asked to make reports during your senior year and is under a moral obligation to report any serious problems that arise. Forewarned is forearmed.

Karen Clagett has taught English at public and private secondary schools in the U.S. and abroad. She is a former Lecturer in English at Boston College. Now a college counselor in New Hampshire, she has written on various issues related to college admissions.

Sources of Information on Financial Aid: U.S. Dept. of Education Regional Offices

Region I
Connecticut, Maine, Massachusetts, New Hampshire, Rhode Island, Vermont

U.S. Dept. of Education
Office of Student Financial Assistance
J.W. McCormack Post Office and Courthouse Building, Room 502
Boston, MA 02109
(617) 223-9338

Region II
New Jersey, New York, Puerto Rico, Virgin Islands, Panama Canal Zone

U.S. Dept. of Education
Office of Student Financial Assistance
26 Federal Plaza, Room 3954
New York, NY 10278
(212) 264-4426

Region III
Delaware, District of Columbia, Maryland, Pennsylvania, Virginia, West Virginia

U.S. Dept. of Education
Office of Student Financial Assistance
3535 Market Street, Room 16200
Philadelphia, PA 19104
(215) 596-0247

Region IV
Alabama, Florida, Georgia, Kentucky, Mississippi, North Carolina, South Carolina, Tennessee

U.S. Dept. of Education
Office of Student Financial Assistance
101 Marietta Tower, Suite 323
Atlanta, GA 30323
(404) 331–2502

Region V
Illinois, Indiana, Michigan, Minnesota, Ohio, Wisconsin

U.S. Dept. of Education
Office of Student Financial Assistance
401 South State Street, 12th Floor, Room 700D
Chicago, IL 60605
(312) 353-8103

Region VI
Arkansas, Louisiana, New Mexico, Oklahoma, Texas

U.S. Dept. of Education
Office of Student Financial Assistance
1200 Main Tower, Room 2150
Dallas, TX 75202
(214) 767-3811

Region VII
Iowa, Kansas, Missouri, Nebraska

U.S. Dept. of Education
Office of Student Financial Assistance
10220 N. Executive Hills Boulevard, 9th Floor
Kansas City, MO 64153
(816) 891-8055

Region VIII
Colorado, Montana, North Dakota, South Dakota, Utah, Wyoming

U.S. Dept. of Education
Office of Student Financial Assistance
1244 Speer Boulevard, Suite 310
Denver, CO 80204
(303) 844-3676

Region IX
Arizona, California, Hawaii, Nevada, American Samoa, Guam, Federated States of Micronesia, Marshall Islands, Republic of Palau, Wake Island

U.S. Dept. of Education
Office of Student Financial Assistance
50 United Nations Plaza
San Francisco, CA 94102
(415) 556-1630

Region X
Alaska, Idaho, Oregon, Washington

U.S. Dept. of Education
Office of Student Financial Assistance
915 Second Avenue, Room 3388
Seattle, WA 98174
(206) 220-7813

UNCF Member Institutions

Barber-Scotia College, NC

Benedict College, SC

Bennett College, NC

Bethune-Cookman College, FL

Claflin College, SC

Clark Atlanta University, GA

Dillard University, LA

Edward Waters College, FL

Fisk University, TN

Florida Memorial College, FL

Huston-Tillotson College, TX

Interdenominational Theological Center, GA

Jarvis Christian College, TX

Johnson C. Smith University, NC

Knoxville College, TN

Lane College, TN

LeMoyne-Owen College, TN

Livingstone College, NC

Miles College, AL

Morehouse College, GA

Morgan State University, MD

Morris Brown College, GA

Morris College, SC

Oakwood College, AL

Paine College, GA

Paul Quinn College, TX

Philander Smith College, AR

Rust College, MS

Saint Augustine's College, NC

Saint Paul's College, VA

Shaw University, NC

Spelman College, GA

Stillman College, AL

Talladega College, AL

Texas College, TX

Tougaloo College, MS

Tuskegee University, AL

Virginia Union University, VA

Voorhees College, SC

Wilberforce University, OH

Wiley College, TX

Xavier University of Louisiana, LA

How to Use This Book

Organization of This Book

High school students looking toward college are faced with a maze of choices. The purpose of Arco's *Historically Black Colleges and Universities* is to help those who are considering such an institution by providing current data on each of the HBCUs in a standard format that allows for easy comparison.

In addition to helping choose a particular school, *Historically Black Colleges and Univeristies* has several other useful sections. One section includes forewords by two prominent Black educators, followed by a statement from NAFEO, the organization that oversees all of the HBCUs.

Another section describes the step-by-step procedure for applying to a college or university, including advice concerning the application, the essay, and the personal interview. Also mentioned in this section is a brief overview of the financial aid process and sources of information on aid. To help with the specialized terminology of higher education, the book also includes a Glossary and a list of Abbreviations.

At the end of the book is a general index showing the ranges of costs, enrollments, and test scores at each college, along with its religious affiliation, and whether it has a Phi Beta Kappa chapter and/or ROTC military training.

The heart of *Historically Black Colleges and Universities* is the college entries, which cover more than 90 accredited four-year, bachelor's degree-granting colleges and universities in the United States. Information provided in each entry is described in the sections titled "The Capsule" and "The Entry." After the full school listings are a group of names and addresses of NAFEO-member schools which offer only associate or graduate degree programs or which did not respond to information requests.

The Capsule

The capsule (sample on following page) is both a preview of what is developed more fully in the entry and a compilation of all the essential data the reader is likely to want at a glance.

School Name, Address, Telephone Number
The school name, address, and general telephone number are prominently displayed in the shaded region for easy reference.

Undergraduate Profile
Listed here are the percentages of students who are members of various ethnic/racial groups, followed by the percentages of state residents and transfers, and then the average age of undergraduates.

Enrollment
The number of full-time undergraduates is listed. These numbers are also broken down by gender to indicate whether the institution is coeducational or a women's or men's college.

This section also provides statistics on freshman enrollment, listing the number of applicants for admission, the number accepted, and the number who chose to enroll.

Faculty
This entry lists the numbers of both full-time and part-time faculty members employed by the institution. Next is the ethnic/racial distribution of faculty members. The percentage of

faculty members who have earned doctorates follows; some institutions choose to provide the percentage of faculty who have earned the highest degree in their field as an alternative. The current student/faculty ratio is then listed.

Test Scores

For institutions that use SAT I scores in their admissions process, average scores for the verbal and math sections and/or a range of scores for the middle 50% of freshmen are provided. For those that request ACT scores, averages are given for the English and math components and a composite score is generally provided; as in the case of SAT I scores, the range of scores for the middle 50% of freshmen is sometimes provided. Some institutions accept, and provide data for, both SAT I and ACT scores. Other institutions, including those that do not rely on SAT I or ACT scores in making admissions determinations, do not provide any information; these are designated as *N/A*.

Costs

First, the tuition for the upcoming academic year is given. For institutions that charge tuition by the credit hour rather than for the year or semester, the cost has been calculated at 30 credit hours per year to reflect the average full-time course load. For institutions that have different tuition rates for state residents and out-of-state students, both figures are provided. For those that had not determined their tuition for the 1995-96 academic year by the deadline of this book, tuition for 1994-95 is given.

Second, housing costs are given. At institutions where housing costs vary, the figures appear as a range.

Next are board costs. As with housing, the figures given are sometimes a range of costs.

Last are fees, books, and miscellaneous academic expenses. This figure comprises such costs as activities and library fees and charges for use of athletic and other facilities. Travel costs are not included.

Name of School

City, State, Zip Code   Telephone Number

Undergraduate profile. The percentages of Black, Other Minority, and White students; the percentage of state residents; percentage of transfers; the average age of undergraduates.

Enrollment. The number of full-time undergraduates; the size of the freshman class, with the number of applicants, the number accepted, and the number who chose to attend; and the number of graduate students enrolled.

Faculty. The number of full-time and part-time faculty members; the ethnic/racial distribution of faculty members; the percentage of faculty who hold a doctoral degree or the highest degree in their field; and the student/faculty ratio.

Test score averages/ranges. Average SAT I scores, SAT I scores of the middle 50%, average ACT scores, and/or ACT scores of the middle 50% of enrolled freshmen.

1995-96 Costs. The full-time tuition (for in-state and out-of-state students, if applicable); the room and board costs; and fees, books, and miscellaneous academic expenses.

The Entry

The entry for each institution is written in a standardized format for the reader's convenience in locating data and comparing colleges. Each entry begins with a ***Profile*** and continues with major sections entitled ***Student Body***, ***Programs of Study***, ***Student Life***, ***Ath-***

letics, **Admissions**, **Financial Aid**, **Student Employment**, **Computer Facilities**, **Graduate Career Data**, and **Prominent Alumni/ae**. If an institution has supplied no information for a particular subsection of these sections, that subsection heading has been omitted.

PROFILE

Each profile provides an overview of the college or university, including such information as background on the founding and history of the institution, noting whether the schools is an HBCU, its academic organization and religious orientation, and relevant name changes. The profile also contains information on whether an institution is single-sex or not, whether control is public or private, and whether the institution emphasizes the liberal arts and sciences, business, or fine arts; and it may provide additional information, including campus size and a description of its architecture, its prominent buildings, the type of neighborhood in which it is located, and its proximity to landmarks and large cities.

Accreditation. Each of the colleges and universities described in the book has been granted accreditation by one of the following national and/or regional accreditation agencies, all members of the American Council on Education for the Commission on Recognition of Postsecondary Accreditation (CORPA):

Assn. of Independent Schools and Colleges
Middle States Assn. of Colleges and Schools
New England Assn. of Schools and Colleges
North Central Assn. of Colleges and Schools
Northwest Assn. of Schools and Colleges
Southern Assn. of Colleges and Schools
Western Assn. of Schools and Colleges

Religious orientation. If a college is sponsored or governed by a religious organization, its affiliation is described here. Institutions that are nondenominational are listed as such.

Library. This section indicates the number of volumes, periodical subscriptions, microform items, and CD-ROMs in the institution's library.

Special facilities/museums. Noteworthy scientific, educational, cultural, and entertainment facilities operated by the institution are listed here.

Athletic facilities. This section lists both intercollegiate and intramural sports and recreation facilities, from bowling alleys to football fields.

STUDENT BODY

The Student Body section's freshman profile, the academic achievement and foreign student subsections, together with the undergraduate profile in the capsule, describe the students enrolled at an institution.

Freshman profile. This lists the percentages and scores of freshmen who took SAT I or ACT tests and the percentage of freshmen from public schools.

Undergraduate achievement. This section gives the percentage of freshmen who returned for the fall semester following their freshman year, the percentage of the entering class who graduate, and the percentage of graduates who go on to graduate study.

Foreign students. Here, the number of students from outside the U.S. is given; a list or number of countries represented by the foreign student body also may be given.

PROGRAMS OF STUDY

The Programs of Study section describes an institution's academic offerings by listing its undergraduate degrees and majors, most popular programs, academic requirements and regulations, special programs, honor societies, and remedial services.

Degrees. Bachelor's degrees granted by the institution are listed.

Majors. This is a complete list of the institution's undergraduate majors. Majors are presented in alphabetical order and are listed as closely as possible to the way they are named by the colleges.

Distribution of degrees. The majors with the highest enrollments are listed in descending order; when available, the programs with the lowest enrollments are also listed.

Academic regulations. If an institution has established a minimum academic performance level, it is described in this subsection. This generally includes the minimum GPA required to remain in good standing.

Special. Since the range of special programs available through American institutions of higher education is extremely broad, this is the most inclusive subsection in most entries.

Minors are often noted, as well as many courses of study offered in areas other than those of major programs. The availability of associate degrees, self-designed majors, double majors, dual degrees, independent and accelerated study, pass/fail grading option, internships, and cooperative education programs is also noted.

Preprofessional programs, programs of cooperative study (programs wherein course work is taken at two institutions for completion of degree study) and dual-degree programs are listed in this subsection. Also noted is the availability of teacher certification in early childhood, elementary, secondary, vo-tech, bilingual/bicultural, and special education and in special subject areas.

Also listed are semester-away and study-abroad programs, as well as cooperative programs with foreign institutions. ROTC, AFROTC, and NROTC programs are noted as well.

Honors. The availability of Phi Beta Kappa, honors programs, and academic honor societies appears.

Academic assistance. The availability of academic assistance services such as tutoring and learning centers is listed.

STUDENT LIFE

The Student Life section surveys a college's social and extracurricular activities through descriptions of its housing, social atmosphere, student services programs, campus organizations, religious organizations, and minority/foreign student organizations.

Housing. The housing subsection describes the type of facilities available and specifies any rules concerning who must live on campus. Also included is the percentage of the student population who live in college housing.

Social atmosphere. To sample the social atmosphere of colleges, a student representative from each institution was asked to describe campus social life. These comments mention on-campus and off-campus student gathering spots, the groups and organizations that have widespread influence on social life, and the popular sports and entertainment events on campus. General comments on the college's social and cultural life are also given.

Services and counseling/handicapped student services. Listed here are psychological, career, and academic counseling services; testing services; reader services for the blind; hearing-impaired student services; and many other student services.

Campus organizations. This subsection lists extracurricular activities, including newspapers and literary magazines, ethnic organizations, musical groups and ensembles, departmental and special-interest groups, and student government. Also noted is the availability of national fraternities and sororities and the percentage of students who join a Greek organization.

Religious organizations. Lists the religious organizations operating on campus.

Foreign student organizations. Organizations on campus serving foreign students are listed.

ATHLETICS
This section lists the intercollegiate, intramural, and club sports available to students and indicates whether intercollegiate and club sports are offered to men and/or women. Also listed are percentages of students participating in intercollegiate and intramural sports, as well as intercollegiate sports associations. In addition, any physical education requirements are described.

ADMISSIONS
This section describes basic admissions information, such as deadlines and criteria for filing, special admissions programs, admissions procedures for transfer students, and specific requirements for admission.

Academic basis for candidate selection. Presented in order of priority are specific indicators of academic performance that each college uses to judge its applicants. Such indicators generally include the student's secondary school record; class rank; the secondary school's recommendation; SAT I, ACT, or SAT II scores; and the essay.

Nonacademic basis for candidate selection. Listed here are the often intangible elements a college considers in its admissions process. These elements normally include qualities such as character and personality, extracurricular participation, alumni/ae relationship, geographical distribution, and talent and ability.

Requirements. This section describes specific requirements for admission, including the number of units the secondary school student must present as well as the distribution by subject, if applicable. Also included are the standardized tests a student must take to be considered for admission.

Procedure. This entry details when a student should submit the appropriate paperwork and fees to be considered for admission and notes the dates by which admission notices are sent and by which students must reply. The availability of admissions for terms other than fall is also mentioned.

Special programs. Listed here are such options as admission deferral, advanced placement and credit programs, and the college's participation in early decision, early admissions, and concurrent enrollment programs.

Transfer students. Information provided for transfer students includes the academic terms during which transfers may be accepted and the percentage of new students who were transfers in the most recent year of recorded figures. Also listed are the number of transfer applications received and accepted, the minimum GPA required, the lowest course grade accepted for credit, the maximum allowable number of transferable credits, and the minimum number of new credits required to graduate.

Admissions Contact. This is the name and phone number of the person applicants must contact for admissions information.

FINANCIAL AID
The statistical picture of an institution's financial aid is presented in this section.

Available aid. The types of scholarships, grants and loans, and payment plans available to students are listed.

Financial aid statistics. Noted are the percentages of freshmen and of all undergraduates who received aid in the most recent year of recorded statistics. The range of aid available and the average amount awarded also may be listed.

Supporting data/closing dates. Any forms needed to apply for financial aid (such as FAFSA) are listed here, as well as priority and deadline dates.

Financial aid contact. The chief financial aid officer of the institution is listed as the contact person.

STUDENT EMPLOYMENT

This section includes such information as the availability of Federal Work/Study and institutional employment, the average amount a student may expect to earn through on-campus employment, the percentage of full-time undergraduates who work during the school year, and a rating of the off-campus employment opportunities ("excellent," "good," "fair," "poor").

COMPUTER FACILITIES

This section describes the primary types of computer equipment available to students, along with types of local and wide area networks students may access. Also listed are availability of computer facilities in residence halls, any restrictions imposed on student access to computers, hours computers may be used, and any fees charged for computer use.

GRADUATE CAREER DATA

Information included in the graduate career section may include the percentage of graduates who enter graduate school, the percentages who enter various types of graduate schools (e.g., law, medicine, business), and a list of the graduate schools that have enrolled the highest numbers of the college's graduates.

PROMINENT ALUMNI/AE

Listed here are both contemporary and historically significant alumni/ae, along with their fields of endeavor.

Glossary

Academic unit. One year of study of one academic subject in secondary school.

Accelerated study. Completion of a college program of study in fewer than the usual number of years, most often by attending summer sessions and carrying extra courses during regular academic terms.

Accreditation. Formal approval granted for meeting certain standards of quality. Colleges and universities listed in this book are accredited by one of six regional accrediting boards. In addition, specific academic programs may be accredited by a professional association.

ACCSCT (Accrediting Commission for Career Schools/Colleges of Technology). A national accrediting agency of vocational-technical institutions.

ACT (American College Testing Program). The American College Testing Program's standardized test battery for secondary school students, used by colleges and universities for admissions and placement purposes.

Advanced Placement. Waiver of introductory courses and placement in higher-level courses for students who demonstrate knowledge in a given subject. Some colleges administer their own placement exams to entering freshmen, and many evaluate the CEEB Advanced Placement exams, the CLEP exams, and other standardized tests for placement purposes.

AFROTC (Air Force Reserve Officers' Training Corps). The United States Air Force's college-based training program.

Associate degree. A degree granted upon completion of a two-year program of study.

Baccalaureate/bachelor's degree. A degree granted upon completion of a four-year program of study.

Calendar. The system an institution uses to organize its academic year.

CEEB (College Entrance Examination Board). The agency that administers the SAT I, SAT II, and CEEB Advanced Placement exams. Also referred to as the College Board.

Class rank. The relative position of a student in his or her graduating class, calculated according to grade point average.

CLEP (College-Level Examination Program). General and subject exams administered by the CEEB, for students with nontraditional learning such as work experience, independent reading, or correspondence courses. Many colleges award advanced placement and/or degree credit based on CLEP results.

Concurrent enrollment. A program enabling secondary school students to attend a nearby college part-time while completing secondary school.

Consortium. An arrangement between colleges for the sharing of faculties, facilities, and programs.

Cooperative education. A program in which a student alternates terms of academic study with terms of employment, often in a job related to the student's major field. Most cooperative education programs take five years to complete a bachelor's degree. Also called "Cooperative Work/Study."

Cross-registration. A system whereby students enrolled at one institution may take courses at another institution without having to apply to the second institution.

DANTES (Defense Activity for Non-Traditional Educational Support). A test used to grant college-level credit or advanced placement.

Deferred admission. A practice of allowing an accepted candidate to postpone enrollment in a college, generally for a period of an academic term or year.

Double major. A program of study in which a student completes the requirements of two majors at the same time.

Dual degree. A program of study in which a student receives two degrees from the same institution.

Early admission. A program allowing well-qualified high school students to enter college full-time before completing secondary school.

Early decision. Notification of acceptance into college early in the applicant's 12th year of secondary school. Some colleges stipulate that a student must withdraw all other college applications if accepted under early decision. Others require that the student apply only to that institution.

Eligibility index. A number calculated from secondary school GPA and SAT I or ACT scores; used by California state colleges and universities for admissions purposes.

EOP (Educational Opportunity Program). An academic and economic support program.

ESL (English as a Second Language). A course of study designed specifically for students whose native language is not English. Also see TESOL.

FAF (Financial Aid Form). The College Board's College Scholarship Service form, supplemental to the FAFSA.

FAFSA (Free Application for Federal Student Aid). The federal form used to determine eligibility for federal aid, including Pell Grants and student loans. It establishes a single estimate of a student's or family's ability to pay and is generally available from high school guidance offices.

Federal Work/Study Program. A federally subsidized part-time employment program. Students work on or off campus throughout the academic year, frequently in positions relating to their educational goals.

4-1-4. An academic calendar consisting of two long semesters separated by a short (generally month-long) intersession for nontraditional study programs.

GED (General Educational Development Test). A high school equivalency exam accepted by many colleges in lieu of a secondary school diploma.

General education requirement. The group of courses required of all students regardless of their particular majors. General education courses usually include a range of arts and sciences.

GPA (Grade Point Average). The translation of a student's letter grades into a numeric system reflecting academic performance. The most common system counts four points for an "A," three points for a "B," two points for a "C," one point for a "D," and no points for an "F."

GRE (Graduate Record Examination). A standardized test battery of general and subject exams designed for college graduates interested in applying to graduate school. Administered by the Educational Testing Service.

Guaranteed Tuition Rate. An agreement by a college to charge the student the same tuition each year of attendance as was charged during the student's freshman year.

HEOP (Higher Education Opportunity Program). A New York State admissions program for applicants not normally admissible due to economic or academic disadvantages.

Honors program. An enriched academic program for students of high ability and motivation, often leading to a degree granted with honors.

HPL (Health Professions Loan). A loan program for undergraduates planning to pursue degrees in the health professions.

Independent study. Academic work earning college credit that is undertaken outside the regular class structure.

Interdisciplinary study. Study in a combination of academic disciplines rather than within one discipline.

Internships. Short-term, supervised work experiences, generally relating to the student's field of interest and receiving degree credit.

January interim. The short, usually month-long, session of a 4-1-4 calendar during which one course of study is pursued intensively.

MEChA (Movimiento Estudiantil Chicano de Azt-lan). A national ethnic student organization.

Michigan Test. A test of English usage including grammar and vocabulary, devised by the University of Michigan English Language Institute. Some colleges may accept the Michigan Test in lieu of TOEFL (see TOEFL).

MSACS (Middle States Association of Colleges and Schools). One of six regional accrediting agencies and a member of the American Council on Education for CORPA.

NASC (Northwest Association of Schools and Colleges). One of six regional accrediting agencies and a member of the American Council on Education for CORPA.

NEASC (New England Association of Schools and Colleges). One of six regional accrediting agencies and a member of the American Council on Education for CORPA.

NCACS (North Central Association of Colleges and Schools). One of six regional accrediting agencies and a member of the American Council on Education for CORPA.

New England Regional Student Program. A cooperative program through which a student may enroll in another state university offering a program not offered at the home state university and pay the same costs as at the home state university.

NROTC (Naval Reserve Officers' Training Corps). The United States Navy's college-based training program.

NSL (Nursing Student Loan). A program of federally funded, college-administered loans for nursing students.

NSS (Nursing Student Scholarship). A program of federally funded, college-administered scholarships for nursing students.

Open admissions. An admissions policy granting acceptance to all secondary school graduates without regard to additional qualifications.

Pass-fail grading option (or credit/no credit grading option). A simplified grading method whereby a student receives a "pass" or "fail" notation in a course rather than a letter grade.

Pell Grant. A gift-aid program sponsored by the federal government, available to undergraduates who are pursuing their first bachelor's degree.

Perkins Loan (formerly NDSL). A program of federally funded, college-administered loans available to students from low-income families.

Phi Beta Kappa. A national honor society recognizing outstanding collegiate academic achievement.

PLUS (Parent Loan for Undergraduate Students). A loan program that is not need-based; available to the parents of dependent students.

PSAT/NMSQT (Preliminary Scholastic Assessment Test/National Merit Scholarship Qualifying Test). A CEEB standardized test usually taken by secondary school students in their sophomore or junior year. The test functions as a trial run for the SAT I; junior-year PSAT scores are used as qualification for National Merit Scholarship and the National Hispanic Scholar Awards Programs.

Quarter system. A calendar in which the academic year is broken into four units of roughly 11 weeks each. Under a quarter system, students normally enroll in three of the four quarters per year.

R.N. (Registered Nurse). Nursing certification.

Rolling admissions. A policy in which colleges without a specific date for notification of admission inform the applicant as soon as the admissions decision is made.

ROTC (Reserve Officers' Training Corps). The United States Army's two- and four-year college-based training program leading to an officer's commission upon graduation and generally including liberal financial aid.

SACS (Southern Association of Colleges and Schools). One of six regional accrediting agencies and a member of the American Council on Education for CORPA.

SAT I (Scholastic Assessment Test). The College Entrance Examination Board's standardized test battery for secondary school students, used by colleges and universities for admissions and placement purposes.

SAT II: Subject Tests. Subject exams administered by the CEEB, used in measuring academic achievement and for student placement purposes.

SEEK (Search for Education, Elevation, and Knowledge). A support program for economically disadvantaged residents of New York City who have graduated from secondary school or hold equivalency diplomas.

Semester system. A calendar in which the academic year is broken into two units of roughly 18 weeks each.

SEOG (Supplemental Educational Opportunity Grant). Federally funded gift aid for students with extreme financial need.

Stafford Loan. A student loan administered and guaranteed by a nonprofit, private institution.

State high school equivalency certificate. A certificate granted after successful completion of a secondary school equivalency exam; accepted by many colleges in lieu of a secondary school diploma. Also see GED.

TESOL (Teaching of English to Speakers of Other Languages). A program designed specifically for the training of educators of English as a Second Language. Also see ESL.

3-2 program. A cooperative academic program involving three years attendance at one institution and two years at another, upon completion of which two degrees are generally granted. 2-2 and 3-1 programs are also available.

TOEFL (Test of English as a Foreign Language). An exam designed to evaluate the English proficiency of students whose native language is not English.

Trimester system. A calendar in which the academic year is broken down into three units. Sometimes called a "quarter" or "three-term" system.

Upper-division college or university. An institution offering only the last two years of a bachelor's degree program. Students must have completed their freshman and sophomore years at other colleges.

WASC (Western Association of Schools and Colleges). One of six regional accrediting agencies and a member of the American Council on Education for CORPA.

Abbreviations

The following are some standard usages and abbreviations for degrees that may be listed in this book:

A.B. Bachelor of Arts
B.A. Bachelor of Arts
B.A./B.F.A. Bachelor of Arts/Bachelor of Fine Arts
B.A.Classics Bachelor of Arts in Classics
B.A.Ed. Bachelor of Arts in Education
B.A.Interdis.Studies Bachelor of Arts in Interdisciplinary Studies
B.A.Internat.Studies Bachelor of Arts in International Studies
B.A.Journ. Bachelor of Arts in Journalism
B.A.Lib.Arts Bachelor of Arts in Liberal Arts
B.A.Lib.Studies Bachelor of Arts in Liberal Studies
B.A.Mus. Bachelor of Arts in Music
B.A.Soc.Work Bachelor of Arts in Social Work
B.A.Teach. Bachelor of Arts in Teaching
B.Acct. Bachelor of Accounting
B.Aero.Eng. Bachelor of Aeronautical Engineering
B.Appl.Arts Bachelor of Applied Arts
B.Appl.Arts/Sci. Bachelor of Applied Arts and Sciences
B.Appl.Sci. Bachelor of Applied Science
B.Arch. Bachelor of Architecture
B.Arch.Eng. Bachelor of Architectural Engineering
B.Art Bachelor of Art
B.Art Ed. Bachelor of Art Education
B.Arts/Sci. Bachelor of Arts and Sciences
B.Avia.Mgmt. Bachelor of Aviation Management
B.Bus.Admin. Bachelor of Business Administration
B.Bus.Ed. Bachelor of Business Education
B.Chem.Eng. Bachelor of Chemical Engineering
B.Church Mus. Bachelor of Church Music
B.Civil Eng. Bachelor of Civil Engineering
B.Comp.Eng. Bachelor of Computer Engineering
B.Comp.Sci. Bachelor of Computer Science
B.Crim.Just. Bachelor of Criminal Justice
B.Dent.Hyg.Ed. Bachelor of Dental Hygiene Education
B.Ed. Bachelor of Education
B.Elec.Eng. Bachelor of Electrical Engineering
B.Elect.Studies Bachelor of Elective Studies
B.Eng. Bachelor of Engineering
B.Eng.Tech. Bachelor of Engineering Technology
B.Env.Design Bachelor of Environmental Design
B.F.A. Bachelor of Fine Arts
B.Gen.Studies Bachelor of General Studies
B.Gen.Tech. Bachelor of General Technology

B.Hlth.Info.Mgmt. Bachelor of Health Information Management
B.Hlth.Sci. Bachelor of Health Science
B.Human. Bachelor of Humanities
B.Indiv.Studies Bachelor of Individual Studies
B.Indust.Design Bachelor of Industrial Design
B.Indust.Eng. Bachelor of Industrial Engineering
B.Indust.Mgmt. Bachelor of Industrial Management
B.Info.Sys. Bachelor of Information Systems
B.Inter.Arch. Bachelor of Interior Architecture
B.Inter.Design Bachelor of Interior Design
B.Interdis.Studies Bachelor of Interdisciplinary Studies
B.Internat.Studies Bachelor of International Studies
B.Journ. Bachelor of Journalism
B.Land.Arch. Bachelor of Landscape Architecture
B.Lib.Arts Bachelor of Liberal Arts
B.Lib.Studies Bachelor of Liberal Studies
B.Mech.Eng. Bachelor of Mechanical Engineering
B.Med.Tech. Bachelor of Medical Technology
B.Minis. Bachelor of Ministry
B.Mus. Bachelor of Music
B.Mus.Arts Bachelor of Musical Arts
B.Mus.Ed. Bachelor of Music Education
B.Mus.Perf. Bachelor of Music Performance
B.Mus.Ther. Bachelor of Music Therapy
B.Phil. Bachelor of Philosophy
B.Phys.Ed. Bachelor of Physical Education
B.Prof.Studies Bachelor of Professional Studies
B.Pub.Admin. Bachelor of Public Administration
B.Relig.Ed. Bachelor of Religious Education
B.S. Bachelor of Science
B.S./B.A. Bachelor of Science/Bachelor of Arts
B.S.Acct. Bachelor of Science in Accounting
B.S.Admin. Bachelor of Science in Administration
B.S.Aero.Eng. Bachelor of Science in Aeronautical Engineering
B.S.Agri. Bachelor of Science in Agriculture
B.S.Agri.Eng. Bachelor of Science in Agricultural Engineering
B.S.Appl.Sci. Bachelor of Science in Applied Science
B.S.Arch. Bachelor of Science in Architecture
B.S.Art Ed. Bachelor of Science in Art Education
B.S.Bus. Bachelor of Science in Business
B.S.Bus.Admin. Bachelor of Science in Business Administration
B.S.Chem. Bachelor of Science in Chemistry
B.S.Chem.Eng. Bachelor of Science in Chemical Engineering
B.S.Civil Eng. Bachelor of Science in Civil Engineering
B.S.Comm.Disorders Bachelor of Science in Communication Disorders
B.S.Commerce Bachelor of Science in Commerce
B.S.Comp.Eng. Bachelor of Science in Computer Engineering
B.S.Comp.Sci. Bachelor of Science in Computer Science

B.S.Comp.Sys.Eng. Bachelor of Science in Computer Systems Engineering
B.S.Constr. Bachelor of Science in Construction
B.S.Crim.Just. Bachelor of Science in Criminal Justice
B.S.Dent. Bachelor of Science in Dentistry
B.S.Dent.Hyg. Bachelor of Science in Dental Hygiene
B.S.Design Bachelor of Science in Design
B.S.Diet. Bachelor of Science in Dietetics
B.S.Econ. Bachelor of Science in Economics
B.S.Ed. Bachelor of Science in Education
B.S.Elec.Eng. Bachelor of Science in Electrical Engineering
B.S.Elec.Eng.Tech. Bachelor of Science in Electrical Engineering Technology
B.S.Elem.Ed. Bachelor of Science in Elementary Education
B.S.Eng. Bachelor of Science in Engineering
B.S.Eng.Sci. Bachelor of Science in Engineering Science
B.S.Eng.Tech. Bachelor of Science in Engineering Technology
B.S.Env.Hlth. Bachelor of Science in Environmental Health
B.S.Fam./Cons.Sci. Bachelor of Science in Family and Consumer Science
B.S.Forestry Bachelor of Science in Forestry
B.S.Gen.Studies Bachelor of Science in General Studies
B.S.Geol. Bachelor of Science in Geology
B.S.Hlth.Care Admin. Bachelor of Science in Health Care Admin.
B.S.Hlth.Sci. Bachelor of Science in Health Science
B.S.Home Econ. Bachelor of Science in Home Economics
B.S.Human Sci. Bachelor of Science in Human Science
B.S.Indust.Eng. Bachelor of Science in Industrial Engineering
B.S.Indust.Mgmt. Bachelor of Science in Industrial Management
B.S.Indust.Tech. Bachelor of Science in Industrial Technology
B.S.Info.Sci. Bachelor of Science in Information Science
B.S.Interdis.Studies Bachelor of Science in Interdisciplinary Studies
B.S.Journ. Bachelor of Science Journalism
B.S.Land.Arch. Bachelor of Science in Landscape Architecture
B.S.Mat.Eng. Bachelor of Science in Materials Engineering
B.S.Math. Bachelor of Science in Mathematics
B.S.Mech.Eng. Bachelor of Science in Mechanical Engineering
B.S.Med. Bachelor of Science in Medicine
B.S.Med.Rec.Admin. Bachelor of Science in Medical Records Administration
B.S.Med.Tech. Bachelor of Science in Medical Technology
B.S.Mgmt. Bachelor of Science in Management
B.S.Mus. Bachelor of Science in Music
B.S.Mus.Ed. Bachelor of Science in Music Education
B.S.Nat.Res. Bachelor of Science in Natural Resources
B.S.Nurs. Bachelor of Science in Nursing
B.S.Occup.Ther. Bachelor of Science in Occupational Therapy
B.S.Petrol.Eng. Bachelor of Science in Petroleum Engineering
B.S.Pharm. Bachelor of Science in Pharmacy
B.S.Phys.Ed. Bachelor of Science in Physical Education
B.S.Phys.Ther. Bachelor of Science in Physical Therapy
B.S.Physics Bachelor of Science in Physics

B.S.Pub.Admin. Bachelor of Science in Public Administration
B.S.Pub.Aff. Bachelor of Science in Public Affairs
B.S.Radiol.Tech. Bachelor of Science in Radiology Technology
B.S.Recr. Bachelor of Science in Recreation
B.S.Sec.Ed. Bachelor of Science in Secondary Education
B.S.Soc.Work Bachelor of Science in Social Work
B.S.Speech/Hear.Sci. Bachelor of Science in Speech and Hearing Science
B.S.Tech. Bachelor of Science in Technology
B.S.Textile Eng. Bachelor of Science in Textile Engineering
B.S.Voc.Tech.Ed. Bachelor of Science in Vocational Technology Education
B.Sacred Mus. Bachelor of Sacred Music
B.Soc.Work Bachelor of Social Work
B.Spec.Studies Bachelor of Special Studies
B.Tech. Bachelor of Technology
B.Theol. Bachelor of Theology
B.Univ.Studies Bachelor of University Studies
B.Voc.Ed. Bachelor of Vocational Education
Regents B.A. Regents Bachelor of Arts
S.B. Bachelor of Science
Theol.B. Bachelor of Theology

The Colleges and Universities

Alabama Agricultural and Mechanical University

Normal, AL 35762   **205 851-5000**

Undergraduate profile. 93% Black, 5% White, 2% Other. 72% are state residents; 20% are transfers. Average age of undergraduates is 19.
Enrollment. Undergraduates: 1,889 men, 2,069 women (full-time). Freshman class: 2,830 applicants, 1,929 accepted, 985 enrolled. Graduate enrollment: 547 men, 783 women.
Faculty. 311 full-time; 168 Black, 74 White, 69 Other. 59% of faculty holds doctoral degree. Student/faculty ratio: 18 to 1.
Test score averages/ranges. Average ACT scores: 16 English, 17 math, 17 composite. Range of ACT scores of middle 50%: 12-17 English, 12-17 math.
1995-96 Costs. Tuition: $1,786 (state residents), $3,572 (out-of-state). Room & board: $2,670-$3,300. Fees, books, misc. academic expenses (school's estimate): $736.

PROFILE. Alabama A&M, founded in 1875, is a public, land-grant university. Undergraduate courses are offered through the Schools of Agriculture, Environmental Science, and Home Economics; Arts and Sciences; Business; Education; and Technology. Its 1,700-acre campus (200-acre main campus) is located in northern Alabama.

Accreditation: SACS. Professionally accredited by the Accreditation Board for Engineering and Technology, Inc., the Council on Social Work Education, the National Council for Accreditation of Teacher Education.

Religious orientation: Alabama Agricultural and Mechanical University is nonsectarian; no religious requirements.

Library: Collections totaling 339,272 volumes, 1,606 periodical subscriptions, and 488,759 microform items.

Athletic facilities: Gymnasiums, tennis courts, football and soccer fields, track, swimming pool, weight room.

STUDENT BODY. Freshman profile: 6% of freshmen who took ACT scored 24 or over on English, 5% scored 24 or over on math, 4% scored 24 or over on composite; 39% scored 18 or over on English, 39% scored 18 or over on math, 40% scored 18 or over on composite; 93% scored 12 or over on English, 97% scored 12 or over on math, 99% scored 12 or over on composite; 99% scored 6 or over on English, 99% scored 6 or over on math, 100% scored 6 or over on composite. 79% of accepted applicants took ACT.

Undergraduate achievement: 90% of fall 1993 freshmen returned for fall 1994 term.

Foreign students: 223 students are from out of the country. Countries represented include Bermuda, China, India, Jamaica, Kuwait, and Nigeria; 41 in all.

PROGRAMS OF STUDY. Degrees: B.A., B.S.

Majors: Accounting, Agribusiness, Agribusiness Management, Agricultural Economics, Agriculture, Animal Science, Apparel Merchandising/Design, Applied Physics, Art Education, Biology, Business Administration, Chemistry, Civil Engineering, Civil Engineering Technology, Commercial/Advertising Art, Computer Science, Crop Science, Early Childhood Education, Economics, Electrical Engineering Technology, Elementary Education, English, Environmental Science, Finance, Food Sciences, Forest Management, French, General Business, History, Home Economics, Horticulture, Human Development/Family Studies, Industrial Arts Education, Industrial Technology, Management, Marketing, Mathematics, Mechanical Drafting/Design Technology, Middle School/Junior High School Principal, Music Education/Choral, Music Education/Instrumental, Music Education/Vocal, Nutrition/Hospitality Management, Office Administration, Physical Education, Physical Education/Non-teaching, Physics, Plant/Soil Science, Political Science, Pre-Nursing, Pre-Veterinary, Printing Production/Management, Psychology, Reading, Secondary Education, Social Work, Sociology, Soil Science, Special Education, Speech Pathology, Systems

Management, Telecommunications, Trade/Industrial Education, Urban/Regional Planning, Urban Studies.

Distribution of degrees: The majors with the highest enrollments are business administration, education, and computer science; social work, engineering technology, and urban studies have the lowest.

Requirements: General education requirement.

Academic regulations: Freshmen must maintain minimum 1.6 GPA; sophomores, 1.8 GPA; juniors, 2.0 GPA; seniors, 2.2 GPA.

Special: Minors offered in most majors. Associate degrees offered. Double majors. Dual degrees. Accelerated study. Internships. Cooperative education programs. Graduate school at which qualified undergraduates may take graduate-level courses. Preprofessional programs in law, medicine, veterinary science, and dentistry. 2-2 nursing program with Emory U. 3-2 engineering program with Georgia Tech. Other programs with Alabama State U, Miles Coll, Oakwood Coll, Stillman Coll, and Talladega Coll. Cross-registration with Athens State Coll, John C. Calhoun State Comm Coll, Oakwood Coll, and U of Alabama at Huntsville. Teacher certification in early childhood, elementary, secondary, and special education. Certification in specific subject areas. ROTC.

Honors: Honors program. Honor societies.

Academic Assistance: Remedial reading, writing, math, and study skills. Nonremedial tutoring.

STUDENT LIFE. Housing: Students may live on or off campus. Women's dorms. School-owned/operated apartments. 38% of students live in college housing.

Services and counseling/handicapped student services: Placement services. Health service. Counseling services for veteran students. Personal counseling. Career and academic guidance services. Religious counseling. Physically disabled student services. Learning disabled services. Tutors. Reader services for the blind.

Campus organizations: Undergraduate student government. Student newspaper (Maroon and White). Yearbook. Radio and TV stations. NAACP. Choir, concert, marching, and jazz bands, modern dance group, radio club, service and special-interest groups, 40 organizations in all. Four fraternities, no chapter houses; three sororities, no chapter houses. 23% of men join a fraternity. 25% of women join a sorority.

Religious organizations: Angelic Voices of Faith, Bahai Faith Club, Baptist Student Union, Christian Student Organization, YWCA.

Foreign student organizations: International Student Organization, Caribbean Student Club, Nigerian Student Organization.

ATHLETICS. Physical education requirements: None.

Intercollegiate competition: 6% of students participate. Baseball (M), basketball (M,W), cheerleading (W), cross-country (M,W), football (M), soccer (M), tennis (M), track (indoor) (M,W), track (outdoor) (M,W), track and field (indoor) (M,W), track and field (outdoor) (M,W), volleyball (W). Member of NCAA Division I for soccer, NCAA Division II, SIAC.

Intramural and club sports: 6% of students participate. Intramural basketball, football, swimming, volleyball.

ADMISSIONS. Academic basis for candidate selection (in order of priority): Secondary school record, standardized test scores, class rank, school's recommendation, essay.

Nonacademic basis for candidate selection: Particular talent or ability is important. Character and personality and extracurricular participation are considered.

Requirements: Graduation from secondary school is required; GED is accepted. 22 units and the following program of study are required: 4 units of English, 2 units of math, 2 units of science, 3 units of social studies, 11 units of electives. Minimum "C" grade average required. Audition required of music program applicants. Conditional admission possible for applicants not meeting standard requirements. ACT is required; SAT I may be substituted. Campus visit recommended. Off-campus interviews available with admissions and alumni representatives.

Procedure: Take SAT I or ACT by February 1 of 12th year. Visit college for interview by January of 12th year. Suggest filing application by April 1; no deadline. Notification of admission on rolling basis. $100 nonrefundable room deposit. Freshmen accepted for all terms.

Special programs: Admission may be deferred one year. Credit and/or placement may be granted through CEEB Advanced Placement exams for scores of 3 or higher. Credit and/or placement may be granted through CLEP general and subject exams. Credit may be granted through DANTES exams and for military experience. Early entrance/early admission program. Concurrent enrollment program.

Transfer students: Transfer students accepted for all terms. In fall 1994, 20% of all new students were transfers into all classes. 469 transfer applications were received, 303 were accepted. Application deadline is July 15 for fall; December 1 for spring. Minimum 2.0 GPA required. Lowest course grade accepted is "C." At least 30 semester hours must be completed at the university to receive degree.

Admissions contact: James Heyward, M.Ed., Director of Admissions. 205 851-5245.

FINANCIAL AID. Available aid: Pell grants, SEOG, state grants, school scholarships and grants, private scholarships, ROTC scholarships, academic merit scholarships, and athletic scholarships. Tuition waivers. Perkins Loans (NDSL), PLUS, Stafford Loans (GSL), state loans, and private loans.

Financial aid statistics: 27% of aid is not need-based. In 1994-95, 85% of all undergraduate aid applicants received aid. Average amounts of aid awarded freshmen: Scholarships and grants, $1,838.

Supporting data/closing dates: FAFSA/FAF: Accepted on rolling basis. School's own aid application: Deadline is April 1. Notification of awards on rolling basis.

Financial aid contact: Percy N. Lanier, Director of Financial Aid. 205 851-5400.

STUDENT EMPLOYMENT. Federal Work-Study Program. Institutional employment. 32% of full-time undergraduates work on campus during school year. Students may expect to earn an average of $1,954 during school year. Freshmen are discouraged from working during their first term. Off-campus part-time employment opportunities rated "excellent."

COMPUTER FACILITIES. 850 IBM/IBM-compatible and Apple/Macintosh microcomputers. Students may access IBM minicomputer/mainframe systems, Internet. Client/LAN operating systems include Apple/Macintosh, DOS. Computer facilities are available to all students.

Fees: None.

Hours: 8:30 AM-9:30 PM (M-F); 8:30 AM-4:30 PM (Sa).

GRADUATE CAREER DATA. Companies and businesses that hire graduates: IBM, government agencies, education boards/systems.

PROMINENT ALUMNI/AE. James A. Chapman, corporate manager; John Stallworth, professional athlete, Pittsburgh Steelers; D.B. Robinson, owner, D.B. Robinson Corp., trustee, Alabama A&M U; Marilyn Gurley Foreman, doctor; Frankie F. Smith, judge; William Cox, publisher.

Alabama State University

Montgomery, AL 36101-0271   205 293-4200

Undergraduate profile. 97% Black, 2% White, 1% Other. 59% are state residents; 3% are transfers. Average age of undergraduates is 19.

Enrollment. Undergraduates: 1,834 men, 2,325 women (full-time). Freshman class: 5,377 applicants, 3,623 accepted, 1,071 enrolled. Graduate enrollment: 99 men, 349 women.

Faculty. 201 full-time, 98 part-time; 185 Black, 89 White, 25 Other. 43% of faculty holds doctoral degree. Student/faculty ratio: 19 to 1.

Test score averages/ranges. Average ACT scores: 16 composite.

1995-96 Costs. Tuition: $1,500 (state residents), $3,000 (out-of-state). Room & board: $3,300. Fees, books, misc. academic expenses (school's estimate): $700.

PROFILE. Alabama State is a historically Black, public university. It was founded as a Normal school in 1866, joined the state university system in 1887, and gained university status in 1969. Programs are offered through the Colleges of Arts and Sciences, Business Administration, Education, and Music; University College; Division of Aerospace Studies; and the School of Graduate Studies. Its 138-acre campus is located near downtown Montgomery.

Accreditation: SACS. Professionally accredited by the Association of Collegiate Business Schools and Programs, the National Association of Schools of Music, the National Council for Accreditation of Teacher Education.

Religious orientation: Alabama State University is nonsectarian; no religious requirements.

Library: Collections totaling 226,907 volumes, 1,111 periodical subscriptions, and 365,336 microform items.

Special facilities/museums: Early childhood center.

Athletic facilities: Swimming pool, basketball and tennis courts, sports arena, weight room, baseball, and football fields.

STUDENT BODY. Freshman profile: 27% of accepted applicants took SAT I; 83% took ACT.

Undergraduate achievement: 53% of fall 1993 freshmen returned for fall 1994 term.

Foreign students: Five students are from out of the country. Countries represented include Jamaica and Nigeria; four in all.

PROGRAMS OF STUDY. Degrees: B.A., B.Mus.Ed., B.S., B.Soc.Work.

Majors: Accounting, Art, Biology, Business Education, Chemistry, Communications Media, Computer Information Systems, Computer Science, Criminal Justice, Early Childhood Education, Economics, Elementary Education, English, Finance, French, Graphic Arts, History, Laboratory Technology, Management, Management/Technology, Marine Biology, Marketing, Mathematics, Mathematics/Engineering, Music, Office Administration, Physics, Political Science, Psychology, Secondary Education, Secretarial Studies, Social Work, Sociology, Spanish, Special Education, Speech Communication, Theatre Arts.

Distribution of degrees: The majors with the highest enrollments are accounting, elementary education, and criminal justice; art, mathematics/engineering, and laboratory technology have the lowest.

Requirements: General education requirement.

Academic regulations: Minimum 2.0 GPA must be maintained.

Special: Minors offered in most majors and in anthropology, library science, and philosophy. Associate degrees offered. Double majors. Dual degrees. Independent study. Internships. Cooperative education programs. Graduate school at which qualified undergraduates may take graduate-level courses. Combined-degree medical lab technology program with U of Alabama. 3-2 engineering program with Auburn U. Member of Alabama Marine Environmental Sciences Consortium; off-campus study possible at Dauphin Island Sea Lab. Teacher certification in early childhood, elementary, secondary, and special education. Certification in specific subject areas. AFROTC. ROTC at Auburn U.

Honors: Honors program. Honor societies.

Academic Assistance: Nonremedial tutoring.

STUDENT LIFE. Housing: Students may live on or off campus. Women's and men's dorms. School-owned/operated apartments. 41% of students live in college housing.

Services and counseling/handicapped student services: Placement services. Health service. Counseling services for military, veteran, and older students. Birth control, personal, and psychological counseling. Career and academic guidance services.

Campus organizations: Undergraduate student government. Student newspaper (Hornet Tribune, published once/two months). Yearbook. Radio station. Marching band, choir, instrumental and vocal groups, athletic and departmental groups, service and special-interest groups. Five fraternities, no chapter houses; four sororities, no chapter houses.

Religious organizations: Baptist Student Union, United Methodist group.

ATHLETICS. Physical education requirements: Two semesters of physical education required.

Intercollegiate competition: 10% of students participate. Baseball (M), basketball (M,W), cheerleading (M,W), cross-country (M,W), football (M), golf (M,W), tennis (M,W), track (indoor) (M,W), track (outdoor) (M,W), track and field (indoor) (M,W), track and field (outdoor) (M,W), volleyball (W). Member of NCAA Division I, NCAA Division I-AA for football, Southwestern Athletics Conference.

Intramural and club sports: 25% of students participate. Intramural basketball.

ADMISSIONS. Academic basis for candidate selection (in order of priority): Standardized test scores, secondary school record, class rank, school's recommendation, essay.

Nonacademic basis for candidate selection: Alumni/ae relationship is important. Extracurricular participation and particular talent or ability are considered.

Requirements: Graduation from secondary school is recommended; GED is accepted. 12 units and the following program of study are recommended: 4 units of English, 2 units of math, 2 units of science, 2 units of foreign language, 2 units of social studies. Minimum composite ACT score of 15 and minimum 1.5 GPA recommended of in-state applicants; minimum 2.0 GPA recommended of out-of-state applicants. Audition required of music and theatre program applicants. Portfolio required of art program applicants. Developmental program for applicants not normally admissible. ACT is recommended; SAT I may be substituted. Campus visit and interview recommended. Off-campus interviews available with admissions and alumni representatives.

Procedure: Take SAT I or ACT by October of 12th year. Visit college for interview by November of 12th year. Suggest filing application by November. Application deadline is June 30. Notification of admission on rolling basis. Freshmen accepted for all terms.

Special programs: Admission may be deferred one year. Credit and/or placement may be granted through CEEB Advanced Placement exams for scores of 4 or higher. Credit may be granted through CLEP general and subject exams. Credit may be granted through challenge exams and for military experience. Credit and placement may be granted for life experience. Early decision program. Deadline for applying for early decision is January 3. Early entrance/early admission program. Concurrent enrollment program.

Transfer students: Transfer students accepted for all terms. In fall 1994, 3% of all new students were transfers into all classes. 595 transfer applications were received, 277 were accepted. Application deadline is June 30. Minimum 2.0 GPA required. Lowest course grade accepted is "C." Maximum number of transferable credits is 64 semester hours. At least 30 semester hours must be completed at the university to receive degree.

Admissions contact: Billy Brooks, M.Ed., Director of Admissions. 205 293-4291.

FINANCIAL AID. Available aid: Pell grants, SEOG, state scholarships and grants, school scholarships and grants, private scholarships and grants, ROTC scholarships, academic merit scholarships, and athletic scholarships. Perkins Loans (NDSL), PLUS, and Stafford Loans (GSL). Deferred payment plan.

Financial aid statistics: 7% of aid is not need-based. In 1994-95, 90% of all undergraduate aid applicants received aid; 85% of freshman aid applicants. Average amounts of aid awarded freshmen: Scholarships and grants, $1,800; loans, $2,625.

Supporting data/closing dates: FAFSA/FAF: Priority filing date is March 1; accepted on rolling basis. School's own aid application: Priority filing date is March 1; accepted on rolling basis. State aid form: Priority filing date is March 1. Notification of awards on rolling basis.

Financial aid contact: Dorenda Adams, M.S., Director of Financial Aid. 205 293-4323.

STUDENT EMPLOYMENT. Federal Work-Study Program. Institutional employment. 45% of full-time undergraduates work on campus during school year. Students may expect to earn an average of $1,591 during school year. Off-campus part-time employment opportunities rated "excellent."

COMPUTER FACILITIES. 259 IBM/IBM-compatible and Apple/Macintosh microcomputers; 199 are networked. Students may access Cray, IBM minicomputer/mainframe systems, Internet. Residence halls may be equipped with networked microcomputers. Client/LAN operating systems include Apple/Macintosh, DOS, OS/2, Windows NT, Novell. Computer facilities are available to all students.

Fees: $15 computer fee per lab course.

Hours: 24 hours (M-F); weekend hours vary.

GRADUATE CAREER DATA. Highest graduate school enrollments: Alabama State U, Auburn U at Montgomery, Howard U, U of Alabama. Companies and businesses that hire graduates: Warren Robins, AFB, IBM, NCR.

PROMINENT ALUMNI/AE. Eugene Sawyer, former mayor of Chicago; Yvonne Kennedy, president, Bishop Coll; James E. Walker, president, Middle Tennessee State U.

Albany State College

Albany, GA 31705   912 430-4600

Undergraduate profile. 88% Black, 1% Native American, 11% White. 90% are state residents; 25% are transfers. Average age of undergraduates is 20.

Enrollment. Undergraduates: 765 men, 1,443 women (full-time). Freshman class: 1,887 applicants, 1,342 accepted, 577 enrolled. Graduate enrollment: 104 men, 199 women.

Faculty. 143 full-time, 22 part-time; 100 Black, 24 White, 19 Other. 64% of faculty holds doctoral degree. Student/faculty ratio: 20 to 1.

Test score averages/ranges. Average SAT I scores: 367 verbal, 415 math.

1995-96 Costs. Tuition: $1,494 (state residents), $4,704 (out-of-state). Room & board: $3,045. Fees, books, misc. academic expenses (school's estimate): $860.

PROFILE. Albany State, a public, liberal arts college, was founded in 1903 as the Albany Bible and Manual Training Institute. In 1932 it became a member of the state university system, and in 1954 assumed its present name. Its 202-acre campus is located in southwest Georgia, 180 miles from Atlanta.

Accreditation: SACS. Professionally accredited by the Association of Collegiate Business Schools and Programs, the National Council for Accreditation of Teacher Education, the National League for Nursing.

Religious orientation: Albany State College is nonsectarian; no religious requirements.

Library: Collections totaling 180,000 volumes, 1,066 periodical subscriptions, and 15,787 microform items.

Special facilities/museums: Electron microscope lab.

Athletic facilities: Gymnasium, tennis courts, weight room, swimming pool, athletic fields.

STUDENT BODY. Freshman profile: 90% of accepted applicants took SAT I; 10% took ACT. 99% of freshmen come from public schools.

Undergraduate achievement: 69% of fall 1993 freshmen returned for fall 1994 term. 65% of entering class graduates. 10% of students who complete a degree program immediately go on to graduate study.

Foreign students: Five students are from out of the country. Countries represented include Nigeria.

PROGRAMS OF STUDY. Degrees: B.A., B.S., B.Soc.Work.

Majors: Accounting, Art, Biology, Chemistry, Computer Science, Criminal Justice, Early Childhood Education, English, Health/Physical Education, History, Management, Marketing, Mathematics, Middle Grades Education, Modern Languages, Music, Nursing, Office Administration, Political Science, Psychology, Sociology, Special Education, Speech/Theatre.

Distribution of degrees: The majors with the highest enrollments are criminal justice, nursing, and accounting; art, computer science, and chemistry have the lowest.

Requirements: General education requirement.

Academic regulations: Freshmen must maintain minimum 1.5 GPA; sophomores, 1.75 GPA; juniors, 2.0 GPA; seniors, 2.0 GPA.

Special: Specialist degrees offered in educational administration and educational leadership. Courses offered in Black studies, geography, German, humanities, and physics. Associate degrees offered. Double majors. Dual degrees. Internships. Cooperative education programs. Preprofessional programs in law, medicine, pharmacy, and dentistry. 2-2 and 3-2 engineering programs with Georgia Tech. Teacher certification in early childhood, elementary, and secondary education. Certification in specific subject areas. ROTC.

Honors: Honors program. Honor societies.

Academic Assistance: Remedial reading, writing, math, and study skills.

STUDENT LIFE. Housing: Students may live on or off campus. Women's and men's dorms. 31% of students live in college housing.

Services and counseling/handicapped student services: Health service. Counseling services for military and veteran students. Personal counseling. Career and academic guidance services.

Campus organizations: Undergraduate student government. Student newspaper (Student Voice, published once/quarter). Radio station. Concert and gospel choirs, concert and marching band, theatre group, 18 organizations in all. Four fraternities, no chapter houses; four sororities, no chapter houses. 15% of men join a fraternity. 15% of women join a sorority.

Religious organizations: Baptist Student Union, Religious Life Organization.

ATHLETICS. Physical education requirements: Six quarter hours of health/physical education required.

Intercollegiate competition: 5% of students participate. Baseball (M), basketball (M,W), cheerleading (M,W), cross-country (M,W), football (M), track and field (indoor) (M,W), track and field (outdoor) (M,W), volleyball (W). Member of NCAA Division II, SIAC.

Intramural and club sports: 5% of students participate. Intramural basketball, flag football, swimming, tennis.

ADMISSIONS. Academic basis for candidate selection (in order of priority): Secondary school record, standardized test scores.

Requirements: Graduation from secondary school is required; GED is accepted. 15 units and the following program of study are required: 4 units of English, 3 units of math, 3 units of lab science, 2 units of foreign language, 3 units of social studies. Minimum SAT I scores of 350 math and 350 verbal (composite ACT score of 17) required. Additional application required of nursing program applicants. College placement exams and/or development studies courses required of applicants not meeting standard requirements. SAT I or ACT is required. Campus visit recommended.

Procedure: Suggest filing application by April 15. Application deadline is September 1. Notification of admission on rolling basis. $50 nonrefundable room deposit. Freshmen accepted for all terms.

Special programs: Admission may be deferred. Credit and/or placement may be granted through CEEB Advanced Placement exams. Credit may be granted through CLEP general and subject exams. Credit may be granted through DANTES exams and for life experience. Early decision program. Deadline for applying for early decision is September 1. Early entrance/early admission program. Concurrent enrollment program.

Transfer students: Transfer students accepted for all terms. In fall 1994, 25% of all new students were transfers into all classes. 345 transfer applications were received, 203 were accepted. Application deadlines are September 1 for fall; December 1 for winter; March 1 for spring. Minimum 2.0 GPA required. Lowest course grade accepted is "C." Maximum number of transferable credits is 135 quarter hours. At least 45 quarter hours must be completed at the college to receive degree.

Admissions contact: Kathleen Caldwell, M.S., Director of Admissions and Financial Aid. 912 430-4646.

FINANCIAL AID. Available aid: Pell grants, SEOG, Federal Nursing Student Scholarships, state scholarships and grants, school scholarships, private scholarships and grants, ROTC scholarships, and athletic scholarships. Perkins Loans (NDSL), PLUS, Stafford Loans (GSL), NSL, state loans, private loans, and unsubsidized Stafford Loans.

Financial aid statistics: 15% of aid is not need-based. In 1994-95, 90% of all undergraduate aid applicants received aid; 90% of freshman aid applicants. Average amounts of aid awarded freshmen: Scholarships and grants, $1,772; loans, $2,000.

Supporting data/closing dates: FAFSA: Priority filing date is April 15. FAF. School's own aid application: Priority filing date is April 15; accepted on rolling basis. Income tax forms: Accepted on rolling basis. Notification of awards on rolling basis.

Financial aid contact: Kathleen Caldwell, M.S., Director of Admissions and Financial Aid. 912 430-4650.

STUDENT EMPLOYMENT. Federal Work-Study Program. Institutional employment. 30% of full-time undergraduates work on campus during school year. Students may expect to earn an average of $900 during school year. Freshmen are discouraged from working during their first term. Off-campus part-time employment opportunities rated "good."

COMPUTER FACILITIES. 90 IBM/IBM-compatible and Apple/Macintosh microcomputers. Computer facilities are available to all students.
Fees: None.
Hours: 8 AM-5 PM (M-F).

GRADUATE CAREER DATA. Graduate school percentages: 1% enter law school. 2% enter medical school. 2% enter dental school. 1% enter graduate business programs. 1% enter graduate arts and sciences programs. Highest graduate school enrollments: Albany State Coll, Georgia Tech, Iowa State U, Medical Coll of Georgia, Ohio State U. Companies and businesses that hire graduates: Miller Brewing Co., AT&T, Procter & Gamble.

PROMINENT ALUMNI/AE. Joseph Jordan and Benjamin Jaudon, medical doctors; Daryl Chapman, dentist; Robert White, plant manager, Procter & Gamble; Sam Russell, Miller Brewing Co.

Alcorn State University
Lorman, MS 39096   **601 877-6147**

Undergraduate profile. 94% Black, 6% White. 87% are state residents; 14% are transfers. Average age of undergraduates is 21.
Enrollment. Undergraduates: 915 men, 1,430 women (full-time). Freshman class: 3,715 applicants, 1,252 accepted, 615 enrolled. Graduate enrollment: 67 men, 120 women.
Faculty. 174 full-time, 19 part-time; 112 Black, 34 White, 28 Other. 45% of faculty holds doctoral degree. Student/faculty ratio: 16 to 1.
Test score averages/ranges. Average ACT scores: 18 English, 17 math, 18 composite.
1995-96 Costs. Tuition: $2,389 (state residents), $4,580 (out-of-state). Room & board: $2,159.

PROFILE. Alcorn State, founded in 1871, is the oldest historically Black, land-grant university in the country. Programs are offered through the Divisions of Agriculture and Applied Science, Arts and Sciences, Business, Education and Psychology, Graduate Studies, and Nursing. Its 1,700-acre campus is located in Lorman, 90 miles southwest of Jackson.
Accreditation: SACS. Professionally accredited by the National Association of Schools of Music, the National Council for Accreditation of Teacher Education, the National League for Nursing.
Religious orientation: Alcorn State University is nonsectarian; no religious requirements.
Library: Collections totaling 168,058 volumes, 964 periodical subscriptions, 368,927 microform items, and seven CD-ROMs.
Athletic facilities: Gymnasium, basketball courts, swimming pool, handball court, dance studio, wrestling and gymnastics rooms.
STUDENT BODY. Freshman profile: 10% of freshmen who took ACT scored 24 or over on English, 4% scored 24 or over on math, 4% scored 24 or over on composite; 47% scored 18 or over on English, 36% scored 18 or over on math, 44% scored 18 or over on composite; 96% scored 12 or over on English, 100% scored 12 or over on math, 100% scored 12 or over on composite; 100% scored 6 or over on English. 5% of accepted applicants took SAT I; 95% took ACT. 99% of freshmen come from public schools.
Undergraduate achievement: 72% of fall 1993 freshmen returned for fall 1994 term. 11% of entering class graduates. 36% of students who complete a degree program go on to graduate study within three years.
Foreign students: Three students are from out of the country.
PROGRAMS OF STUDY. Degrees: B.A., B.Mus., B.S.
Majors: Accounting, Administrative Office Management, Agribusiness Management, Agricultural Economics, Agricultural Education, Agronomy, Animal Science, Biology, Business Administration, Business Education, Chemistry, Computer Science, Criminal Justice, Economics, Educational

Psychology, Elementary Education, English, Food Sciences/Human Nutrition, General Agriculture, General Home Economics, General Studies, Health/Physical Education, Health Sciences, History, Industrial Arts Education, Industrial Technology, Mass Communication, Mathematics, Medical Technology, Music, Music Education, Music/Instrumental, Music/Piano, Music/Voice, Nursing, Physical Therapy, Political Science, Recreation, Sociology/Social Work, Special Education, Technical Education, Textile Chemistry, Vocational-Technical Education.

Distribution of degrees: The majors with the highest enrollments are business, agricultural economics, and biology; technical education has the lowest.

Requirements: General education requirement.

Academic regulations: Minimum 2.0 GPA must be maintained.

Special: Associate degrees offered. Double majors. Independent study. Internships. Cooperative education programs. Graduate school at which qualified undergraduates may take graduate-level courses. Preprofessional programs in law, medicine, veterinary science, pharmacy, dentistry, and optometry. Cooperative physics program with Howard U. 2-2 pre-engineering program. Teacher certification in elementary and secondary education. ROTC.

Honors: Honors program. Honor societies.

Academic Assistance: Remedial reading, writing, math, and study skills. Nonremedial tutoring.

STUDENT LIFE. Housing: All students receiving institutional aid must live on campus. Women's and men's dorms. 73% of students live in college housing.

Services and counseling/handicapped student services: Placement services. Health service. Counseling services for military students. Personal counseling. Career and academic guidance services.

Campus organizations: Undergraduate student government. Student newspaper (Alcorn Herald). Yearbook. Radio station. Alcorn Players, concert and marching bands, glee club, jazz and wind ensembles, gospel choir, interfaith choir, Student Council, departmental and special-interest groups, 46 organizations in all. Four fraternities, no chapter houses; four sororities, no chapter houses. 15% of men join a fraternity. 20% of women join a sorority.

Religious organizations: Baptist Student Union, Newman Center, Sunday School, Church of God in Christ, United Methodist Campus Ministry.

ATHLETICS. Physical education requirements: Four semesters of physical education required.

Intercollegiate competition: 1% of students participate. Baseball (M), basketball (M,W), cross-country (M,W), football (M), golf (M), tennis (M,W), track (indoor) (M,W), track and field (indoor) (M,W), track and field (outdoor) (M,W), volleyball (W). Member of NCAA Division 1-A for basketball, NCAA Division 1-AA, NCAA Division I, Southwestern Athletic Conference.

Intramural and club sports: Intramural basketball, bowling, flag football, softball, volleyball.

ADMISSIONS. Academic basis for candidate selection (in order of priority): Standardized test scores, class rank, secondary school record, school's recommendation, essay.

Nonacademic basis for candidate selection: Character and personality are important. Particular talent or ability and alumni/ae relationship are considered.

Requirements: Graduation from secondary school is required; GED is accepted. 13.5 units and the following program of study are required: 4 units of English, 3 units of math, 3 units of science, 1 unit of foreign language, 2.5 units of social studies. Minimum composite ACT score of 15 and minimum 2.0 GPA required of in-state applicants; minimum composite ACT score of 18 and minimum 2.0 GPA required of out-of-state applicants. Audition required of music program applicants. ACT is required; SAT I may be substituted. Campus visit recommended. Admissions interview required of nursing program applicants. Off-campus interviews available with an admissions representative.

Procedure: Application deadline is July 15. Notification of admission on rolling basis. $75 room deposit, refundable upon graduation or withdrawal from housing. Freshmen accepted for all terms.

Special programs: Admission may be deferred two years. Credit and/or placement may be granted through CEEB Advanced Placement exams for scores of 3 or higher. Credit and/or placement may be granted through CLEP general and subject exams. Credit and placement may be granted through challenge exams. Early entrance/early admission program. Concurrent enrollment program.

Transfer students: Transfer students accepted for all terms. In fall 1994, 14% of all new students were transfers into all classes. 129 transfer applications were received, 100 were accepted. Application deadline is in July for fall; in October for spring. Minimum 2.0 GPA required. Lowest course grade accepted is "C." Maximum number of transferable credits is 64 semester hours. At least 36 semester hours must be completed at the university to receive degree.

Admissions contact: Emanuel Barnes, M.S., Director of Admissions. 601 877-6147, 800 222-6790.

FINANCIAL AID. Available aid: Pell grants, SEOG, state grants, school scholarships, private scholarships, ROTC scholarships, academic merit scholarships, and athletic scholarships. PLUS and Stafford Loans (GSL).

Financial aid statistics: 15% of aid is not need-based. In 1994-95, 88% of all undergraduate aid applicants received aid; 93% of freshman aid applicants. Average amounts of aid awarded freshmen: Scholarships and grants, $1,118; loans, $1,000.

Supporting data/closing dates: FAFSA: Priority filing date is April 1; accepted on rolling basis. School's own aid application: Priority filing date is April 1. Income tax forms: Priority filing date is April 1. Notification of awards on rolling basis.

Financial aid contact: Dyann Moses, M.S., Acting Director of Financial Aid. 601 877-6190.

STUDENT EMPLOYMENT. Federal Work-Study Program. Institutional employment. 30% of full-time undergraduates work on campus during school year. Students may expect to earn an average of $500 during school year. Freshmen are discouraged from working during their first term. Off-campus part-time employment opportunities rated "poor."

COMPUTER FACILITIES. 150 IBM/IBM-compatible microcomputers. Client/LAN operating systems include DOS, OS/2. Computer facilities are available to all students.
Fees: None.
Hours: 8 AM-6 PM.

GRADUATE CAREER DATA. Graduate school percentages: 2% enter law school. 2% enter medical school. 1% enter dental school. 5% enter graduate business programs. 10% enter graduate arts and sciences programs. 1% enter theological school/seminary. Highest graduate school enrollments: Iowa State U, Meharry Medical Sch, Mississippi State U, U of Mississippi. 65% of graduates choose careers in business and industry. Companies and businesses that hire graduates: Allstate, Dow Chemical, federal government, IBM, State Farm Insurance.

PROMINENT ALUMNI/AE. Alex Haley, author, *Roots*; Medgar Evers, civil rights leader.

Arkansas Baptist College

Little Rock, AR 72202   501 374-7856

Undergraduate profile. 98% Black, 2% Other. 95% are state residents.
Enrollment. Undergraduates: 411 (full-time). Freshman class: 47 enrolled.
Faculty. 17% of faculty holds highest degree in specific field.
Test score averages/ranges. N/A.
1994-95 Costs. Tuition: $2,000. Room & board: $2,200. Fees, books, misc. academic expenses (school's estimate): $600.

PROFILE. Arkansas Baptist, founded in 1884, is a private, church-affiliated, liberal arts college located in Little Rock.

Accreditation: NCACS.

Religious orientation: Arkansas Baptist College is affiliated with the American Baptist Churches in the USA; no religious requirements.

PROGRAMS OF STUDY. Degrees: B.A., B.S.

Majors: Business/Management, Computer/Information Sciences, Elementary Education, Religion, Secondary Education, Social Sciences.

Requirements: General education requirement.

Academic regulations: Freshmen must maintain minimum 2.0 GPA.

Special: Associate degrees offered. Double majors. Independent study. Teacher certification in elementary and secondary education.

Academic Assistance: Remedial writing and math.

STUDENT LIFE. Housing: Women's and men's dorms.

Services and counseling/handicapped student services: Placement services. Health service. Day care. Counseling services for veteran students. Personal counseling. Career guidance services. Learning disabled services.

Campus organizations: Undergraduate student government. Choral groups, student teacher organization.

Religious organizations: Baptist Student Union.

ATHLETICS. Physical education requirements: None.

Intercollegiate competition: Basketball (M,W), softball (M,W). Member of NJCAA.

ADMISSIONS. Academic basis for candidate selection (in order of priority): Secondary school record, school's recommendation.

Nonacademic basis for candidate selection: Particular talent or ability and alumni/ae relationship are important.

Requirements: Graduation from secondary school is required; GED is not accepted. 18 units and the following program of study are recommended: 4 units of English, 4 units of math, 2 units of science, 1 unit of social studies. Conditional admission possible for applicants not meeting standard requirements. Admissions interview recommended.

Procedure: Application deadline is September 30. Notification of admission on rolling basis. Freshmen accepted for fall term only.

Special programs: Credit and placement may be granted through challenge exams.

FINANCIAL AID. Supporting data/closing dates: FAFSA: Deadline is May 1. Notification of awards begins August 15.

Barber-Scotia College

Concord, NC 28025   704 786-5171

Undergraduate profile. 99% Black, 1% White. 53% are state residents; 3% are transfers.

Enrollment. Undergraduates: 352 men, 352 women (full-time). Freshman class: 933 applicants, 933 accepted, 480 enrolled.

Faculty. 50 full-time, 5 part-time; 28 Black, 21 White. 50% of faculty holds doctoral degree. Student/faculty ratio: 14 to 1.

Test score averages/ranges. Average SAT I scores: 300 verbal, 350 math. Range of SAT I scores of middle 50%: 250-349 verbal, 250-349 math.

1995-96 Costs. Tuition: $4,841. Room: $1,504. Board: $1,566. Fees, books, misc. academic expenses (school's estimate): $1,053.

PROFILE. Barber-Scotia is a private, church-affiliated, liberal arts college. Founded in 1867, it adopted coeducation in 1954. Its 23-acre campus is located in the town of Concord, 20 miles from Charlotte.

Accreditation: SACS. Professionally accredited by the National Council for Accreditation of Teacher Education.

Religious orientation: Barber-Scotia College is affiliated with the Presbyterian Church (USA); no religious requirements.

Library: Collections totaling 26,356 volumes, 193 periodical subscriptions, and 1,100 microform items.

STUDENT BODY. Freshman profile: 2% of freshmen who took SAT I scored 500 or over on math; 6% scored 400 or over on verbal; 8% scored 400 or over on math; 38% scored 300 or over on verbal; 57% scored 300 or over on math. 19% of accepted applicants took SAT I. 100% of freshmen come from public schools.

Undergraduate achievement: 10% of students who complete a degree program immediately go on to graduate study.

Foreign students: Six students are from out of the country. Countries represented include Bermuda, Jamaica, Kenya, and Nigeria; four in all.

PROGRAMS OF STUDY. Degrees: B.A., B.S.

Majors: Administration of Justice, Anthropology, Biology, Business Administration, Communication/Journalism, Education, English, Mathematics, Medical Technology, Political Science, Recreation Administration, Sociology.

Distribution of Degrees: The majors with the highest enrollments are sociology, business administration, and biology; English, recreation administration, and mathematics have the lowest.

Requirements: General education requirement.

Academic regulations: Minimum 2.0 GPA must be maintained.

Special: Minors offered in art, chiropractic, chemistry, computer science, gerontology, history, music, physics, pre-engineering, pre-law, social work, sociology, and theatre. Double majors. Internships. Cooperative education programs. Preprofessional programs in law and chiropractic. Charlotte Area Educational Consortium. Teacher certification in elementary and secondary education. Certification in specific subject areas. ROTC at Davidson Coll. AFROTC at U of North Carolina at Charlotte.

Honors: Honors program. Honor societies.

Academic Assistance: Nonremedial tutoring.

STUDENT LIFE. Housing: All unmarried students under age 21 must live on campus unless living near campus with relatives. Women's and men's dorms. School-owned/operated apartments. 89% of students live in college housing.

Services and counseling/handicapped student services: Placement services. Health service. Personal and psychological counseling. Career and academic guidance services. Religious counseling.

Campus organizations: Undergraduate student government. Student newspaper (Scotia Express, published once/semester). Yearbook. UNCF, Pre-Alumni Council. Four fraternities, no chapter houses; four sororities, no chapter houses.

ATHLETICS. Physical education requirements: Two semesters of physical education required.

ADMISSIONS. Academic basis for candidate selection (in order of priority): Secondary school record, class rank, school's recommendation, standardized test scores.

Nonacademic basis for candidate selection: Geographical distribution and alumni/ae relationship are important. Character and personality, extracurricular participation, and particular talent or ability are considered.

Requirements: Graduation from secondary school is required; GED is accepted. The following program of study is required: 4 units of English, 3 units of math, 3 units of science, 2 units of social studies. SAT I or ACT is required. Campus visit recommended. Off-campus interviews available with admissions and alumni representatives.

Procedure: Application deadline is August 1. Notification of admission on rolling basis. $100 room deposit, refundable until August 15. Freshmen accepted for all terms.

Special programs: Credit and/or placement may be granted through CEEB Advanced Placement exams for scores of 3 or higher. Credit and/or placement may be granted through CLEP general and subject exams. Placement may be granted through ACT PEP exams.

Transfer students: Transfer students accepted for all terms. Application deadline is August 1 for fall; December 1 for spring. Minimum 2.0 GPA required. Lowest course grade accepted is "C." Maximum number of transferable credits is 65 semester hours. At least 60 semester hours must be completed at the college to receive degree.

Admissions contact: Abbie Butler, Director of Admissions. 704 786-5171, extension 247.

FINANCIAL AID. Available aid: Pell grants, SEOG, state scholarships and grants, school scholarships and grants, private scholarships and grants, ROTC scholarships, athletic scholarships, and United Negro College Fund. Perkins Loans (NDSL), PLUS, Stafford Loans (GSL), and state loans.

Financial aid statistics: 5% of aid is not need-based.

Supporting data/closing dates: FAFSA. FAF: Accepted on rolling basis. School's own aid application: Accepted on rolling basis. State aid form: Accepted on rolling basis. Income tax forms: Accepted on rolling basis. Notification of awards on rolling basis.

Financial aid contact: Patsy Nwagbaraocha, Director of Financial Aid. 704 786-5171, extension 247.

STUDENT EMPLOYMENT. Federal Work-Study Program. Institutional employment. 75% of full-time undergraduates work on campus during school year. Students may expect to earn an average of $500 during school year. Off-campus part-time employment opportunities rated "fair."

COMPUTER FACILITIES. 120 IBM/IBM-compatible and Apple/Macintosh microcomputers. Residence halls may be equipped with stand-alone microcomputers. Computer facilities are available to all students.

Fees: None.

PROMINENT ALUMNI/AE. Dr. Mabel McClean, president emeritus, Barber-Scotia Coll; Dr. Mabel Phifer, president, Black College Satellite; Mrs. Vivian Allen, director, New American Museum.

Benedict College

Columbia, SC 29204   **803 256-4220**

Undergraduate profile. 97% Black, 3% Other. 86% are state residents; 8% are transfers. Average age of undergraduates is 21.

Enrollment. Undergraduates: 578 men, 834 women (full-time). Freshman class: 2,561 applicants, 2,153 accepted, 429 enrolled.

Faculty. 77 full-time, 23 part-time; 56 Black, 20 White, 24 Other. 47% of faculty holds doctoral degree. Student/faculty ratio: 15 to 1.

Test score averages/ranges. N/A.

1995-96 Costs. Tuition: $5,728. Room & board: $3,294. Fees, books, misc. academic expenses (school's estimate): $1,018.

PROFILE. Benedict, founded in 1870, is a private, liberal arts college. Its 20-acre campus is located in Columbia.

Accreditation: SACS. Professionally accredited by the Council on Social Work Education.

Religious orientation: Benedict College is affiliated with the Baptist Church; two semesters of religion required. Attendance is mandatory for chapel, assemblies, and convocations.

Library: Collections totaling 134,167 volumes, 573 periodical subscriptions, and 37,065 microform items.

Special facilities/museums: Language lab.

Athletic facilities: Gymnasium, swimming pool, tennis courts, weight room.

STUDENT BODY. Freshman profile: 100% of freshmen come from public schools.

Foreign students: 32 students are from out of the country. Countries represented include the Bahamas, Jamaica, Kuwait, Lebanon, Nigeria, and Saudi Arabia; eight in all.

PROGRAMS OF STUDY. Degrees: B.A., B.S., B.Soc.Work.

Majors: Accounting, Art, Biology, Business Administration, Chemistry, Child/Family Development, Computer Science, Criminal Justice, Early Childhood Education, Economics, Elementary Education, English, Environmental Health Science, History, Mathematics, Media Arts, Physics, Political Science, Recreation, Religion/Philosophy, Social Work.

Distribution of degrees: The majors with the highest enrollments are business administration, criminal justice, and social work; religion/philosophy and chemistry have the lowest.

Requirements: General education requirement.

Academic regulations: Freshmen must maintain minimum 1.5 GPA; sophomores, 1.6 GPA; juniors, 1.8 GPA; seniors, 1.9 GPA.

Special: Dual degrees. Independent study. Internships. Cooperative education programs. Preprofessional programs in medicine, dentistry, and allied health. 3-2 engineering programs with Clemson U, Georgia Tech, and Southern Tech Inst. Washington Semester, UN Semester, and Sea Semester. Teacher certification in early childhood, elementary, and secondary education. Study abroad in Mexico. ROTC. AFROTC at U of South Carolina.

Honors: Honors program. Honor societies.

Academic Assistance: Remedial reading, writing, math, and study skills. Nonremedial tutoring.

STUDENT LIFE. Housing: All students must live on campus unless living with family. Women's and men's dorms. 65% of students live in college housing.

Social atmosphere: The College Corner, Food Lion, and Five Points area are the most popular student gathering-spots. Greeks are a major influence on student social life. The annual basketball tournament, Springfest, Coronation, and Homecoming are highlights of the school year. Movies, the student center, and student lounge provide some opportunities for social and cultural life at Benedict; most of it is found off campus.

Services and counseling/handicapped student services: Placement services. Health service. Day care. Freshman seminars. Counseling services for military, veteran, and older students. Birth control, personal, and psychological counseling. Career and academic guidance services. Physically disabled student services. Tape recorders. Tutors. Reader services for the blind.

Campus organizations: Undergraduate student government. Student newspaper (Benedict Tiger, published once/month). Yearbook. Choir, concert band, gospel choir, drama club, departmental clubs, service societies, special-interest groups, 29 organizations in all. Four fraternities, no chapter houses; four sororities, no chapter houses. 5% of men join a fraternity. 8% of women join a sorority.

Religious organizations: Pretheological Association, Religious Awareness Association.

Foreign student organizations: Foreign Student Association.

ATHLETICS. Physical education requirements: Two semester hours of physical education required.

Intercollegiate competition: 1% of students participate. Baseball (M), basketball (M,W), softball (W), track and field (indoor) (M,W), track and field (outdoor) (M,W), volleyball (W). Member of EIAC Conference, NAIA.

Intramural and club sports: Intramural baseball, basketball.

ADMISSIONS. Academic basis for candidate selection (in order of priority): Secondary school record, class rank, standardized test scores, school's recommendation, essay.

Nonacademic basis for candidate selection: Extracurricular participation and geographical distribution are emphasized. Character and personality, particular talent or ability, and alumni/ae relationship are important.

Requirements: Graduation from secondary school is required; GED is accepted. 20 units and the following program of study are recommended: 4 units of English, 3 units of math, 2 units of science, 4 units of social studies, 7 units of electives. SAT I or ACT is required. Campus visit recommended. Off-campus interviews available with admissions and alumni representatives.

Procedure: Take SAT I or ACT by February of 12th year. Visit college for interview by April 15 of 12th year. Notification of admission on rolling basis. $50 nonrefundable tuition deposit. $50 room deposit, refundable until August 15. Freshmen accepted for all terms.

Special programs: Admission may be deferred three years. Credit and/or placement may be granted through CLEP general exams. Credit may be granted through CLEP subject exams. Credit may be granted through DANTES exams and for military and life experience. Placement may be granted through challenge exams. Early decision program. Deadline for applying for early decision is in August. Early entrance/early admission program. Concurrent enrollment program.

Transfer students: Transfer students accepted for all terms. In fall 1994, 8% of all new students were transfers into all classes. 207 transfer applications were received, 154 were accepted. Application deadline is rolling for fall; rolling for spring. Minimum 2.0 GPA required. Lowest course grade accepted is "C." Maximum number of transferable credits is 60 semester hours. At least 30 semester hours must be completed at the college to receive degree.

Admissions contact: Wanda Scott, M.A., Acting Director of Enrollment Management. 803 253-5143, 800 868-6598.

FINANCIAL AID. Available aid: Pell grants, SEOG, state grants, school scholarships and grants, private scholarships, ROTC scholarships, academic merit scholarships, athletic scholarships, and United Negro College Fund. Perkins Loans (NDSL), PLUS, and Stafford Loans (GSL). Deferred payment plan.

Financial aid statistics: 14% of aid is not need-based. In 1994-95, 97% of all undergraduate aid applicants received aid; 95% of freshman aid applicants. Average amounts of aid awarded freshmen: Scholarships and grants, $6,000; loans, $2,625.

Supporting data/closing dates: FAFSA/FAF: Priority filing date is April 15. School's own aid application: Priority filing date is April 15; accepted on rolling basis. State aid form: Priority filing date is April 15; accepted on rolling basis. Income tax forms: Priority filing date is April 15. Notification of awards on rolling basis.

Financial aid contact: Carl Bradsher, Director of Financial Aid. 803 253-5105.

STUDENT EMPLOYMENT. Federal Work-Study Program. Institutional employment. 36% of full-time undergraduates work on campus during school year. Students may expect to earn an average of $1,000 during school year. Off-campus part-time employment opportunities rated "good."

COMPUTER FACILITIES. 150 IBM/IBM-compatible and Apple/Macintosh microcomputers; 75 are networked. Students may access Digital minicomputer/mainframe systems. Residence halls may be equipped with stand-alone microcomputers, networked microcomputers, networked terminals. Client/LAN operating systems include DOS, Novell. Computer facilities are available to all students.

Fees: None.

Hours: 7:30 AM-11 PM (M-Th); 7:30 AM-6 PM (F); 2-5 PM (Sa-Su).

GRADUATE CAREER DATA. Highest graduate school enrollments: Clark Atlanta U, Clemson U, Ohio State U, U of South Carolina. 42% of graduates choose careers in business and industry. Companies and businesses that hire graduates: Equitable Life, IBM, Michelin Tire, South Carolina Electric and Gas Co.

PROMINENT ALUMNI/AE. Walter Simon, vice president, Kentucky Fried Chicken, Inc.; Dr. Clarence Vaughn, president, Southfield Cancer Institute; Dr. Leroy Walker, president, U.S. Olympic Committee.

Bennett College

Greensboro, NC 27401   **910 273-4431**

Undergraduate profile. 99% Black, 1% Hispanic. 32% are state residents; 11% are transfers. Average age of undergraduates is 20.

Enrollment. 650 women (full-time). Freshman class: 774 applicants, 542 accepted, 193 enrolled.

Faculty. 52 full-time; 6 part-time. 38 Black, 14 White, 6 Other. 63% of faculty holds doctoral degree. Student/faculty ratio: 11 to 1.

Test score averages/ranges. Average SAT I scores: 385 verbal, 395 math. Average ACT scores: 18 composite.

1995-96 Costs. Tuition: $10,056 (comprehensive). Fees, books, misc. academic expenses (school's estimate): $750.

PROFILE. Bennett is a church-affiliated college. It was founded as a coeducational seminary in 1873, gained college status in 1889, and became a senior college for women in 1926. Its 55-acre campus is located in Greensboro.

Accreditation: SACS. Professionally accredited by the American Dietetic Association, the Council on Social Work Education, the National Council for Accreditation of Teacher Education.

Religious orientation: Bennett College is affiliated with the United Methodist Church; three semester hours of religion/theology required.

Library: Collections totaling 95,293 volumes, 325 periodical subscriptions, and 1,800 microform items.

Special facilities/museums: Children's House, Constance Maiteena collection, college archives, telecommunications satellite dish.

Athletic facilities: Gymnasium, swimming pool, ball courts, fitness equipment.

STUDENT BODY. Freshman profile: 1% of freshmen who took SAT I scored 600 or over on verbal, 2% scored 600 or over on math; 4% scored 500 or over on verbal, 7% scored 500 or over on math; 27% scored 400 or over on verbal, 33% scored 400 or over on math; 62% scored 300 or over on verbal, 60% scored 300 or over on math. 21% of freshmen who took ACT scored 24 or over on composite; 80% scored 18 or over on composite; 100% scored 12 or over on composite. 89% of accepted applicants took SAT I; 11% took ACT. 91% of freshmen come from public schools.
Undergraduate achievement: 26% of entering class graduated. 35% of students who complete a degree program immediately go on to graduate study.
Foreign students: 16 students are from out of the country. Countries represented include Gambia, Ghana, Jamaica, Liberia, Zambia, and Zimbabwe; 10 in all.

PROGRAMS OF STUDY. Degrees: B.A., B.A./S.Interdis.Studies, B.S., B.Soc.Work.
Majors: Accounting, Arts Management, Biology, Business Administration, Chemistry, Clothing/Fashion Merchandising, Communications, Computer Science, Elementary Education, English, English Education, Home Economics, Interdisciplinary Studies, Mathematics, Mathematics Education, Medical Technology, Middle Grades Education, Music, Music Education, Nutrition/Dietetics, Political Science, Psychology, Science Education, Social Work, Sociology, Special Education, Visual Arts.
Distribution of degrees: The majors with the highest enrollments are business administration, education, and interdisciplinary studies; music, chemistry, and computer science have the lowest.
Requirements: General education requirement.
Academic regulations: Freshmen must maintain minimum 1.75 GPA; sophomores, juniors, seniors, 2.0 GPA.
Special: Minors offered in economics, history, and women's studies. Volunteer or paid career-related experience required of all students for graduation. Associate degrees offered. Self-designed majors. Dual degrees. Independent study. Internships. Preprofessional programs in medicine, pharmacy, and dentistry. 3-1 medical technology program with the Bowman Gray Sch of Medicine at Wake Forest U. 3-2 nursing program with North Carolina A&T State U. Five-year dual degree program in electrical or mechanical engineering with North Carolina A&T State U. Special programs with five areas of concentration offered in conjunction with North Carolina A&T State U and U of North Carolina at Greensboro. Member of the Piedmont Independent College Association (PICA) and Greater Greensboro Consortium. Washington Semester. Exchange programs with Mt. Vernon Coll, New York U, Randolph-Macon Coll, and Union Coll. Teacher certification in early childhood, elementary, secondary, and special education. Certification in specific subject areas. ROTC and AFROTC at North Carolina A&T State U.
Honors: Honors program. Honor societies.
Academic Assistance: Remedial reading, writing, math, and study skills. Nonremedial tutoring.

STUDENT LIFE. Housing: All students must live on campus for first two years. Women's dorms. 80% of students live in college housing.
Social atmosphere: The most popular on-campus gathering spot at Bennett is the student union. Four sororities have widespread influence on student life. Founder's Day and the Bennett Coronation highlight the school year. "We are a private, religious college," reports the editor of the school newspaper. Many students participate in the social activities at the local state university, only three blocks away.
Services and counseling/handicapped student services: Placement services. Health service. Day care. Student Support Services Program. Personal and psychological counseling. Career and academic guidance services. Religious counseling. Learning disabled services.
Campus organizations: Undergraduate student government. Student newspaper (Bennett Banner, published once/quarter). Yearbook. Choir, theatre group, Academic/Cultural Enrichment Series, community service and departmental groups, 28 organizations in all. Four sororities, no chapter houses. 20% of women join a sorority.
Religious organizations: Belles of Harmony, Christian Fellowship.
Foreign student organizations: International Students Organization.

ATHLETICS. Physical education requirements: Four semester hours of physical education required.
Intercollegiate competition: Member of NCAA Division III.
ADMISSIONS. Academic basis for candidate selection (in order of priority): Secondary school record, standardized test scores, class rank, school's recommendation, essay.
Nonacademic basis for candidate selection: Character and personality and extracurricular participation are emphasized. Particular talent or ability is important. Geographical distribution and alumni/ae relationship are considered.
Requirements: Graduation from secondary school is required; GED is accepted. 16 units and the following program of study are required: 4 units of English, 2 units of math, 1 unit of science, 2 units of foreign language, 1 unit of social studies, 6 units of electives. HEOP for applicants not normally admissible. Special student status possible for applicants not meeting standard requirements. SAT I is required; ACT may be substituted. Campus visit and interview recommended. Off-campus interviews available with an alumni representative.
Procedure: Take SAT I or ACT by spring of 12th year. Suggest filing application by February 15; no deadline. Notification of admission is sent within two weeks of receipt of all credentials. Reply is required by June 30. $70 tuition deposit. $100 refundable room deposit. Freshmen accepted for all terms.
Special programs: Admission may be deferred one semester. Credit and/or placement may be granted through CLEP general and subject exams. Early entrance/early admission program.
Transfer students: Transfer students accepted for all terms. In fall 1993, 11% of all new students were transfers into all classes. 74 transfer applications were received, 40 were accepted. Application deadline is rolling for fall; rolling for spring. Minimum 2.0 GPA recommended. Lowest course grade accepted is "C." At least 36 semester hours must be completed at the college to receive degree.
Admissions contact: Yolanda Johnson, Acting Director of Admissions. 910 370-8624.

FINANCIAL AID. Available aid: Pell grants, SEOG, state grants, school scholarships and grants, private scholarships and grants, academic merit scholarships, and United Negro College Fund. Perkins Loans (NDSL), PLUS, Stafford Loans (GSL), and unsubsidized Stafford Loans. Deferred payment plan.
Financial aid statistics: 36% of aid is not need-based. In 1993-94, 89% of all undergraduate aid applicants received aid; 86% of freshman aid applicants. Average amounts of aid awarded freshmen: Scholarships and grants, $1,678; loans, $5,037.
Supporting data/closing dates: FAFSA. FAF: Accepted on rolling basis. Notification of awards on rolling basis.

STUDENT EMPLOYMENT. Federal Work-Study Program. Institutional employment. 32% of full-time undergraduates work on campus during school year. Students may expect to earn an average of $1,080 during school year. Off-campus part-time employment opportunities rated "good."

COMPUTER FACILITIES. 110 IBM/IBM-compatible microcomputers; 60 are networked. Students may access Digital, IBM minicomputer/mainframe systems. Client/LAN operating systems include DOS, Novell. Computer facilities are available to all students.
Fees: None.
Hours: 8 AM-9 PM.

GRADUATE CAREER DATA. Graduate school percentages: 1% enter law school. 35% enter medical school. 10% enter dental school. 8% enter graduate business programs. 25% enter graduate arts and sciences programs. Highest graduate school enrollments: Howard U, Meharry Medical Coll, U of North Carolina. 30% of graduates choose careers in business and industry. Companies and businesses that hire graduates: federal government, public and private schools.

PROMINENT ALUMNI/AE. Mayde Norman, actress; Glendora Putnam, attorney; Dorothyn Brown, surgeon.

Bethune-Cookman College
Daytona Beach, FL 32114-3099   **904 255-1401**

Undergraduate profile. 97% Black, 1% Asian-American, 1% Hispanic, 1% White. 82% are state residents; 5% are transfers. Average age of undergraduates is 18.

Enrollment. Undergraduates: 914 men, 1,319 women (full-time). Freshman class: 1,699 applicants, 1,309 accepted, 711 enrolled.

Faculty. 124 full-time, 60 part-time; 112 Black, 56 White, 16 Other. 50% of faculty holds doctoral degree. Student/faculty ratio: 17 to 1.

Test score averages/ranges. Average SAT I scores: 370 verbal, 412 math. Average ACT scores: 16 English, 16 math, 16 composite.

1995-96 Costs. Tuition: $6,458. Room: $1,558. Board: $1,964. Fees, books, misc. academic expenses (school's estimate): $600.

PROFILE. Bethune-Cookman is a church-affiliated, historically Black college. It is the product of the 1923 merger of Cookman Institute for Boys (founded in 1872) and the Daytona Normal and Industrial Institute for Girls (founded in 1904). Its 52-acre campus is located near the downtown section of Daytona Beach.

Accreditation: SACS. Professionally accredited by the American Medical Association (CAHEA), the National Council for Accreditation of Teacher Education.

Religious orientation: Bethune-Cookman College is affiliated with the United Methodist Church; two semesters of religion required.

Library: Collections totaling 149,108 volumes, 770 periodical subscriptions, 38,691 microform items, and 25 CD-ROMs.

Special facilities/museums: Historic archives, founder's home and gravesite (historic landmark), outreach center, telecommunications satellite network.

Athletic facilities: Gymnasium, racquetball and volleyball courts, weight room, track, football and soccer fields, tennis courts.

STUDENT BODY. Freshman profile: 1% of freshmen who took SAT I scored 600 or over on math; 1% scored 500 or over on verbal, 3% scored 500 or over on math; 10% scored 400 or over on verbal, 23% scored 400 or over on math; 52% scored 300 or over on verbal, 74% scored 300 or over on math. 22% of accepted applicants took SAT I; 21% took ACT. 90% of freshmen come from public schools.

Undergraduate achievement: 78% of fall 1993 freshmen returned for fall 1994 term. 22% of entering class graduates. 23% of students who complete a degree program immediately go on to graduate study.

Foreign students: 92 students are from out of the country. Countries represented include the Bahamas, China, Japan, Kenya, and the West Indies; 10 in all.

PROGRAMS OF STUDY. Degrees: B.A., B.S.

Majors: Accounting, Biology, Biology Education, Business Administration, Business Education, Chemistry, Chemistry Education, Computer Information Systems, Computer Science, Criminal Justice, Elementary Education, English, English Education, History, Hospitality Management, Liberal Studies, Mass Communication, Mathematics, Mathematics Education, Medical Technology, Modern Language Education, Modern Languages, Music, Music Education, Nursing, Physical Education, Physical Education/Recreation, Physics, Physics Education, Political Science, Psychology, Religion/Philosophy, Social Studies Education, Sociology, Specific Learning Disabilities.

Distribution of degrees: The majors with the highest enrollments are business administration, criminal justice, and elementary education; chemistry, modern languages, and social studies education have the lowest.

Requirements: General education requirement.

Academic regulations: Freshmen must maintain minimum 1.85 GPA; sophomores, juniors, seniors, 2.0 GPA.

Special: Minors offered in most majors and in French, German, journalism, management, marketing, and Spanish. Double majors. Dual degrees. Accelerated study. Internships. Cooperative education programs. Preprofessional programs in law, medicine, veterinary science, pharmacy, and dentistry. 3-2 engineering programs with Florida A&M U, Florida Atlantic U, Tuskegee U, and U of Florida. Teacher certification in elementary, secondary, and special education. Study abroad in France, Germany, and Spain. ROTC. AFROTC at Embry-Riddle Aeronautical U.

Honors: Honors program. Honor societies.

Academic Assistance: Remedial reading, writing, math, and study skills. Nonremedial tutoring.

STUDENT LIFE. Housing: All freshmen must live on campus unless living with family. Women's and men's dorms. 57% of students live in college housing.

Services and counseling/handicapped student services: Placement services. Health service. Counseling services for military, veteran, and older students. Birth control, personal, and psychological counseling. Career and academic guidance services. Religious counseling. Physically disabled student services. Tape recorders. Tutors.

Campus organizations: Undergraduate student government. Student newspaper (Voice, published once/month). Yearbook. Radio station. NAACP. Concert chorale, gospel choir, marching band, drama group, Men's Senate, Women's Senate, 40 organizations in all. Four fraternities, no chapter houses; four sororities, no chapter houses. 2% of men join a fraternity. 5% of women join a sorority.

Religious organizations: Religion and Philosophy Club, Religious Fellowship Club.

Foreign student organizations: International Relations Club, Federation of Bahamian Students.

ATHLETICS. Physical education requirements: Two semesters of physical education required.

Intercollegiate competition: 12% of students participate. Baseball (M), basketball (M,W), cheerleading (M,W), cross-country (M,W), football (M), golf (M,W), softball (W), tennis (M,W), track (indoor) (W), track (outdoor) (M,W), track and field (indoor) (W), track and field (outdoor) (M,W), volleyball (W). Member of MEAC, NCAA Division I, NCAA Division I-AA for football.

Intramural and club sports: 2% of students participate. Intramural baseball, basketball, football, softball, table tennis, volleyball. Men's club soccer.

ADMISSIONS. Academic basis for candidate selection (in order of priority): Secondary school record, school's recommendation, class rank, essay, standardized test scores.

Nonacademic basis for candidate selection: Character and personality are emphasized. Extracurricular participation and particular talent or ability are important.

Requirements: Graduation from secondary school is required; GED is accepted. 26 units and the following program of study are required: 4 units of English, 3 units of math, 3 units of science, 2 units of foreign language, 5 units of social studies, 9 units of academic electives. Minimum 2.0 GPA required. Special Services program for applicants not meeting standard requirements. SAT I or ACT is recommended.

Procedure: Take SAT I or ACT by July of 12th year. Visit college for interview by January of 12th year. Application deadline is July 30. Notification of admission on rolling basis. $100 room deposit, refundable until registration. Freshmen accepted for all terms.

Special programs: Admission may be deferred one year. Credit may be granted through CEEB Advanced Placement for scores of 3 or higher. Credit may be granted through CLEP general and subject exams. Early decision program.

Transfer students: Transfer students accepted for all terms. In fall 1994, 5% of all new students were transfers into all classes. 250 transfer applications were received, 195 were accepted. Application deadline is July 30 for fall; November 30 for spring. Minimum 2.0 GPA required. Lowest course grade accepted is "C." Maximum number of transferable credits is 60 semester hours. At least 30 semester hours must be completed at the college to receive degree.

Admissions contact: Catherine Cook, Ph.D., Interim Director of Admissions. 904 238-3803, 800 448-0228.

FINANCIAL AID. Available aid: Pell grants, SEOG, state scholarships and grants, school scholarships and grants, private scholarships and grants, ROTC scholarships, academic merit scholarships, athletic scholarships, and United Negro College Fund. Perkins Loans (NDSL), PLUS, Stafford Loans (GSL), state loans, and unsubsidized Stafford Loans. Tuition Plan Inc., AMS, and Tuition Management Systems.

Financial aid statistics: 20% of aid is not need-based. In 1994-95, 85% of all undergraduate aid applicants received aid; 95% of freshman aid applicants. Average amounts of aid awarded freshmen: Scholarships and grants, $2,500; loans, $2,700.

Supporting data/closing dates: FAFSA/FAF: Priority filing date is March 1. Notification of awards begins March 1.

Financial aid contact: Joseph L. Coleman, Director of Financial Aid. 904 255-1401.

STUDENT EMPLOYMENT. Federal Work-Study Program. Institutional employment. 20% of full-time undergraduates work on campus during school year. Students may expect to earn an average of $1,400 during school year. Off-campus part-time employment opportunities rated "fair."

COMPUTER FACILITIES. 150 IBM/IBM-compatible and Apple/Macintosh microcomputers; 100 are networked. Students may access Digital minicomputer/mainframe systems. Residence halls may be equipped with stand-alone microcomputers. Client/LAN operating systems include Apple/Macintosh, DOS, DEC. Computer facilities are available to all students.

Fees: $20 computer fee per academic year; included in tuition/fees.

Hours: 8 AM-10 PM.

GRADUATE CAREER DATA. Graduate school percentages: 2% enter law school. 1% enter medical school. 9% enter graduate business programs. 5% enter graduate arts and sciences programs. 1% enter theological school/seminary. Highest graduate school enrollments: Florida A&M U, Florida International U, Nova U, U of Central Florida. 30% of graduates choose careers in business and industry. Companies and businesses that hire graduates: IBM, Bell South, State Farm Insurance, Wal-Mart, Sears, local school districts.

PROMINENT ALUMNI/AE. Anthony Godbolt, Theodore Nicholson, and David Moore, physicians; Zelle Blunt, neurosurgeon; Andre Samuels, professional athlete, Tampa Bay Buccaneers; Ricky Claitt, professional athlete, Washington Redskins; Carl Cannon and Edward Dawkins, lawyers; Dr. Oswald P. Bronson, Sr., president, Bethune-Cookman Coll.

Bluefield State College

Bluefield, WV 24701   **304 327-4000**

Undergraduate profile. 8.6% Black, .5% Asian-American, .3% Hispanic, .3% Native American, 90.3% White. 90% are state residents; 37% are transfers. Average age of undergraduates is 26.

Enrollment. Undergraduates: 622 men, 841 women (full-time). Freshman class: 1,046 applicants, 832 accepted, 518 enrolled.

Faculty. 91 full-time, 65 part-time; 4 Black, 82 White, 4 Other. 20% of faculty holds doctoral degree. Student/faculty ratio: 16 to 1.

Test score averages/ranges. Average SAT I scores: 380 verbal, 410 math. Range of SAT I scores of middle 50%: 360-480 verbal, 390-450 math. Average ACT scores: 17 English, 18 math, 18 composite. Range of ACT scores of middle 50%: 14-18 English, 14-19 math.

1995-96 Costs. Tuition: $1,854 (state residents), $4,498 (out-of-state). Housing: None. Fees, books, misc. academic expenses (school's estimate): $500.

PROFILE. Bluefield State was founded in 1895 as a public Black teachers college. Programs are offered through the Divisions of Business, Continuing Education, Education, Engineering Technology, Health Services, Humanities and Social Sciences, and Natural Science. Its 100-acre campus is located one mile from downtown Bluefield.

Accreditation: NCACS. Professionally accredited by the Accreditation Board for Engineering and Technology, Inc., the National League for Nursing.

Religious orientation: Bluefield State College is nonsectarian; no religious requirements.

Library: Collections totaling 108,490 volumes, 524 periodical subscriptions, and 242,251 microform items.

Athletic facilities: Swimming pool, gymnasium, tennis courts, football field, fitness room.

STUDENT BODY. Freshman profile: 1% of freshmen who took ACT scored 30 or over on composite; 14% scored 24 or over on composite; 44% scored 18 or over on composite; 92% scored 12 or over on composite; 100% scored 6 or over on composite. 5% of accepted applicants took SAT I; 95% took ACT. 98% of freshmen come from public schools.

Undergraduate achievement: 25% of entering class graduates. 5% of students who complete a degree program immediately go on to graduate study.

Foreign students: 14 students are from out of the country. Countries represented include Canada, India, Japan, Jordan, Kuwait, and the Philippines; nine in all.

PROGRAMS OF STUDY. Degrees: B.A., B.S., B.S.Eng.Tech., B.S.Nurs.

Majors: Accountancy, Adolescent Education, Applied Science, Architectural Engineering Technology, Business Administration, Civil Engineering Technology, Computer Science, Criminal Justice Administration, Early/Middle Education, Education, Electrical Engineering Technology, Humanities, Mathematics, Middle/Adolescent Education, Mining Engineering Technology, Nursing, Regents Bachelor of Arts, Social Sciences.

Distribution of degrees: The majors with the highest enrollments are business administration, education, and criminal justice; mathematics has the lowest.

Requirements: General education requirement.

Academic regulations: Freshmen must maintain minimum 1.8 GPA; sophomores, 1.8 GPA; juniors, 1.9 GPA; seniors, 2.0 GPA.

Special: Minors offered in some majors and in art, biology, chemistry, international studies, physics, political science, psychology, sociology, and technical communications. Associate degrees offered. Double majors. Independent study. Internships. Combined degree programs in computer science, engineering technology, and nursing. Teacher certification in early childhood, elementary, secondary, and special education. Certification in specific subject areas.

Honors: Honor societies.

Academic Assistance: Remedial reading, writing, math, and study skills. Nonremedial tutoring.

STUDENT LIFE. Housing: Commuter campus; no student housing.

Social atmosphere: Students gather at the student union and cafeteria on campus and at City Park and the Mercer Mall off campus. Influential campus groups include the Greeks, newspaper and yearbook staffs, and the Model United Nations. Popular annual events include Homecoming, Greek Week, athletic events, and concerts and plays.

Services and counseling/handicapped student services: Placement services. Health service. Counseling services for veteran and older students. Birth control and personal counseling. Career and academic guidance services. Physically disabled student services. Learning disabled services. Tutors.

Campus organizations: Undergraduate student government. Student newspaper (Bluefieldian, published twice/month). Yearbook. Rainbow, Minorities On The Move. Gospel choir, jazz band, drama club, civil engineering technology club, criminal justice club, education association, physical education/recreation club, Society of Mining Engineering, Student Nurses Association, radiographers association, Rotaract, ski club, Young Republicans, Phi Beta Lambda, 35 organizations in all. Six fraternities, no chapter houses; four sororities, no chapter houses. 5% of men join a fraternity. 4% of women join a sorority.

Religious organizations: Christian Fellowship Organization.

Foreign student organizations: International Student Association.

ATHLETICS. Physical education requirements: Two semester hours of physical education required.

Intercollegiate competition: 3% of students participate. Baseball (M), basketball (M,W), cheerleading (W), cross-country (M,W), golf (M), softball (W), tennis (M,W). Member of NAIA, NCAA Division II, WVIAC.

Intramural and club sports: Intramural badminton, basketball, billiards, bowling, darts, flag football, golf, horseshoes, inner-tube water polo, racquetball, skiing, soccer, softball, swimming, table tennis, tennis, volleyball. Men's club softball.

ADMISSIONS. Requirements: Graduation from secondary school is recommended; GED is accepted. 17 units and the following program of study are required: 4 units of English, 2 units of math, 2 units of lab science, 3 units of social studies, 1 unit of history, 3 units of academic electives. Minimum composite ACT score of 17, rank in top half of secondary school class, and minimum 2.0 GPA recommended. Higher secondary school standards and minimum composite ACT score of 20 required of health science program applicants. Portfolio required of Regents Bachelor of Arts (R.B.A.) program applicants. PPST required of teacher education program applicants. R.N. required of nursing program applicants. Conditional admission possible for applicants not meeting standard requirements. SAT I or ACT is required. Campus visit and interview recommended. Off-campus interviews available with an admissions representative.

Procedure: Take SAT I or ACT by June 1 of 12th year. Suggest filing application by June 1. Notification of admission on rolling basis. Freshmen accepted for all terms.

Special programs: Admission may be deferred. Credit and/or placement may be granted through CEEB Advanced Placement exams for scores of 5 or higher. Credit and/or placement may be granted through CLEP general and subject exams. Credit may be granted for life experience. Credit and placement may be granted through ACT PEP and DANTES exams and for military experience. Deadline for applying for early decision is December 15. Early entrance/early admission program. Concurrent enrollment program.

Transfer students: Transfer students accepted for all terms. In fall 1993, 37% of all new students were transfers into all classes. 879 transfer applications were received, 796 were accepted. Application deadline is August 1 for fall; December 1 for spring. Minimum 2.0 GPA recommended. Lowest course grade accepted is "D." Maximum number of transferable credits is 72 semester hours from a two-year school and 96 semester hours from a four-year school. At least 32 semester hours must be completed at the college to receive degree.

Admissions contact: John C. Cardwell, M.A., Director of Admissions. 304 327-4065.

FINANCIAL AID. Available aid: Pell grants, SEOG, state scholarships and grants, school scholarships, private scholarships and grants, academic merit scholarships, and athletic scholarships. Perkins Loans (NDSL), PLUS, and Stafford Loans (GSL). Institutional payment plan.

Financial aid statistics: 24% of aid is not need-based. In 1993-94, 70% of all undergraduate aid applicants received aid; 70% of freshman aid applicants. Average amounts of aid awarded freshmen: Scholarships and grants, $500.

Supporting data/closing dates: FAFSA: Priority filing date is March 1. School's own aid application: Priority filing date is March 1. State aid form: Priority filing date is March 1. Notification of awards begins June 1.

Financial aid contact: Audrey C. Clay, M.A., Director of Financial Aid. 304 327-4022.

STUDENT EMPLOYMENT. Federal Work-Study Program. Institutional employment. 16% of full-time undergraduates work on campus during school year. Students may expect to earn an average of $1,000 during school year. Off-campus part-time employment opportunities rated "fair."

COMPUTER FACILITIES. 300 IBM/IBM-compatible and Apple/Macintosh microcomputers; 150 are networked. Students may access Digital minicomputer/mainframe systems, Internet. Client/LAN operating systems include Apple/Macintosh, DOS, Windows NT, DEC. Computer facilities are available to all students.

Fees: None.

Hours: 7 AM-midn.

GRADUATE CAREER DATA. Graduate school percentages: 1% enter law school. 1% enter medical school. 4% enter graduate business programs. 1% enter graduate arts and sciences programs. Highest graduate school enrollments: Radford U, Virginia Polytech Inst and State U, West Virginia Coll of Graduate Studies, West Virginia U. 55% of graduates choose careers in business and industry. Companies and businesses that hire graduates: school districts, hospitals.

PROMINENT ALUMNI/AE. Noel Taylor, mayor of Roanoke, Va.; Bernard Robertson, deputy assistant secretary for African affairs, U.S. Department of State.

Bowie State University
Bowie, MD 20715   **301 464-3000**

Undergraduate profile. 80% Black, 1% Asian-American, 1% Hispanic, .3% Native American, 16% White, 1.7% Other. 90% are state residents. Average age of undergraduates is 21.
Enrollment. Undergraduates: 859 men, 1,326 women (full-time). Freshman class: 1,780 applicants, 856 accepted, 418 enrolled. Graduate enrollment: 1,206 men, 2,032 women.
Faculty. 126 full-time, 93 part-time; 130 Black, 77 White, 13 Other. Student/faculty ratio: 22 to 1.
Test score averages/ranges. Average SAT I scores: 370 verbal, 404 math.
1995-96 Costs. Tuition: $3,018 (state residents), $6,017 (out-of-state). Room: $2,396-$2,696. Board: $1,578-$1,740.

PROFILE. Bowie State, founded in 1865, is a public university of liberal arts and technology studies. Programs are offered through the Departments of Behavioral Sciences and Human Services; Business, Economics, and Public Administration; Communications; Education and Physical Education; History, Politics, and International Studies; Humanities and Fine Arts; Military Science; Natural Sciences, Mathematics, and Computer Science; and Nursing. Its 267-acre campus is located in Bowie, 22 miles from Washington, D.C.

Accreditation: MSACS. Professionally accredited by the Council on Social Work Education, the National Council for Accreditation of Teacher Education.
Religious orientation: Bowie State University is nonsectarian; no religious requirements.
Library: Collections totaling 255,282 volumes, 1,287 periodical subscriptions, and 598,007 microform items.
Special facilities/museums: Science and math labs, computer academy.
Athletic facilities: Gymnasium, fitness, Universal, and weight rooms, swimming pool, basketball, racquetball, and volleyball courts, baseball, soccer, and softball fields, track.

STUDENT BODY. Freshman profile: 2% of freshmen who took SAT I scored 600 or over on math; 1% scored 500 or over on verbal, 6% scored 500 or over on math; 22% scored 400 or over on verbal, 40% scored 400 or over on math; 84% scored 300 or over on verbal, 95% scored 300 or over on math. 92% of accepted applicants took SAT I.
Undergraduate achievement: 15% of fall 1993 freshmen returned for fall 1994 term. 7% of entering class graduates.
Foreign students: 49 students are from out of the country. Countries represented include Cameroon, China, India, and Nigeria; 48 in all.
PROGRAMS OF STUDY. Degrees: B.A., B.S., B.S.Ed., B.S.Nurs.
Majors: Biology, Business Administration, Communications Media, Computer Science, Early Childhood, Elementary Education, Engineering, English, English Education, History, History Education, International Studies, Mathematics, Mathematics Education, Nursing, Political Science, Psychology, Science Education, Social Work Education, Sociology/Anthropology, Technology.
Distribution of degrees: The majors with the highest enrollments are business administration, communications media, and elementary education; science education has the lowest.
Requirements: General education requirement.
Academic regulations: Freshmen must maintain minimum 1.7 GPA; sophomores, 1.9 GPA; juniors, 2.0 GPA; seniors, 2.0 GPA.
Special: Minors offered in some majors and in approximately 15 other fields including Hispanic culture and literature of the Third World. Double majors. Dual degrees. Independent study. Pass/fail grading option. Internships. Cooperative education programs. Preprofessional programs in law, medicine, and dentistry. Dual-degree programs in dentistry with Maryland Dental Sch and in engineering with George Washington U, Morgan State U, and U of Maryland at College Park. Teacher certification in early childhood, elementary, secondary, and special education. Certification in specific subject areas. ROTC. AFROTC at U of Maryland at College Park.

Honors: Phi Beta Kappa. Honors program. Honor societies.
Academic Assistance: Remedial reading, writing, math, and study skills. Nonremedial tutoring.
STUDENT LIFE. Housing: Students may live on or off campus. Women's and men's dorms. School-owned/operated apartments. 18% of students live in college housing.
Services and counseling/handicapped student services: Placement services. Health service. Counseling services for military, veteran, and older students. Birth control, personal, and psychological counseling. Career and academic guidance services. Religious counseling. Learning disabled services.
Campus organizations: Undergraduate student government. Student newspaper (Spectrum, published four times/semester). Literary magazine. Yearbook. Radio and TV stations. Jazz ensemble, marching and pep bands, University Singers, gospel choir, departmental clubs, 40 organizations in all. Four fraternities, no chapter houses; four sororities, no chapter houses. 25% of men join a fraternity. 18% of women join a sorority.
Religious organizations: Campus Christian Fellowship.
Foreign student organizations: International Student Association.

ATHLETICS. Physical education requirements: Two semesters of physical education required.
Intercollegiate competition: 13% of students participate. Baseball (M), basketball (M,W), cheerleading (M,W), cross-country (M,W), football (M), softball (W), track (indoor) (M,W), track (outdoor) (M,W), volleyball (W). Member of CIAA, NCAA Division II.
Intramural and club sports: 52% of students participate. Intramural basketball, flag football, softball, swimming, volleyball. Men's club soccer. Women's club soccer.

ADMISSIONS. Academic basis for candidate selection (in order of priority): Secondary school record, standardized test scores, school's recommendation.
Nonacademic basis for candidate selection: Character and personality, extracurricular participation, particular talent or ability, geographical distribution, and alumni/ae relationship are considered.
Requirements: Graduation from secondary school is required; GED is accepted. 20 units and the following program of study are required: 4 units of English, 3 units of math, 2 units of lab science, 2 units of foreign language, 3 units of social studies, 6 units of academic electives. Minimum combined SAT I score of 700 and minimum 2.0 GPA required of in-state applicants; minimum combined SAT I score of 800 and minimum 2.5 GPA required of out-of-state applicants. R.N. required of nursing program applicants. Summer Emerging Scholars program. SAT I or ACT is required. Campus visit recommended.
Procedure: Take SAT I or ACT by December of 12th year. Visit college for interview by April 1 of 12th year. Suggest filing application by January 1. Application deadline is April 1. Notification of admission on rolling basis. $50 nonrefundable tuition deposit. $50 nonrefundable room deposit. Freshmen accepted for all terms.
Special programs: Admission may be deferred one semester. Credit and/or placement may be granted through CEEB Advanced Placement exams for scores of 3 or higher. Credit may be granted through CLEP general and subject exams. Credit may be granted for military and life experience. Credit and placement may be granted through ACT PEP, DANTES, and challenge exams. Early decision program. Deadline for applying for early decision is November 1. Concurrent enrollment program.
Transfer students: Transfer students accepted for all terms. In fall 1994, 1,005 transfer applications were received, 649 were accepted. Application deadline is May 1 for fall; November 1 for spring. Minimum 2.0 GPA required. Lowest course grade accepted is "C." Maximum number of transferable credits is 70 semester hours from a two-year school and 90 semester hours from a four-year school. At least 30 semester hours must be completed at the university to receive degree.
Admissions contact: Dharmi Chaudhari, Acting Registrar. 301 464-6570.

FINANCIAL AID. Available aid: Pell grants, SEOG, state scholarships and grants, school scholarships and grants, private scholarships and grants, ROTC scholarships, academic merit scholarships, and athletic scholarships. Perkins Loans (NDSL), PLUS, Stafford Loans (GSL), Federal Direct Student Loans, and unsubsidized Stafford Loans. AMS and deferred payment plan.
Financial aid statistics: 34% of aid is not need-based.

Supporting data/closing dates: FAFSA: Priority filing date is May 1. FAF. School's own aid application: Priority filing date is May 1. State aid form: Priority filing date is March 1. Student Aid Report: Priority filing date is May 1. Notification of awards begins May 1.

Financial aid contact: Donald Kiah, M.Ed., Director of Financial Aid. 301 464-6544.

STUDENT EMPLOYMENT. Federal Work-Study Program. Institutional employment. 22% of full-time undergraduates work on campus during school year. Students may expect to earn an average of $1,200 during school year. Off-campus part-time employment opportunities rated "good."

COMPUTER FACILITIES. 55 IBM/IBM-compatible and Apple/Macintosh microcomputers; 20 are networked. Students may access Digital minicomputer/mainframe systems, BITNET, Internet. Client/LAN operating systems include Novell. Computer facilities are available to all students.

Fees: Computer fee is included in tuition/fees.

Hours: 8 AM-10 PM (M-Th); 8 AM-5 PM (F); 10 AM-5 PM (Sa-Su).

GRADUATE CAREER DATA. Highest graduate school enrollments: Bowie State U. Companies and businesses that hire graduates: Giant Food, government agencies, IBM, NASA contractors, Xerox.

PROMINENT ALUMNI/AE. Sharon Christa McAuliffe, teacher selected for Challenger spaceflight; William Missouri, judge, Prince George's County, Md.; Dr. Roland Smith, assistant to president of Notre Dame U.

Central State University

Wilberforce, OH 45384   513 376-6011

Undergraduate profile. 90% Black, 5% White, 5% Other. 65% are state residents; 3% are transfers. Average age of undergraduates is 19.

Enrollment. Undergraduates: 1,185 men, 1,119 women (full-time). Freshman class: 3,461 applicants, 2,493 accepted, 673 enrolled. Graduate enrollment: 4 men, 14 women.

Faculty. 127 full-time; 20 part-time. 46% of faculty holds doctoral degree. Student/faculty ratio: 15 to 1.

Test score averages/ranges. N/A.

1995-96 Costs. Tuition: $3,088 (state residents), $6,767 (out-of-state). Room & board: $4,575. Fees, books, misc. academic expenses (school's estimate): $646.

PROFILE. Central State, founded in 1887, is a comprehensive, public university. Programs are offered through the Colleges of Arts and Sciences, Business Administration, and Education. Its 550-acre campus is located in Wilberforce, 18 miles east of Dayton.

Accreditation: NCACS. Professionally accredited by the Accreditation Board for Engineering and Technology, Inc., the National Association of Schools of Music.

Religious orientation: Central State University is nonsectarian; no religious requirements.

Library: Collections totaling 155,643 volumes, 890 periodical subscriptions, and 555,443 microform items.

Special facilities/museums: Museum/gallery, TV studio, language lab.

Athletic facilities: Gymnasiums, nautilus and dance rooms, swimming pool, baseball and softball fields.

STUDENT BODY. Freshman profile: Majority of accepted applicants took ACT.

Undergraduate achievement: 65% of students who complete a degree go on to graduate study within five years.

Foreign students: Countries represented include Ethiopia, Jamaica, Jordan, Kenya, Lebanon, and Zimbabwe.

PROGRAMS OF STUDY. Degrees: B.A., B.Mus., B.S., B.S.Ed., B.S.Mus.Ed.

Majors: Accounting, Allied Health, Art Education, Biology, Business Administration/Management, Chemistry, Community Health, Community Recreation, Computer Technology, Construction, Drawing/Design/Planning, Economics, Electronics, Elementary Education, English, English Literature, Finance, French, Geography, Geology, Graphic Arts, Graphic/Commercial Art, Health

Education, Health/Physical Education/Recreation, History, Hospitality Management, Industrial Arts Education, Industrial Technology, International Business, Journalism, Management, Management Information Systems, Manufacturing Engineering, Marketing Management/Research, Mathematics, Military Science, Music, Music Education, Music Performance, Philosophy, Physical Education, Physics, Political Science/Government, Psychology, Public Administration, Radio/Television, Secondary Education, Social Welfare, Sociology/Anthropology, Spanish, Special Education, Speech/Debate/Forensics, Studio Art, Systems Engineering, Theatre, Water Resources Management.

Distribution of degrees: The majors with the highest enrollments are business administration and education; water resources management and manufacturing engineering have the lowest.

Requirements: General education requirement.

Academic regulations: Minimum 2.0 GPA must be maintained.

Special: Minors offered in most majors. Associate degrees offered. Double majors. Independent study. Internships. Cooperative education programs. Graduate school at which qualified undergraduates may take graduate-level courses. Preprofessional programs in law, medicine, veterinary science, pharmacy, dentistry, and engineering. 2-2 and 3-2 engineering programs with Wright State U. Member of Southwestern Ohio Council for Higher Education (SOCHE); cross-registration possible. Teacher certification in elementary, secondary, and special education. ROTC. AFROTC at Wright State U.

Honors: Honors program. Honor societies.

Academic Assistance: Remedial reading, writing, and math. Nonremedial tutoring.

STUDENT LIFE. Housing: All freshmen must live on campus unless living with family. Coed, women's, and men's dorms. 50% of students live in college housing.

Services and counseling/handicapped student services: Placement services. Health service. Counseling services for military students. Personal and psychological counseling. Career and academic guidance services. Religious counseling. Physically disabled student services. Notetaking services.

Campus organizations: Undergraduate student government. Student newspaper (Gold Torch, published twice/month). Yearbook. Radio station. Concert/jazz band, choirs, marching band, drama groups, service and special-interest groups. Four fraternities, no chapter houses; three sororities, no chapter houses. 35% of men join a fraternity. 25% of women join a sorority.

Religious organizations: Interfaith Campus Ministry.

ATHLETICS. Physical education requirements: Five quarter hours of physical education required.

Intercollegiate competition: 8% of students participate. Baseball (M), basketball (M,W), cross-country (M,W), football (M), track and field (indoor) (M,W), track and field (outdoor) (M,W), volleyball (W). Member of NAIA Division I.

Intramural and club sports: 15% of students participate. Intramural basketball, flag football, softball, volleyball.

ADMISSIONS. Academic basis for candidate selection (in order of priority): Secondary school record, class rank, standardized test scores, school's recommendation, essay.

Requirements: Graduation from secondary school is required; GED is accepted. The following program of study is recommended: 4 units of English, 3 units of math, 3 units of science, 2 units of foreign language, 1 unit of social studies, 2 units of history, 1 unit of electives. Minimum 2.0 GPA required of out-of-state applicants. Ohio applicants must pass secondary school proficiency test. ACT is required. Campus visit and interview recommended. No off-campus interviews.

Procedure: Take ACT before filing application. Suggest filing application by June 15. Application deadline is August 1. Notification of admission on rolling basis. $60 nonrefundable room deposit. Freshmen accepted for all terms.

Special programs: Admission may be deferred. Early entrance/early admission program. Concurrent enrollment program.

Transfer students: Transfer students accepted for all terms. In fall 1994, 3% of all new students were transfers into all classes. 279 transfer applications were received, 198 were accepted. Application deadline is June 15 for fall; February 15 for spring. Minimum 2.0 GPA required. Lowest course grade accepted is "C." At least 45 credits must be completed at the university to receive degree. **Admissions contact:** Robert E. Johnson, M.Ed., Director of Admissions. 513 376-6348.

FINANCIAL AID. Available aid: Pell grants, SEOG, state grants, school scholarships and grants, ROTC scholarships, academic merit scholarships, and athletic scholarships. Perkins Loans (NDSL), PLUS, Stafford Loans (GSL), state loans, and unsubsidized Stafford Loans. Institutional payment plan.
Supporting data/closing dates: FAFSA/FAF: Priority filing date is March 31; accepted on rolling basis. School's own aid application: Priority filing date is March 31; accepted on rolling basis. State aid form: Priority filing date is March 31; accepted on rolling basis. Notification of awards on rolling basis.
Financial aid contact: Sunny Terrell, M.A., Director of Financial Aid. 513 376-6579.

STUDENT EMPLOYMENT. Federal Work-Study Program. 30% of full-time undergraduates work on campus during school year. Students may expect to earn an average of $1,200 during school year. Off-campus part-time employment opportunities rated "fair."

COMPUTER FACILITIES. IBM/IBM-compatible and Apple/Macintosh microcomputers. Students may access IBM minicomputer/mainframe systems. Computers are available to all students; use is supervised.
Fees: $25 computer fee per quarter.
Hours: 8 AM-4 PM, 6-11 PM (M-F).

GRADUATE CAREER DATA. Companies and businesses that hire graduates: General Electric Aircrafts, MCI Telecommunications, Procter & Gamble.

Cheyney University of Pennsylvania
Cheyney, PA 19319   **610 399-2000**

Undergraduate profile. 97% Black, .4% Asian-American, 1.3% Hispanic, .3% Native American, 1% White. 79% are state residents; 20% are transfers. Average age of undergraduates is 21.
Enrollment. Undergraduates: 449 men, 462 women (full-time). Freshman class: 1,104 applicants, 767 accepted, 287 enrolled. Graduate enrollment: 98 men, 226 women.
Faculty. 93 full-time, 16 part-time; 54 Black, 26 White, 13 Other. 52% of faculty holds doctoral degree. Student/faculty ratio: 14 to 1.
Test score averages/ranges. N/A.
1995-96 Costs. Tuition: $3,086 (state residents), $7,844 (out-of-state). Room & board: $7,496 (state residents), $8,348 (out-of-state). Books, misc. academic expenses (school's estimate): $400.

PROFILE. Cheyney, founded in 1837, is a public, historically Black university. Programs are offered through the Departments of Arts and Sciences, Education, and Technical and Applied Sciences. Its 275-acre campus is located 24 miles west of Philadelphia.

Accreditation: MSACS. Professionally accredited by the National Council for Accreditation of Teacher Education.
Religious orientation: Cheyney University of Pennsylvania is nonsectarian; no religious requirements.
Library: Collections totaling 237,780 volumes, 655 periodical subscriptions, and 517,955 microform items.
Special facilities/museums: Afro-American history/culture collection, planetarium, weather station, satellite communication network.
Athletic facilities: Gymnasiums, basketball and tennis courts, football, soccer, and softball fields, indoor pool, stadium, weight rooms.

STUDENT BODY. Freshman profile: 93% of accepted applicants took SAT I; 2% took ACT. 90% of freshmen come from public schools.

Undergraduate achievement: 12% of students who complete a degree program immediately go on to graduate study.

Foreign students: 12 students are from out of the country. Countries represented include Bermuda, Jamaica, Korea, Nigeria, Taiwan, and Zimbabwe; nine in all.

PROGRAMS OF STUDY. Degrees: B.A., B.S., B.S.Ed.

Majors: Art, Biology, Broadcast Communication Technology, Business Administration, Chemistry, Clothing/Textiles, Communication Arts, Computer/Information Sciences, Dietetics, Early Childhood Education, Elementary Education, English, General Science, Geography, History, Home Economics, Hotel/Restaurant/Institutional Management, Industrial Management, Industrial Technology, Mathematics, Medical Technology, Music, Music Merchandising, Political Science, Psychology, Recreation, Secondary Education, Social Relations, Social Sciences, Special Education, Technology Education, Theatre Arts.

Distribution of degrees: The majors with the highest enrollments are business administration, education, and social relations; geography, industrial management, and home economics have the lowest.

Requirements: General education requirement.

Academic regulations: Freshmen must maintain minimum 1.6 GPA; sophomores, 1.75 GPA; juniors, 1.85 GPA; seniors, 2.0 GPA.

Special: Concentrations offered in some majors. Courses offered in design/merchandising and guidance/counseling. Seminars and special-topic courses. Field experience in art and community health. Associate degrees offered. Double majors. Dual degrees. Independent study. Pass/fail grading option. Cooperative education programs. Graduate school at which qualified undergraduates may take graduate-level courses. Member of Allied Health Careers Opportunity Program, Cheyney-Lincoln-Temple Cluster, and Compact for Lifelong Educational Opportunities. Teacher certification in elementary, secondary, and special education. Certification in specific subject areas. ROTC.

Honors: Honor societies.

Academic Assistance: Remedial reading, writing, math, and study skills. Nonremedial tutoring.

STUDENT LIFE. Housing: Students may live on or off campus. Women's and men's dorms. 65% of students live in college housing.

Services and counseling/handicapped student services: Placement services. Health service. Personal and psychological counseling. Career and academic guidance services. Religious counseling. Physically disabled student services. Learning disabled services.

Campus organizations: Undergraduate student government. Student newspaper (Record, published once/month). Yearbook. Radio station. Band, concert choir, karate and martial arts clubs, chess club, social and cultural group, Toastmasters International, commuter student association, departmental, professional, and special-interest groups, 56 organizations in all. Four fraternities, no chapter houses; four sororities, no chapter houses. 4% of men join a fraternity. 3% of women join a sorority.

Religious organizations: Evangelical Christian Students, Muslim Student Association.

Foreign student organizations: International Student Association.

ATHLETICS. Physical education requirements: Two semesters of physical education required.

Intercollegiate competition: 20% of students participate. Basketball (M,W), cheerleading (M,W), cross-country (M,W), football (M), tennis (M,W), track (indoor) (M,W), track (outdoor) (M,W), track and field (indoor) (M,W), track and field (outdoor) (M,W), volleyball (W), wrestling (M). Member of NCAA Division II, Pennsylvania State Athletic Conference.

Intramural and club sports: 30% of students participate. Intramural basketball, softball, touch football, volleyball.

ADMISSIONS. Academic basis for candidate selection (in order of priority): Secondary school record, standardized test scores, essay, class rank, school's recommendation.

Nonacademic basis for candidate selection: Extracurricular participation, particular talent or ability, and geographical distribution are considered.

Requirements: Graduation from secondary school is required; GED is accepted. 17 units and the following program of study are recommended: 4 units of English, 3 units of math, 2 units of science, 1 unit of social studies, 2 units of history, 5 units of electives. Minimum combined SAT I score of 650 and minimum 2.0 GPA required; others may be considered on an individual basis. Act 101 program for in-state applicants not normally admissible; Freshman Studies Program for out-of-state applicants not normally admissible. SAT I is required; ACT may be substituted. Campus visit and interview recommended. Off-campus interviews available with an admissions representative.

Procedure: Take SAT I or ACT by October 31 of 12th year. Visit college for interview by October 31 of 12th year. Suggest filing application by June 30; no deadline. Notification of admission on rolling basis. $35 nonrefundable tuition deposit. $100 refundable room deposit. Freshmen accepted for all terms.

Special programs: Credit may be granted through CLEP general and subject exams. Credit and placement may be granted through challenge exams and for military and life experience. Early decision program. Deadline for applying for early decision is November 30. Early entrance/early admission program.

Transfer students: Transfer students accepted for all terms. In fall 1993, 20% of all new students were transfers into all classes. 166 transfer applications were received, 107 were accepted. Application deadline is June 30 for fall; November 15 for spring. Minimum 2.0 GPA recommended. Lowest course grade accepted is "C." At least 30 semester hours must be completed at the university to receive degree.

Admissions contact: Sharon Cannon, M.A., Director of Admissions. 800 CHEYNEY.

FINANCIAL AID. Available aid: Pell grants, SEOG, state scholarships and grants, school scholarships and grants, private scholarships and grants, academic merit scholarships, and athletic scholarships. Perkins Loans (NDSL), PLUS, Stafford Loans (GSL), state loans, and unsubsidized Stafford Loans. AMS and Tuition Management Systems.

Financial aid statistics: 4% of aid is not need-based. In 1993-94, 93% of all undergraduate aid applicants received aid; 87% of freshman aid applicants. Average amounts of aid awarded freshmen: Scholarships and grants, $2,450; loans, $2,625.

Supporting data/closing dates: FAFSA: Priority filing date is April 1. State aid form: Priority filing date is May 1. Income tax forms: Priority filing date is April 1. Notification of awards on rolling basis.

Financial aid contact: James Brown, M.Ed., Director of Financial Aid. 610 399-2302.

STUDENT EMPLOYMENT. Federal Work-Study Program. 33% of full-time undergraduates work on campus during school year. Students may expect to earn an average of $1,000 during school year. Off-campus part-time employment opportunities rated "good."

COMPUTER FACILITIES. 150 IBM/IBM-compatible and Apple/Macintosh microcomputers; 8 are networked. Students may access IBM, UNISYS minicomputer/mainframe systems. Client/LAN operating systems include Apple/Macintosh. Computer facilities are available to all students.

Fees: Computer fee is included in tuition/fees.

Hours: 8:30 AM-4:30 PM (M-F).

GRADUATE CAREER DATA. Graduate school percentages: 6% enter graduate business programs. 6% enter graduate arts and sciences programs. Highest graduate school enrollments: Cheyney U of Pennsylvania, , Temple U, U of Delaware. 70% of graduates choose careers in business and industry. Companies and businesses that hire graduates: SmithKline, Beckman; UNISYS; Vanguard Investment Corp.

PROMINENT ALUMNI/AE. Ed Bradley, TV journalist, "60 Minutes"; Jim Vance, news anchor, Washington, D.C.; Andre Waters, professional athlete, Philadelphia Eagles; Charles Grantham, executive director, National Basketball Players Association; Arnold Webster, superintendent of schools, Camden, N.J.

Chicago State University

Chicago, IL 60628   312 995-2000

Undergraduate profile. 92% Black, .6% Asian-American, 3.7% Hispanic, .1% Native American, 3.3% White, .3% Other. 98% are state residents; 52% are transfers. Average age of undergraduates is 26.

Enrollment. Undergraduates: 1,377 men, 3,234 women (full-time). Freshman class: 3,330 applicants, 1,481 accepted, 796 enrolled. Graduate enrollment: 825 men, 1,867 women.

Faculty. 370 full-time; 112 part-time. 64% of faculty holds doctoral degree. Student/faculty ratio: 30 to 1.

Test score averages/ranges. Average ACT scores: 17 composite.

1995-96 Costs. Tuition: $984 (state residents), $2,952 (out-of-state). Room & board: $4,990. Housing: None. Fees, books, misc. academic expenses (school's estimate): $1,009.

PROFILE. Chicago State, a public university, was founded in 1867 as an experimental teacher training school. Programs are now offered through the Colleges of Allied Health, Arts and Sciences, Business and Administration, Education, and Nursing. Its 152-acre campus is located in a residential neighborhood on Chicago's South Side.

Accreditation: NCACS. Professionally accredited by the National Council for Accreditation of Teacher Education, the National League for Nursing.

Religious orientation: Chicago State University is nonsectarian; no religious requirements.

Library: Collections totaling over 270,000 volumes, 1,377 periodical subscriptions, and 513,941 microform items.

Athletic facilities: Gymnasium, dance, aerobic, and weight rooms, swimming pool, tennis courts, indoor and outdoor tracks, softball field.

STUDENT BODY. Freshman profile: 2% of freshmen who took ACT scored 24 or over on composite; 37% scored 18 or over on composite; 100% scored 12 or over on composite. 75% of accepted applicants took ACT. 80% of freshmen come from public schools.

Undergraduate achievement: 55% of fall 1993 freshmen returned for fall 1994 term.

Foreign students: 82 students are from out of the country. Countries represented include Germany, Liberia, Nigeria, and South Korea; eight in all.

PROGRAMS OF STUDY. Degrees: B.A., B.S., B.S.Ed.

Majors: Accounting, Art, Bilingual/Bicultural Education, Biology, Business Education, Chemistry, Computer Science/Data Processing, Corrections, Early Childhood/Elementary Education, Economics, English, Finance, Geography, Health/Safety/Physical Education/Recreation, History, Hotel/Restaurant Management, Industrial Technology, Information Sciences/Systems, Management, Marketing Management/Research, Mathematics, Medical Records Administration, Music, Nursing, Occupational Education, Occupational Therapy, Physics, Political Science/Government, Professional/Technical Writing, Psychology, Radio/Television Broadcasting, Sociology/Anthropology, Spanish, Special Education.

Distribution of degrees: The majors with the highest enrollments are accounting, early childhood/elementary education, and nursing; industrial technology, Spanish, and geography have the lowest.

Requirements: General education requirement.

Academic regulations: Sophomores must maintain minimum 1.8 GPA; juniors, 1.9 GPA; seniors, 2.0 GPA.

Special: Minors offered in many majors and in anthropology, French, philosophy, physical science, real estate, religious studies, social work, theatre arts, and writing. Individualized curriculum, University Without Walls, and Board of Governors programs. Business Lab Program and Presidential Scholars Program. Double majors. Independent study. Internships. Cooperative education programs. Preprofessional programs in law, medicine, veterinary science, pharmacy, dentistry, optometry, and podiatry. 3-2 engineering programs with Illinois Inst of Tech and U of Illinois at Chicago. Teacher certification in early childhood, elementary, secondary, and special education. Certification in specific subject areas. Study abroad in Germany and Nigeria. ROTC. AFROTC at Illinois Inst of Tech.

Honors: Phi Beta Kappa. Honors program.

Academic Assistance: Remedial reading, writing, math, and study skills. Nonremedial tutoring.

STUDENT LIFE. Housing: Coed dorms.

Services and counseling/handicapped student services: Placement services. Health service. Day care. Counseling services for military and veteran students. Personal counseling. Career and academic guidance services. Physically disabled student services. Notetaking services. Tape recorders.

Campus organizations: Undergraduate student government. Student newspaper (Tempo). Yearbook. Radio station. Black Student Psychological Association, Latin American Student Organization. Musical, departmental, social, and special-interest groups, 70 organizations in all. Four fraternities, no chapter houses; four sororities, no chapter houses. 12% of men join a fraternity. 15% of women join a sorority.

Religious organizations: Campus Ministry.

ATHLETICS. Physical education requirements: Three semester hours of physical education required of education majors.

Intercollegiate competition: 2% of students participate. Baseball (M), basketball (M,W), cross-country (M,W), golf (W), tennis (M,W), track (indoor) (M,W), track (outdoor) (M,W), track and field (indoor) (M,W), track and field (outdoor) (M,W), volleyball (W), wrestling (M). Member of Mid-Continent Conference, NCAA Division I.

Intramural and club sports: 2% of students participate. Intramural aerobics, basketball, softball, swimming, track, weight lifting. Women's club cheerleading.

ADMISSIONS. Academic basis for candidate selection (in order of priority): Class rank, standardized test scores, secondary school record.

Requirements: Graduation from secondary school is required; GED is accepted. 15 units and the following program of study are required: 4 units of English, 3 units of math, 3 units of lab science, 3 units of social studies, 2 units of electives, 2 units of art, foreign language, or music. Minimum ACT scores and rank in top quarter of secondary school class required. After admission, completion of university exams and prerequisite courses required of applicants to certain programs. Provisional admission possible for applicants not meeting standard requirements. SAT I or ACT is required. Campus visit and interview recommended. No off-campus interviews.

Procedure: Take SAT I or ACT by April of 12th year. Application deadline is August 1. Notification of admission on rolling basis. Freshmen accepted for all terms.

Special programs: Credit and/or placement may be granted through CEEB Advanced Placement exams for scores of 4 or higher. Credit and/or placement may be granted through CLEP general and subject exams. Credit and placement may be granted for life experience. Concurrent enrollment program.

Transfer students: Transfer students accepted for all terms. In fall 1994, 52% of all new students were transfers into all classes. 2,865 transfer applications were received, 1,350 were accepted. Application deadline is August 1 for fall; December 1 for spring. Minimum 2.0 GPA required. Lowest course grade accepted is "C." Maximum number of transferable credits is 66 credit hours. At least 30 credit hours must be completed at the university to receive degree.

Admissions contact: Romi Lowe, Director of Admissions. 312 995-2513.

FINANCIAL AID. Available aid: Pell grants, SEOG, state scholarships and grants, school scholarships and grants, private scholarships, ROTC scholarships, academic merit scholarships, athletic scholarships, and aid for undergraduate foreign students. Perkins Loans (NDSL), PLUS, and Stafford Loans (GSL). Deferred payment plan.

Financial aid statistics: In 1993-94, 85% of all undergraduate aid applicants received aid; 80% of freshman applicants. Average amounts of aid awarded freshmen: Scholarships and grants, $1,868.

Supporting data/closing dates: FAFSA/FAF: Priority filing date is April 15. School's own aid application: Priority filing date is April 15.

Financial aid contact: George West, Director of Financial Aid. 312 995-2304.

STUDENT EMPLOYMENT. Federal Work-Study Program. Institutional employment. 38% of full-time undergraduates work on campus during school year. Students may expect to earn an average of $2,700 during school year. Off-campus part-time employment opportunities rated "fair."
COMPUTER FACILITIES. 40 IBM/IBM-compatible microcomputers. Students may access IBM minicomputer/mainframe systems. Client/LAN operating systems include DOS. Computer facilities are available to all students.
Fees: None.
Hours: 8:30 AM-10 PM (M-F); 8:30 AM-5 PM (Sa); 1-8 PM (Su).
GRADUATE CAREER DATA. Highest graduate school enrollments: DePaul U, Illinois State U, Loyola U, Roosevelt U, U of Chicago, U of Illinois at Chicago. Companies and businesses that hire graduates: Arthur Andersen, Chicago public schools, federal government, Xerox.
PROMINENT ALUMNI/AE. Edward Gardner, president, Soft Sheen Products; Dr. Margaret Burroughs, founder and president, DuSable Museum of Black History; Dr. James Birren, gerontologist; Jacqueline Vaughn, president, Chicago Teacher's Union; Jolyn Robichaux, president, Baldwin Ice Cream.

City University of New York, Medgar Evers College

Brooklyn, NY 11225   **718 270-4900**

Undergraduate profile. 91% Black, 1% Asian-American, 6% Hispanic, 2% White. 29% are transfers. Average age of undergraduates is 28.
Enrollment. Undergraduates: 706 men, 2,176 women (full-time). Freshman class: 1,261 applicants, 839 accepted, 633 enrolled.
Faculty. 122 full-time; 139 part-time. Student/faculty ratio: 18 to 1.
Test score averages/ranges. N/A.
1995-96 Costs. Tuition: $3,200 (state residents), $6,800 (out-of-state). Housing: None. Fees, books, misc. academic expenses (school's estimate): $44.

PROFILE. Medgar Evers, founded in 1969, is a public institution. Programs are offered through the Divisions of Business Administration, Education, Health Sciences, Humanities, Natural Sciences and Mathematics, and Social Sciences. Its one-acre campus is located in the Central Brooklyn area.
Accreditation: MSACS. Professionally accredited by the National League for Nursing.
Religious orientation: City University of New York, Medgar Evers College is nonsectarian; no religious requirements.
Library: Collections totaling 77,568 volumes.
Special facilities/museums: Language lab.
Athletic facilities: Gymnasium, swimming pool, track.
STUDENT BODY. Freshman profile: 43% of freshmen come from public schools.
Undergraduate achievement: 73% of fall 1993 freshmen returned for fall 1994 term. 6% of entering class graduates.
Foreign students: 59 students are from out of the country. Countries represented include Barbados, Guyana, Haiti, Jamaica, St. Vincent/the Grenadines, and Trinidad/Tobago; 16 in all.
PROGRAMS OF STUDY. Degrees: B.A., B.S.
Majors: Accounting, Biology, Business Administration, Business Administration/Management, Computer Applications, Computer Science, Early Childhood/Elementary Education, Environmental Science, Liberal Arts, Nursing, Psychology, Public Administration, Science, Secretarial Science, Special Education, Teacher Education.
Requirements: General education requirement.
Special: Courses offered in advertising design, anthropology, art, chemistry, communications, economics, English, general studies, health administration/education, history, humanities, math, music, philosophy, physical education, physics, political science, politics/international administration, Spanish, and urban planning. Associate degrees offered. Independent study. Pass/fail grading op-

tion. Cooperative education programs. Graduate school at which qualified undergraduates may take graduate-level courses. Cross-registration with other CUNY colleges. Teacher certification in elementary education.

Honors: Honors program.

Academic Assistance: Remedial reading, writing, and math. Nonremedial tutoring.

STUDENT LIFE. Housing: Commuter campus; no student housing.

Social atmosphere: Popular gathering places include the cafeteria, gym, and auditorium. Influencial groups include the Student Government Association, ADAFI, Back Stage Players, Black & Latino Male Initiative, MESE, and NABA. Popular events include the soccer tournament, fashion show, and presidential lecture series. Basically friendly and outgoing is how the editor of the student newspaper describes the campus. "Being a historically Black institution, most people are very conscious of the Afro-American experience."

Services and counseling/handicapped student services: Placement services. Health service. Counseling services for military students. Personal counseling. Career and academic guidance services. Physically disabled student services. Learning disabled program/services.

Campus organizations: Undergraduate student government. Student newspaper (ADAFI, published three times/semester). Yearbook. Radio station. National Third World Coalition. Dance club, meditation club, swimming club, theatre workshop, 30 organizations in all.

Religious organizations: Christian Club, Muslim Student Club.

Foreign student organizations: African, Caribbean, and Haitian groups.

ATHLETICS. Physical education requirements: One semester of physical education required.

Intercollegiate competition: 4% of students participate. Basketball (M,W), cross-country (M,W), soccer (M), softball (W), track (indoor) (M,W), track (outdoor) (M,W), track and field (indoor) (M,W), track and field (outdoor) (M,W), volleyball (W). Member of CUNY Athletic Conference, ECAC, Hudson Valley Women's Athletic Conference, NCAA Division III.

Intramural and club sports: 8% of students participate. Intramural basketball, bowling, softball, swimming, volleyball. Men's club martial arts. Women's club cheerleading, martial arts.

ADMISSIONS. Academic basis for candidate selection (in order of priority): Secondary school record, class rank.

Nonacademic basis for candidate selection: Geographical distribution is considered.

Requirements: Graduation from secondary school is required; GED is accepted. The following program of study is recommended: 3 units of English, 2 units of math, 1 unit of science. Search for Education, Elevation, and Knowledge (SEEK) and College Discovery programs for applicants not normally admissible.

Procedure: Application deadline is August 23. Notification of admission on rolling basis. Freshmen accepted for all terms.

Special programs: Admission may be deferred one semester. Credit may be granted through CLEP subject exams. Credit may be granted through challenge exams.

Transfer students: Transfer students accepted for all terms. In fall 1994, 29% of all new students were transfers into all classes. 454 transfer applications were received, 415 were accepted. Minimum 2.0 GPA required. Lowest course grade accepted is "D."

Admissions contact: Roberta Danneselser, Ph.D., Director of Admissions. 718 270-6024.

FINANCIAL AID. Available aid: Pell grants, SEOG, and Federal Nursing Student Scholarships. Perkins Loans (NDSL), Stafford Loans (GSL), NSL, and state loans. Tuition Assistance Program.

Supporting data/closing dates: School's own aid application: Deadline is August 15. Notification of awards on rolling basis.

Financial aid contact: Leila Haynes, Director of Financial Aid. 718 270-6038.

STUDENT EMPLOYMENT. Federal Work-Study Program. Students may expect to earn an average of $1,200 during school year. Off-campus part-time employment opportunities rated "fair."

COMPUTER FACILITIES. 25 IBM/IBM-compatible microcomputers. Students may access IBM minicomputer/mainframe systems.

Fees: None.

Hours: 9 AM-9 PM.

GRADUATE CAREER DATA. Highest graduate school enrollments: Columbia U, Long Island U, Pace U, SUNY branches. 56% of graduates choose careers in business and industry. Companies and businesses that hire graduates: IBM, various insurance companies.

PROMINENT ALUMNI/AE. Leroy Richardson and Alford Smith, physicians; Maxine O'Connor, unit coordinator/crisis intervention teacher; Vincent James, senior auditor, Blue Cross/Blue Shield; Winston Dove, senior accountant, Rockefeller Foundation.

City University of New York, New York City Technical College
Brooklyn, NY 11201-2983   **718 260-5000**

Undergraduate profile: 51% Black, 10% Asian-American, 23% Hispanic, 16% White. 99% are state residents; 16% are transfers. Average age of undergraduates is 25.

Enrollment. Undergraduates: 3,668 men, 3,657 women (full-time). Freshman class: 3,820 applicants, 2,335 enrolled.

Faculty. 319 full-time, 565 part-time; 185 Black, 619 White, 80 Other. 90% of faculty holds highest degree in specific field. Student/faculty ratio: 18 to 1.

1995-96 Costs. Tuition: $3,200 (state residents), $6,800 (out-of-state). Housing: None. Fees, books, misc. academic expenses (school's estimate): $460. Additional required fees: $60 (full-time), $19 (part-time).

PROFILE. CUNY New York City Technical College, founded in 1946, is a public institution. Its urban campus is located in Brooklyn.

Accreditation: MSACS. Professionally accredited by the Accreditation Board for Engineering and Technology, Inc., the American Bar Association, the American Dental Association, the National League for Nursing.

Religious orientation: City University of New York, New York City Technical College is non-sectarian; no religious requirements.

Library: Collections totaling 169,771 volumes and 930 periodical subscriptions.

Special facilities/museums: Art gallery, hotel and restaurant dining room, graphic arts lab.

Athletic facilities: Gymnasium, wrestling and weight rooms.

STUDENT BODY. Freshman profile: 63% of freshmen come from New York state public schools.

Undergraduate achievement: 65% of fall 1993 freshmen returned for fall 1994 term. 19% of entering class graduates.

Foreign students: 178 students are from out of the country. Countries represented include China, the Dominican Republic, Jamaica, Russia, the Ukraine, and Vietnam; 44 in all.

PROGRAMS OF STUDY. Degrees: B.S., B.Tech.

Majors: Engineering Technology, Graphic Arts, Hospitality Management, Human Services, Legal Assistant Studies, Telecommunications Technology.

Requirements: General education requirement.

Academic regulations: Minimum 2.0 GPA must be maintained.

Special: Associate degrees offered. Self-designed majors. Pass/fail grading option. Graduate school at which qualified undergraduates may take graduate-level courses. Continuing education. Study abroad in England, France, Germany, and Italy. ROTC at Long Island U, Brooklyn campus. AFROTC at Polytechnic U.

Honors: Honors program.

Academic Assistance: Remedial reading, writing, and math. Nonremedial tutoring.

STUDENT LIFE. Housing: Commuter campus; no student housing. Housing available at Brooklyn campus of Long Island U.

Services and counseling/handicapped student services: Placement services. Health service. Women's center. Counseling services for veteran students. Personal and psychological counseling. Career and academic guidance services. Physically disabled student services. Learning disabled services. Tape recorders. Tutors. Reader services for the blind.

Campus organizations: Undergraduate student government. Student newspaper (New Tech Times, published six times/year). Literary magazine. Yearbook. Black Cultural Workshop, Black Student Organization. Camera and photo club, conversation club, culinary arts club, gymnastics club, musical theatre group, disabled student club.

Foreign student organizations: Hispanic Student Organization. African Dance Club, Chinese Student Association.

ATHLETICS. Physical education requirements: None.

Intercollegiate competition: 1% of students participate. Basketball (M,W), soccer (M), volleyball (W). Member of City University of New York Athletic Conference, NJCAA.

Intramural and club sports: 1% of students participate. Intramural badminton, basketball, softball, table tennis, turkey trot, volleyball, weight training.

ADMISSIONS. Academic basis for candidate selection (in order of priority): Secondary school record or New York state equivalency diploma, class rank, school's recommendation.

Nonacademic basis for candidate selection: Character and personality, extracurricular participation, particular talent or ability, and alumni/ae relationship are considered.

Requirements: Graduation from secondary school is required; GED is accepted. No specific distribution of secondary school units required. CUNY skills assessment tests required.

Procedure: Suggest filing application by March 15. Application deadline is rolling. Notification of admission on rolling basis. Freshmen accepted for all terms.

Special programs: Admission may be deferred. Credit and/or placement may be granted through CEEB Advanced Placement exams for scores of 3 or higher. Credit and/or placement may be granted through CLEP general and subject exams. Credit and placement may be granted through Regents College and challenge exams and for military and life experience. Concurrent enrollment program.

Transfer students: Transfer students accepted for all terms. In fall 1994, 16% of all new students were transfers into all classes. 928 transfer applications were received, 771 were accepted. Application deadline is March 15 for fall; October 15 for spring. Minimum 2.0 GPA required. Lowest course grade accepted is "C." Maximum number of transferable credits is 30 semester hours from a two-year school and 94 semester hours from a four-year school. At least 34 semester hours must be completed at the college to receive degree.

Admissions contact: Arlene Matsumoto Floyd, M.B.A., Director of Admissions. 718 260-5500.

FINANCIAL AID. Available aid: Pell grants, SEOG, state scholarships and grants, school scholarships and grants, private scholarships and grants, and academic merit scholarships. Perkins Loans (NDSL), PLUS, Stafford Loans (GSL), NSL, school loans, and unsubsidized Stafford Loans. AMS and deferred payment plan.

Financial aid statistics: 36% of aid is not need-based. In 1994-95, 65% of all freshman aid applicants received aid.

Supporting data/closing dates: FAFSA/FAF: Priority filing date is June 30. School's own aid application: Priority filing date is June 30. Income tax forms: Priority filing date is June 30. Notification of awards begins in July.

Financial aid contact: Lamont Pittman, Director of Financial Aid. 718 260-5700.

STUDENT EMPLOYMENT. Federal Work-Study Program. 5% of full-time undergraduates work on campus during school year. Off-campus part-time employment opportunities rated "fair."

COMPUTER FACILITIES. 2,000 IBM/IBM-compatible and Apple/Macintosh microcomputers; 900 are networked. Students may access AT&T, IBM minicomputer/mainframe systems, BITNET, Internet. Client/LAN operating systems include Apple/Macintosh, DOS, Windows NT, LocalTalk/AppleTalk, Novell. Computers may be used only in conjunction with relevant courses.

Fees: Computer fee is included in tuition/fees.

GRADUATE CAREER DATA. 70% of graduates choose careers in business and industry. Companies and businesses that hire graduates: MCI, NYNEX.

PROMINENT ALUMNI/AE. Rocky Aoki, CEO, Benihana Restaurants and Foods; Michael Romano, executive chef, Union Square Cafe; Marie Venticinque, crime scene analyst, New York City District Attorney Office.

City University of New York, York College

Jamaica, NY 11451   718 262-2000

Undergraduate profile: 62% Black, 12% Asian-American, 17% Hispanic, 8% White, 1% Other. 48% are transfers. Average age of undergraduates is 31.

Enrollment. Undergraduates: 1,499 men, 2,392 women (full-time). Freshman class: 692 enrolled.

Faculty. 160 full-time, 306 part-time; 114 Black, 264 White, 88 Other. 64% of faculty holds doctoral degree. Student/faculty ratio: 19 to 1.

Test score averages/ranges. Average SAT I scores: 336 verbal, 383 math. Range of SAT I scores of middle 50%: 250-400 verbal, 320-420 math.

1995-96 Costs. Tuition: $3,200 (state residents), $6,800 (out-of-state). Housing: None. Fees, books, misc. academic expenses (school's estimate): $682.

PROFILE. York College, founded in 1966, is a public institution offering liberal and career education. Its 50-acre campus is located in Jamaica.

Accreditation: MSACS. Professionally accredited by the American Medical Association (CAHEA), the Council on Social Work Education.

Religious orientation: City University of New York, York College is nonsectarian; no religious requirements.

Library: Collections totaling over 153,000 volumes, 11,000 periodical subscriptions, and 110,000 microform items.

Special facilities/museums: Center for educational technology.

Athletic facilities: Gymnasium, swimming pool, fitness center, handball and tennis courts, indoor track, outdoor track and field, soccer and softball fields.

STUDENT BODY. Freshman profile: 1% of freshmen who took SAT I scored 600 or over on verbal, 3% scored 600 or over on math; 4% scored 500 or over on verbal, 12% scored 500 or over on math; 29% scored 400 or over on verbal, 37% scored 400 or over on math; 66% scored 300 or over on verbal, 85% scored 300 or over on math. 16% of accepted applicants took SAT I. 46% of freshmen come from public schools.

Undergraduate achievement: 70% of fall 1993 freshmen returned for fall 1994 term. 5% of entering class graduates.

Foreign students: 103 students are from out of the country. Countries represented include Bangladesh, the Dominican Republic, Haiti, India, and Jamaica; 32 in all.

PROGRAMS OF STUDY. Degrees: B.A., B.S.

Majors: Accounting, African-American Studies, Anthropology, Art History, Bilingual Program, Biology, Biotechnology, Business Administration, Chemistry, Community Health Education, Early Childhood Education, Economics, Elementary Education, English, Environmental Health Science, Fine Arts, French, Geology, Gerontology, Health Education, History, Information Systems Management, Italian, Marketing, Mathematics, Medical Technology, Movement Science, Music, Nursing, Occupational Therapy, Philosophy, Physical Education, Physics, Political Science, Psychology, Social Work, Sociology, Spanish, Special Education, Speech, Studio Art.

Distribution of degrees: The majors with the highest enrollments are business administration, accounting, and information systems management; African-American studies, anthropology, and history have the lowest.

Requirements: General education requirement.

Special: Concentrations offered in Judaic, Latin American, and Puerto Rican studies. Courses offered in behavioral science, communications, comparative literature, humanities, and managerial studies. Self-designed majors. Independent study. Pass/fail grading option. Internships. Cooperative education programs. Preprofessional programs in medicine, dentistry, and engineering. Teacher certification in early childhood, elementary, secondary, and special education. Study abroad in France.

Honors: Honors program. Honor societies.

Academic Assistance: Nonremedial tutoring.

STUDENT LIFE. Housing: Commuter campus; no student housing.

Services and counseling/handicapped student services: Placement services. Health service. Counseling services for veteran, and older students. Personal counseling. Career and academic guidance services. Learning disabled services.

Campus organizations: Undergraduate student government. Student newspaper (Pandora's Box). Literary magazine. Yearbook. TV station. Black Student Caucus. Gospel chorus, international dancers company, theatre arts association, biology, chemistry, entrepreneur, environmental health science, future teacher, geology, health/physical education, occupational therapy, psychology, and social work clubs, premed society, GQ fashion club, chess and photography clubs, student activities club, women's club, 55 organizations in all.

Religious organizations: Chinese Christian Fellowship, Joy Christian Fellowship, Muslim Student's Group.

Foreign student organizations: Latin Caucus, Puerto Rican Organization. African Student Association, Bangladesh Student Association, Caribbean Student Association, Chinese Students and Friends, Haitian perspectives, Indian-Pakistan-Bangladesh Club, Islamic Students, Korean Student Club, Latin American folkloric, West Indian cultural clubs.

ATHLETICS. Physical education requirements: Two credits of physical education required.

Intercollegiate competition: 2% of students participate. Basketball (M,W), cheerleading (W), cross-country (M,W), soccer (M), tennis (M), track (indoor) (M,W), track (outdoor) (M,W), track and field (indoor) (M,W), track and field (outdoor) (M,W), volleyball (M,W). Member of CUNY-AC, ECAC, Hudson Valley Women's Athletic Conference, MCTC, NCAA Division III.

Intramural and club sports: 14% of students participate. Intramural badminton, basketball, flag football, soccer, swimming, table tennis, volleyball.

ADMISSIONS. Academic basis for candidate selection (in order of priority): Secondary school record, class rank.

Requirements: Graduation from secondary school is required; GED is accepted. 7 units and the following program of study are required: 4 units of English, 2 units of math, 1 unit of science. Admissions criteria determined by number of openings available and by action of CUNY Board of Trustees (subject to change each semester). Special admissions requirements for health profession, social work, and cooperative education program applicants. Search for Education, Elevation, and Knowledge (SEEK) program for applicants not normally admissible. Flexible requirements for veterans and applicants age 25 and older. Campus visit recommended.

Procedure: Suggest filing application by February 1; no deadline. Notification of admission on rolling basis. Freshmen accepted for all terms.

Special programs: Admission may be deferred one semester. Credit and/or placement may be granted through CEEB Advanced Placement exams for scores of 3 or higher. Credit and/or placement may be granted through CLEP subject exams. Credit and placement may be granted through challenge exams and for military and life experience. Early entrance/early admission program. Concurrent enrollment program.

Transfer students: Transfer students accepted for all terms. In fall 1994, 48% of all new students were transfers into all classes. Minimum 2.0 GPA required. Lowest course grade accepted is "C." Maximum number of transferable credits is 64 semester hours from a two-year school and 98 semester hours from a four-year school. At least 30 semester hours must be completed at the college to receive degree.

Admissions contact: Sally Nelson, M.A., Director of Admissions. 718 262-2165.

FINANCIAL AID. Available aid: Pell grants, SEOG, state scholarships and grants, school scholarships, private scholarships, and aid for undergraduate foreign students. Perkins Loans (NDSL), PLUS, Stafford Loans (GSL), and unsubsidized Stafford Loans. Tuition Plan Inc. and deferred payment plan.

Financial aid statistics: In 1994-95, 85% of all freshman aid applicants received aid; 85% of freshman aid applicants. Average amounts of aid awarded freshmen: Scholarships and grants, $4,802.

Supporting data/closing dates: FAFSA/FAF: Priority filing date is May 1; accepted on rolling basis. School's own aid application: Accepted on rolling basis. Income tax forms: Priority filing date is May 1. Notification of awards on rolling basis.

Financial aid contact: Alan Rumberg, M.P.A., Director of Financial Aid. 718 262-2230.

STUDENT EMPLOYMENT. Federal Work-Study Program. 70% of full-time undergraduates work on campus during school year. Students may expect to earn an average of $1,200 during school year.

COMPUTER FACILITIES. 530 IBM/IBM-compatible and Apple/Macintosh microcomputers; 300 are networked. Students may access Digital, IBM minicomputer/mainframe systems, BITNET, Internet. Client/LAN operating systems include Apple/Macintosh, DOS, DEC. Computer facilities are available to all students.

Fees: $25 computer fee included in tuition/fees.

Hours: 9 AM-9 PM (M-Th); 9 AM-5 PM (F, Sa).

Claflin College

Orangeburg, SC 29115   **803 534-2710**

Undergraduate profile. N/A.

Enrollment. Undergraduates: 360 men, 547 women (full-time). Freshman class: 170 applicants, 564 accepted, 409 enrolled.

Faculty. 54 full-time; 5 part-time. 61% of faculty holds highest degree in specific field. Student/faculty ratio: 13 to 1.

Test score averages/ranges. Range of SAT I scores of middle 50%: 300-400 verbal, 300-400 math.

1995-96 Costs. Tuition: $4,678. Room: $1,120. Board: $1,500.

PROFILE. Claflin, founded in 1869, is a church-affiliated college. Its 25-acre campus is located in Orangeburg.

Accreditation: SACS.

Religious orientation: Claflin College is affiliated with the United Methodist Church; religious observance recommended.

STUDENT BODY. Freshman profile: 100% of accepted applicants took SAT I.

Foreign students: 103 students are from out of the country. Countries represented include Bangladesh, the Dominican Republic, Haiti, India, and Jamaica; 32 in all.

PROGRAMS OF STUDY. Degrees: B.A., B.S., B.S.Ed.

Majors: Art, Biology, Business Administration, Chemistry, Education, Engineering, English, English Education, Fine Arts, History, Mathematics, Mathematics/Computer Science, Mathematics Education, Music, Office Supervision/Management, Physical Education, Secondary Education, Social Sciences, Sociology, Theological Studies.

Requirements: General education requirement.

Special: Courses offered in computer science, French, physics, psychology, and Spanish. Thirteen College Curriculum Program provides intensive counseling, support services, and enriched academic courses during freshman year. Double majors. Internships. Graduate school at which qualified undergraduates may take graduate-level courses. Preprofessional programs in law and medicine. Teacher certification in elementary and secondary education. AFROTC. ROTC at South Carolina State Coll.

Honors: Honors program.

STUDENT LIFE. Housing: Women's and men's dorms.
Services and counseling/handicapped student services: Placement services. Counseling services for military and veteran students. Career and academic guidance services.
Campus organizations: Undergraduate student government. Student newspaper. NAACP. Band, choir, instrumental ensembles, modern dance group, Theatre Guild, Campus Gold (Girl Scouts), academic groups. Four fraternities, no chapter houses; four sororities, no chapter houses.
Religious organizations: Church School, Oxford Club, Student Christian Association.

ATHLETICS. Physical education requirements: Three semester hours of physical education required.
Intramural and club sports: Intramural basketball, softball, table tennis, volleyball.

ADMISSIONS. Academic basis for candidate selection (in order of priority): Secondary school record, standardized test scores, school's recommendation.
Nonacademic basis for candidate selection: Character and personality are important.
Requirements: Graduation from secondary school is required; GED is accepted. 16 units and the following program of study are required: 4 units of English, 2 units of math, 2 units of science, 2 units of foreign language, 1 unit of social studies. Conditional admission possible for applicants not meeting standard requirements. SAT I is required; ACT may be substituted. Admissions interview recommended. No off-campus interviews.
Procedure: Suggest filing application by July 30; no deadline. Notification of admission on rolling basis. $15 room deposit. Freshmen accepted for all terms.
Special programs: Credit and/or placement may be granted through CLEP general and subject exams.
Transfer students: Transfer students accepted for all terms. Lowest course grade accepted is "C."
Admissions contact: George Lee, Director of Admissions.

FINANCIAL AID. Available aid: Pell grants and SEOG. Perkins Loans (NDSL) and Stafford Loans (GSL).
Supporting data/closing dates: FAFSA/FAF: Deadline is June 1.

STUDENT EMPLOYMENT. Federal Work-Study Program.

Clark Atlanta University

Atlanta, GA 30314 | 404 880-8000

Undergraduate profile. 99% Black, 1% Asian-American. 37% are state residents; 30% are transfers. Average age of undergraduates is 20.
Enrollment. Undergraduates: 1,138 men, 2,626 women (full-time). Freshman class: 9,545 applicants, 4,074 accepted, 841 enrolled. Graduate enrollment: 445 men, 834 women.
Faculty. 316 full-time. Student/faculty ratio: 16 to 1.
Test score averages/ranges. Average SAT I scores: 874 combined. Average ACT scores: 19 composite.
1995-96 Costs. Tuition: $8,300. Room: $1,170. Board: $1,085. Fees, books, misc. academic expenses (school's estimate): $745.

PROFILE. Clark Atlanta, founded in 1869, is a private university. Academic divisions include General Education, Humanities, Natural Sciences and Mathematics, and Sociocultural Studies. Its campus is located one mile west of downtown Atlanta.

Accreditation: SACS. Professionally accredited by the American Dietetic Association, the American Physical Therapy Association, the Council on Social Work Education, the National Council for Accreditation of Teacher Education.
Religious orientation: Clark Atlanta University is affiliated with the United Methodist Church; no religious requirements.
Library: Collections totaling over 750,000 volumes.
Special facilities/museums: Language lab.

Athletic facilities: Swimming pool, gymnasium, weight room, football fields, basketball, tennis courts.

STUDENT BODY. Freshman profile: 75% of accepted applicants took SAT I; 25% took ACT.
Undergraduate achievement: 78% of fall 1993 freshmen returned for fall 1994 term.
Foreign students: 255 students are from out of the country. Countries represented include the Bahamas, Bermuda, Ghana, India, Nigeria, and South Africa; 64 in all.

PROGRAMS OF STUDY. Degrees: B.A., B.S., B.Soc.Work.
Majors: Accounting, Art, Art Education, Biology, Bookkeeping, Business Administration, Business Education, Chemistry, Child Development, Computer Science, Dietetics, Drama, Early Childhood, Educational Studies, Elementary Education, English, Fine Arts, French, German, History, Home Economics Education, Human Resources, Mass Communications, Mathematics, Medical Illustration, Medical Records Administration, Medical Technology, Music, Music Education, Nutrition, Office Administration, Philosophy, Physical Education, Physical Therapy, Physics, Political Science, Psychology, Religion, Restaurant/Institutional Management, Social Welfare, Sociology, Spanish, Speech Communication.
Requirements: General education requirement.
Academic regulations: Freshmen must maintain minimum 1.76 GPA; sophomores, juniors, seniors, 2.00 GPA.
Special: Established and self-designed interdepartmental majors. Cooperative general science program for non-science majors. Mandatory freshman orientation seminars. Double majors. Dual degrees. Independent study. Accelerated study. Pass/fail grading option. Preprofessional programs in medicine and pharmacy. 3-2 engineering program with Auburn U, Boston U, Georgia Tech, and North Carolina A&T State U. Member of Atlanta University Center Consortium; all undergraduate majors are open to Clark Atlanta U students. Affiliated with Southern Center for Studies in Public Policy. Teacher certification in early childhood, elementary, secondary, and special education. Study abroad possible. ROTC and NROTC.
Honors: Honors program.
Academic Assistance: Remedial reading, writing, math, and study skills. Nonremedial tutoring.

STUDENT LIFE. Housing: Students may live on or off campus. Coed, women's, and men's dorms. 36% of students live in college housing.
Services and counseling/handicapped student services: Placement services. Health service. Counseling services for veteran students. Personal and psychological counseling. Career and academic guidance services. Religious counseling. Physically disabled student services. Learning disabled services. Tutors.
Campus organizations: Undergraduate student government. Student newspaper (Panther, published once/week). Yearbook. Radio and TV stations. Band, choir, orchestra, jazz ensemble, musical theatre, community service projects, special-interest groups, 60 organizations in all. Four fraternities, no chapter houses; four sororities, no chapter houses.
Religious organizations: Campus Ministry.

ATHLETICS. Physical education requirements: Two semesters of physical education required.
Intercollegiate competition: 1% of students participate. Basketball (M,W), cheerleading (W), football (M), tennis (M,W), track and field (outdoor) (M,W), volleyball (W). Member of NCAA Division II, Southern Intercollegiate Athletic Conference.
Intramural and club sports: 1% of students participate. Intramural basketball, softball, swimming, volleyball, weight lifting. Men's club baseball.

ADMISSIONS. Academic basis for candidate selection (in order of priority): Secondary school record, standardized test scores.
Nonacademic basis for candidate selection: Particular talent or ability is important. Extracurricular participation and alumni/ae relationship are considered.
Requirements: Graduation from secondary school is required; GED is accepted. 18 units and the following program of study are recommended: 4 units of English, 3 units of math, 2 units of science, 2 units of foreign language, 2 units of social studies, 5 units of electives. Applicants not meeting standard requirements may be considered. SAT I is required; ACT may be substituted.

Procedure: Suggest filing application by March 1. Application deadline is rolling. Notification of admission on rolling basis. $100 tuition deposit, refundable until July 1. $750 room deposit, refundable until July 1. Freshmen accepted for all terms.

Special programs: Admission may be deferred one semester. Early entrance/early admission program. Concurrent enrollment program.

Transfer students: Transfer students accepted for all terms. In fall 1994, 30% of all new students were transfers into all classes. 1,478 transfer applications were received, 759 were accepted. Application deadline is March 1 for fall; November 1 for spring. Minimum 2.0 GPA required. Lowest course grade accepted is "C." At least 30 semester hours must be completed at the university to receive degree.

Admissions contact: Clifton B. Rawles, M.A., Director of Admissions. 404 880-8017.

FINANCIAL AID. Available aid: Pell grants, SEOG, state scholarships and grants, school scholarships and grants, ROTC scholarships, academic merit scholarships, athletic scholarships, and United Negro College Fund. Perkins Loans (NDSL), PLUS, and Stafford Loans (GSL). Deferred payment plan.

Financial aid statistics: In 1994-95, 89% of all undergraduate aid applicants received aid; 94% of freshman aid applicants. Average amounts of aid awarded freshmen: Scholarships and grants, $5,800; loans, $3,000.

Supporting data/closing dates: FAFSA: Priority filing date is April 30. Notification of awards begins May 1.

Financial aid contact: Gwendolyn Coleman, M.A., Director of Financial Aid. 404 880-8066.

STUDENT EMPLOYMENT. Federal Work-Study Program. Institutional employment. 20% of full-time undergraduates work on campus during school year. Students may expect to earn an average of $2,000 during school year. Off-campus part-time employment opportunities rated "fair."

COMPUTER FACILITIES. IBM/IBM-compatible microcomputers. Students may access Digital, IBM, SUN minicomputer/mainframe systems, Internet. Residence halls may be equipped with stand-alone microcomputers. Client/LAN operating systems include DOS, Novell. Computer facilities are available to all students.

Fees: Computer fee is included in tuition/fees.

Coppin State College

Baltimore, MD 21216　　　　　　　　　　　　　　**410 383-4500**

Undergraduate profile. 92% Black, .5% Asian-American, .5% Hispanic, 1% Native American, 4% White, 2% Other. 91% are state residents. Average age of undergraduates is 25.

Enrollment. Undergraduates: 771 men, 1,385 women (full-time). Freshman class: 1,976 applicants, 888 accepted, 447 enrolled. Graduate enrollment: 123 men, 301 women.

Faculty. 4 full-time, 119 part-time; 171 Black, 49 White, 12 Other. 85% of faculty holds doctoral degree. Student/faculty ratio: 25 to 1.

Test score averages/ranges. Average SAT I scores: 376 verbal, 411 math. Average ACT scores: 19 English, 21 math, 20 composite.

1995-96 Costs. Tuition: $5,498 (state residents), $11,926 (out-of-state). Room & board: $4,640.

PROFILE. Coppin State, founded in 1900, is a public college. Programs are offered through the Divisions of Arts and Sciences, Continuing Education, Education, and Nursing. Its 38-acre campus is located in Baltimore.

Accreditation: MSACS. Professionally accredited by the National Council for Accreditation of Teacher Education.

Religious orientation: Coppin State College is nonsectarian; no religious requirements.

Library: Collections totaling 134,983 volumes, 665 periodical subscriptions, and 231,573 microform items.

Special facilities/museums: Language lab, school of special education, TV studio.

Athletic facilities: Gymnasium, training, weight, and wrestling rooms, dance studio, basketball, handball, racquetball, tennis, and volleyball courts, swimming pool, baseball and other athletic fields.

STUDENT BODY. Freshman profile: 98% of accepted applicants took SAT I; 2% took ACT. 85% of freshmen come from public schools.

Undergraduate achievement: 60% of entering class graduates. 25% of students who complete a degree program go on to graduate study within five years.

Foreign students: 23 students are from out of the country. Countries represented include Canada, India, Kenya, Liberia, Nigeria, and Trinidad/Tobago; 19 in all.

PROGRAMS OF STUDY. Degrees: B.A., B.S.

Majors: Biology, Computer Science, Criminal Justice, Early Childhood Education, Elementary Education, English, General Science/Chemistry, History, Management Science, Mathematics, Nursing, Philosophy, Psychology, Social Science/Social Work, Social Sciences, Special Education.

Distribution of degrees: The majors with the highest enrollments are management science, psychology, and nursing; history, philosophy, and chemistry have the lowest.

Requirements: General education requirement.

Academic regulations: Freshmen must maintain minimum 1.2 GPA; sophomores, 1.6 GPA; juniors, 1.8 GPA; seniors, 2.0 GPA.

Special: Courses offered in African-American studies, art, economics, French, geography, international studies, journalism, Latin, linguistics, mass communications, music, physical science, physics, political science, Spanish, speech/theatre, and urban recreation. Undergraduate Record Exam, major exam, or professional school entrance exam required for graduation. Double majors. Dual degrees. Internships. Cooperative education programs. Graduate school at which qualified undergraduates may take graduate-level courses. Preprofessional programs in pharmacy, engineering, and physical therapy. Cooperative social work program with U of Maryland at Baltimore County. Dual-degree programs in chemistry/engineering, general science/engineering, mathematics/engineering, predental/general science, and prepharmacy/general science with U of Maryland. Prephysical therapy program with U of Maryland. Member of consortium with Bowie State U, Frostburg State U, Salisbury State U, Towson State U, and U of Maryland at Baltimore, Baltimore County, College Park, and Eastern Shore. Teacher certification in elementary, secondary, and special education. Certification in specific subject areas. ROTC at Morgan State U.

Honors: Honors program. Honor societies.

Academic Assistance: Remedial reading and math. Nonremedial tutoring.

STUDENT LIFE. Housing: Students may live on or off campus. Coed dorms.

Services and counseling/handicapped student services: Placement services. Health service. Counseling services for veteran students. Personal counseling. Career and academic guidance services. Physically disabled student services. Learning disabled services. Reader services for the blind.

Campus organizations: Undergraduate student government. Student newspaper (Courier, published twice/semester). Yearbook. TV station. African-American Student Society, Association of Black Journalists. Gospel choir, Coppin Dancers, Coppin Players, College Democrats, Democrats of America, Women's Symposium, professional and departmental groups, 45 organizations in all. 12 fraternities, no chapter houses; 12 sororities, no chapter houses. 1% of men join a fraternity. 1% of women join a sorority.

Religious organizations: Alpha Nu Omega.

Foreign student organizations: Korean Student Club.

ATHLETICS. Physical education requirements: One semester of physical education required.

Intercollegiate competition: 7% of students participate. Baseball (M), basketball (M,W), bowling (M,W), cheerleading (W), cross-country (M,W), diving (M,W), softball (W), swimming (M,W), tennis (M,W), track (indoor) (M,W), track (outdoor) (M,W), track and field (indoor) (M,W), track and field (outdoor) (M,W), volleyball (W), wrestling (M). Member of Mid-Eastern Athletic Conference, NCAA Division I.

Intramural and club sports: 5% of students participate. Intramural basketball, flag football, rugby, volleyball.

ADMISSIONS. Academic basis for candidate selection (in order of priority): Secondary school record, standardized test scores, school's recommendation, class rank, essay.

Nonacademic basis for candidate selection: Character and personality, extracurricular participation, geographical distribution, and alumni/ae relationship are considered.

Requirements: Graduation from secondary school is required; GED is accepted. The following program of study is required: 4 units of English, 3 units of math, 2 units of lab science, 2 units of foreign language, 3 units of social studies. Minimum composite ACT score of 18 (combined SAT I score of 730) and minimum 2.3 GPA required. Separate application required of nursing program applicants. SAT I is required; ACT may be substituted. Campus visit and interview recommended. Off-campus interviews available with an admissions representative.

Procedure: Take SAT I or ACT by March of 12th year. Suggest filing application by January 15. Application deadline is July 15. Notification of admission on rolling basis. $25 nonrefundable tuition deposit. $100 refundable room deposit. Freshmen accepted for all terms.

Special programs: Admission may be deferred one year. Credit may be granted through CEEB Advanced Placement for scores of 3 or higher. Credit and/or placement may be granted through CLEP general exams. Credit may be granted through CLEP subject exams. Placement may be granted for military experience. Credit and placement may be granted through challenge exams. Early decision program. Deadline for applying for early decision is January 15. Early entrance/early admission program. Concurrent enrollment program.

Transfer students: Transfer students accepted for all terms. In fall 1994, 657 transfer applications were received, 413 were accepted. Application deadline is July 15 for fall; December 15 for spring. Minimum 2.0 GPA required. Lowest course grade accepted is "D." Maximum number of transferable credits is 70 semester hours from a two-year school and 90 semester hours from a four-year school. At least 30 semester hours must be completed at the college to receive degree.

Admissions contact: Allen D. Mosley, M.S., Director of Admissions. 410 383-5990.

FINANCIAL AID. Available aid: Pell grants, SEOG, state scholarships, school scholarships and grants, private scholarships and grants, academic merit scholarships, and athletic scholarships. Perkins Loans (NDSL), PLUS, Stafford Loans (GSL), and unsubsidized Stafford Loans. Deferred payment plan.

Financial aid statistics: 12% of aid is not need-based. In 1993-94, 85% of all undergraduate aid applicants received aid; 85% of freshman aid applicants. Average amounts of aid awarded freshmen: Scholarships and grants, $1,680; loans, $1,500.

Supporting data/closing dates: FAFSA/FAF: Priority filing date is May 3; deadline is July 15. School's own aid application: Priority filing date is May 3; deadline is July 15. State aid form: Priority filing date is January 2; deadline is March 1. Notification of awards on rolling basis.

Financial aid contact: Ron Smith, M.S., Director of Financial Aid. 410 383-5930.

STUDENT EMPLOYMENT. Federal Work-Study Program. Institutional employment. 40% of full-time undergraduates work on campus during school year. Students may expect to earn an average of $2,500 during school year. Off-campus part-time employment opportunities rated "excellent."

COMPUTER FACILITIES. 130 IBM/IBM-compatible and Apple/Macintosh microcomputers. Computer facilities are available to all students.

Fees: None.

GRADUATE CAREER DATA. Highest graduate school enrollments: Johns Hopkins U, U of Maryland at Baltimore County.

PROMINENT ALUMNI/AE. Bishop Robinson, commissioner, Baltimore City Police; Milton Allen, state supreme court justice; Vondalu Clark, assistant superintendent, Baltimore Public Schools; Dr. Patricia Schmoke, optometrist; Quentin Lawson, vice-chairperson, Maryland Commission of Higher Education.

Delaware State University

Dover, DE 19901-2275   **302 739-4917**

Undergraduate profile. 68% Black, 2% Hispanic, 1% Asian-American, 1% Native American, 26% White, 2% Other. 55% are state residents; 23% are transfers. Average age of undergraduates is 21.

Enrollment. Undergraduates: 1,137 men, 1,425 women (full-time). Freshman class: 2,169 applicants, 1,461 accepted, 734 enrolled. Graduate enrollment: 76 men, 164 women.

Faculty. 174 full-time, 50 part-time; 78 Black, 76 White, 20 Other. 67% of faculty holds doctoral degree. Student/faculty ratio: 15 to 1.

Test score averages/ranges. N/A.

1995-96 Costs. Tuition: $2,390 (state residents), $5,872 (out-of-state). Room & board: $4,310. Fees, books, misc. academic expenses (school's estimate): $500.

PROFILE. Delaware State, founded in 1891, is a public university. Its 400-acre campus is located one mile north of Dover's city limits.

Accreditation: MSACS. Professionally accredited by the Council on Social Work Education, the National League for Nursing.

Religious orientation: Delaware State University is nonsectarian; no religious requirements.

Library: Collections totaling 179,082 volumes, 2,850 periodical subscriptions, 81,482 microform items, 30 CD-ROM titles, and 5,641 audiovisual items.

Special facilities/museums: Art gallery, language lab, observatory, herbarium.

Athletic facilities: Gymnasium, swimming pool, racquetball courts, track, playing fields.

STUDENT BODY. Freshman profile: 80% of freshmen come from public schools.

Foreign students: Countries represented include Bermuda, Cameroon, China, Honduras, Kenya, and Nigeria; 46 in all.

PROGRAMS OF STUDY. Degrees: B.A., B.S., B.Tech.

Majors: Accounting, Agribusiness, Agribusiness Technology, Agricultural Education, Agriculture, Airway Science, Art/Business, Art Education, Biology, Botany, Business Administration, Business Education, Business/Secretarial Technologies, Chemical Engineering, Chemical Laboratory Technology/Environmental Technology, Chemistry, Chemistry/Chemical Engineering, Child Development/Family Relations, Civil Engineering, Clothing/Textiles/Related Arts, Community Health, Criminal Justice Technology, Data Processing, Dental Assisting Technology, Distributive Education, Drama/Speech Communication Education, Early Childhood Education, Early Childhood/Exceptional Children, Economics, Electrical Engineering, Elementary Education, Engineering Technology, English, Environmental Health, Fire Protection, Fisheries Management, Food Service Management Technology, Foods/Nutrition, French, General Arts, General Resource Management, Health Education, Health/Physical Education, History, Home Economics, Home Economics Education, Human Services Technology, Journalism, Library Studies, Library Technology, Marketing, Marketing Education, Mathematics, Mathematics/Computer Science, Mathematics Education, Mathematics/Mechanical Engineering, Mechanical/Aerospace Engineering, Medical Laboratory Technologies, Music, Natural Resources Technology, Nursing, Occupational Teacher Education, Occupational/Vocational Guidance of Children, Park Administration/Natural Resources, Park Management/Recreation, Physics, Physics/Civil Engineering, Physics Education, Physics/Electrical Engineering, Physics/Mechanical/Aerospace Engineering, Plant Sciences, Political Science, Pre-Study in Medically Allied Fields, Psychology, Recreation, Science Education, Science Education Technology, Secretarial/Related Business Subjects, Secretarial Science, Social Studies, Social Work, Sociology, Soil/Water Management, Spanish, Special Education, Theatre, Urban Affairs, Vegetation Management.

Distribution of degrees: The majors with the highest enrollments are business administration, marketing, and accounting; physics education has the lowest.

Requirements: General education requirement.

Academic regulations: Minimum 1.7 GPA must be maintained.

Special: Minors offered in Black studies and women's studies. Courses offered in astronomy and philosophy. Technology program. Self-designed majors. Double majors. Dual degrees. Independent study. Accelerated study. Pass/fail grading option. Internships. Cooperative education programs. Graduate school at which qualified undergraduates may take graduate-level courses. Preprofessional programs in law, veterinary science, and dentistry. Exchange program with U of Delaware. Teacher certification in early childhood, elementary, secondary, and special education. Study abroad in China. ROTC and AFROTC.

Honors: Honors program.

Academic Assistance: Remedial reading, writing, math, and study skills. Nonremedial tutoring.

STUDENT LIFE. Housing: Students may live on or off campus. Women's and men's dorms. 36% of students live in college housing.

Services and counseling/handicapped student services: Placement services. Health service. Day care. Counseling services for veteran students. Career and academic guidance services. Physically disabled student services. Notetaking services. Tape recorders.

Campus organizations: Undergraduate student government. Student newspaper (Hornet, published once/month). Yearbook. Radio station. Art, writers, and jazz clubs, band and choir, debating, drama guild, athletic and departmental groups, commuter club, 53 organizations in all. Five fraternities, no chapter houses; four sororities, no chapter houses. 4% of men join a fraternity. 4% of women join a sorority.

Foreign student organizations: International Student Association.

ATHLETICS. Physical education requirements: None.

Intercollegiate competition: 10% of students participate. Baseball (M), basketball (M,W), cheerleading (M,W), cross-country (M,W), football (M), softball (W), tennis (M,W), track (indoor) (M,W), track (outdoor) (M,W), track and field (indoor) (M,W), track and field (outdoor) (M,W), volleyball (W), wrestling (M). Member of ECAC, Mid-Eastern Athletic Conference, NCAA Division I, NCAA Division I-AA for football.

Intramural and club sports: 12% of students participate. Intramural basketball, bowling, football, jogging, racquetball, softball, swimming, tennis, track/field, volleyball, weight lifting. Men's club soccer.

ADMISSIONS. Academic basis for candidate selection (in order of priority): Secondary school record, standardized test scores, school's recommendation, class rank, essay.

Nonacademic basis for candidate selection: Character and personality and extracurricular participation are important. Particular talent or ability and alumni/ae relationship are considered.

Requirements: Graduation from secondary school is required; GED is accepted. 15 units and the following program of study are required: 4 units of English, 2 units of math, 2 units of science including 1 unit of lab, 2 units of social studies, 5 units of academic electives. Minimum 2.0 GPA required. SAT I or ACT is required. Campus visit and interview recommended. Off-campus interviews available with an admissions representative.

Procedure: Take SAT I or ACT by July of 12th year. Suggest filing application by June 1. Application deadline is November 1. Notification of admission on rolling basis. Reply is required by June 30. $100 nonrefundable room deposit. Freshmen accepted for all terms.

Special programs: Placement may be granted through CEEB Advanced Placement exams. Credit and/or placement may be granted through CLEP general and subject exams. Credit and placement may be granted through DANTES exams and for military experience. Concurrent enrollment program.

Transfer students: Transfer students accepted for all terms. In fall 1994, 23% of all new students were transfers into all classes. 598 transfer applications were received, 340 were accepted. Application deadline is June 1 for fall; November 1 for spring. Minimum 2.0 GPA required. Lowest course grade accepted is "C." At least 30 semester hours must be completed at the university to receive degree.

Admissions contact: Jethro C. Williams, Director of Admissions. 302 739-4917.

FINANCIAL AID. Available aid: Pell grants, SEOG, state scholarships and grants, school scholarships and grants, private scholarships and grants, ROTC scholarships, academic merit scholarships, and athletic scholarships. Perkins Loans (NDSL), PLUS, Stafford Loans (GSL), state loans, school loans, private loans, and unsubsidized Stafford loans. Tuition Plan Inc. and deferred payment plan. Education Financing Plan.

Financial aid statistics: In 1994-95, 84% of all undergraduate aid applicants received aid; 83% of freshman aid applicants. Average amounts of aid awarded freshmen: Scholarships and grants, $2,824; loans, $3,096.

Supporting data/closing dates: FAFSA: Priority filing date is February 28. School's own aid application: Priority filing date is May 1. State aid form: Priority filing date is May 1. Notification of awards on rolling basis.

Financial aid contact: Martha Hopkins, M.A., Director of Financial Aid. 302 739-4908.

STUDENT EMPLOYMENT. Federal Work-Study Program. Institutional employment. 7% of full-time undergraduates work on campus during school year. Students may expect to earn an average of $2,000 during school year. Off-campus part-time employment opportunities rated "excellent."

COMPUTER FACILITIES. 192 IBM/IBM-compatible microcomputers; 88 are networked. Students may access IBM minicomputer/mainframe systems, Internet. Client/LAN operating systems include DOS, Novell. Computer facilities are available to all students.

Fees: None.

GRADUATE CAREER DATA. Companies and businesses that hire graduates: DuPont, Kodak, Hercules, banks, retail firms.

PROMINENT ALUMNI/AE. Kent Amos, former vice president, Xerox; John Sims, vice president, Digital Equipment Corp.; William Granville, vice president, Mobil Oil; Wayne Gilcrest, Maryland congressman; Wanda Wilson, veterinarian.

Dillard University

New Orleans, LA 70122   **504 283-8822**

Undergraduate profile. 97% Black, 2% White, .1% Asian-American, .9% Other. 38% are state residents; 26% are transfers.

Enrollment. Undergraduates: 337 men, 1,207 women (full-time). Freshman class: 2,117 applicants, 1,582 accepted, 547 enrolled.

Faculty. 112 full-time, 11 part-time; 84 Black, 36 Other. 63% of faculty holds doctoral degree. Student/faculty ratio: 15 to 1.

Test score averages/ranges. Average SAT I scores: 900 combined. Average ACT scores: 19 composite.

1995-96 Costs. Tuition: $7,000. Room & board: $3,750.

PROFILE. Dillard, a church-affiliated, liberal arts university, was formed through the 1930 merger of New Orleans University and Straight College. Programs are offered through the Divisions of Business Administration, Education, Humanities, Natural Sciences, Nursing, and Social Sciences. Its 46-acre campus is located in a residential section of New Orleans. Campus architecture is predominantly neoclassical in style.

Accreditation: SACS. Professionally accredited by the National Association of Schools of Music, the National League for Nursing.

Religious orientation: Dillard University is an interdenominational Christian school.

Library: Collections totaling over 144,000 volumes and 682 periodical subscriptions.

STUDENT BODY. Freshman profile: Majority of accepted applicants took ACT. 61% of freshmen come from public schools.

Undergraduate achievement: 86% of fall 1993 freshmen returned for fall 1994 term. 79% of entering class graduates. 41% of students who complete a degree program go on to graduate study within five years.

Foreign students: 12 students are from out of the country. Countries represented include Canada, Ghana, Greece, Nigeria, South Africa, and Spain; six in all.

PROGRAMS OF STUDY. Degrees: B.A., B.S., B.S.Nurs.

Majors: Art, Biology, Business Administration/Accounting, Chemistry, Computer Science, Criminal Justice, Drama, Early Childhood Education, Economics, Elementary Education, English, Foreign Languages, French, Health/Physical Education, History, Japanese Studies, Mass Communications, Mathematics, Music, Nursing, Philosophy, Physics, Political Science, Pre-Engineering, Psychology, Public Health, Religion, Secondary Education, Social Welfare, Sociology/Anthropology, Spanish, Special Education, Speech, Urban Studies.

Distribution of degrees: The majors with the highest enrollments are business administration/accounting, pre-engineering, and mass communications; physics, mathematics, and secondary education have the lowest.

Requirements: General education requirement.

Academic regulations: Minimum 2.00 GPA must be maintained.

Special: Dual degrees. Independent study. Internships. Preprofessional programs in law, medicine, veterinary science, pharmacy, dentistry, and optometry. 3-2 program in engineering. Teacher certification in early childhood, elementary, secondary, and special education. ROTC. AFROTC at Tulane U.

Honors: Honors program. Honor societies.

Academic Assistance: Remedial reading, writing, math, and study skills. Nonremedial tutoring.

STUDENT LIFE. Housing: Women's and men's dorms. School-owned/operated apartments. 49% of students live in college housing.

Services and counseling/handicapped student services: Placement services. Health service. Personal counseling. Career and academic guidance services.

Campus organizations: Undergraduate student government. Student newspaper (Courtbouillon). Yearbook. Radio station. Choir, band, gospel choir, drama group, athletic, departmental, political, tand service groups, 20 organizations in all. Eight fraternities, no chapter houses; eight sororities, no chapter houses. 30% of men join a fraternity. 26% of women join a sorority.

Religious organizations: Bible Study Group.

ATHLETICS. Physical education requirements: Four semesters of physical education required.

Intercollegiate competition: Basketball (M,W).

ADMISSIONS. Academic basis for candidate selection (in order of priority): Secondary school record, school's recommendation, standardized test scores, class rank, essay.

Nonacademic basis for candidate selection: Character and personality are important. Extracurricular participation, particular talent or ability, and alumni/ae relationship are considered.

Requirements: Graduation from secondary school is recommended; GED is accepted. 18 units and the following program of study are required: 4 units of English, 3 units of math, 3 units of lab science, 2 units of social studies, 6 units of electives including 4 units of academic electives. Biology and chemistry required of nursing program applicants. Audition required of music program applicants. SAT I or ACT is required. Campus visit and interview recommended. No off-campus interviews.

Procedure: Take SAT I or ACT by December of 12th year. Application deadline is July 1. Notification of admission on rolling basis. $50 nonrefundable tuition deposit. $100 nonrefundable room deposit. Freshmen accepted for all terms.

Special programs: Credit and/or placement may be granted through CEEB Advanced Placement exams for scores of 3 or higher. Credit and/or placement may be granted through CLEP general and subject exams. Credit may be granted through DANTES and challenge exams. Early entrance/early admission program. Concurrent enrollment program.

Transfer students: Transfer students accepted for all terms. In fall 1994, 26% of all new students were transfers into all classes. 68 transfer applications were received, 42 were accepted. Application deadline is July 1 for fall; December 1 for spring. Minimum 2.0 GPA required. Lowest course grade accepted is "C." Maximum number of transferable credits is 60 semester hours. At least 60 semester hours must be completed at the university to receive degree.

Admissions contact: Vernese B. O'Neal, M.S., Director of Admissions. 504 286-4670.

FINANCIAL AID. Available aid: Pell grants, SEOG, Federal Nursing Student Scholarships, state grants, school scholarships, private scholarships, ROTC scholarships, academic merit scholarships, athletic scholarships, and United Negro College Fund. Perkins Loans (NDSL), PLUS, Stafford Loans (GSL), and NSL. AMS and deferred payment plan.

Financial aid statistics: In 1994-95, 82% of all undergraduate aid applicants received aid. Average amounts of aid awarded freshmen: Loans, $2,500.
Supporting data/closing dates: FAFSA/FAF: Deadline is June 1. School's own aid application: Deadline is June 1. Notification of awards on rolling basis.
Financial aid contact: Rosie C. Toney, Director of Financial Aid. 504 286-4677.
STUDENT EMPLOYMENT. Federal Work-Study Program. 48% of full-time undergraduates work on campus during school year. Students may expect to earn an average of $2,000 during school year. Off-campus part-time employment opportunities rated "excellent."
COMPUTER FACILITIES. 70 IBM/IBM-compatible and Apple/Macintosh microcomputers; 40 are networked. Students may access IBM minicomputer/mainframe systems. Client/LAN operating systems include Apple/Macintosh, DOS, UNIX/XENIX/AIX, Windows NT. Computer facilities are available to all students.
Fees: Computer fee is included in tuition/fees.
Hours: 8 AM-9 PM daily.
GRADUATE CAREER DATA. Highest graduate school enrollments: Columbia U, U of New Orleans. Companies and businesses that hire graduates: Cargill, AETNA.
PROMINENT ALUMNI/AE. Rheta Dumas, dean of nursing, U of Michigan; D. Mitchell Spelman, dean, Harvard Medical School; Bishop Alfred Norris, Texas/New Mexico.

Edward Waters College

Jacksonville, FL 32209   **904 366-2506**

Undergraduate profile. 94% Black, 6% White. 83% are state residents.
Enrollment. Undergraduates: 587 (full-time).
Faculty. N/A.
Test score averages/ranges. N/A.
1995-96 Costs. Tuition: $4,400. Room & board: $3,400. Fees, books, misc. academic expenses (school's estimate): $1,150.

PROFILE. Edward Waters is a church-affiliated, liberal arts college. It was founded as Brown Theological Institute in 1870, was renamed Brown University in 1872 and East Florida Conference High School in 1883, and acquired its present name in 1892. Its 20-acre campus is located in the eastern section of Jacksonville.

Accreditation: SACS.
Religious orientation: Edward Waters College is affiliated with the African Methodist Episcopal Church; no religious requirements.
Athletic facilities: Baseball and softball fields, volleyball and tennis courts, local high school gymnasium.
PROGRAMS OF STUDY. Degrees: B.A., B.S.
Majors: Biological/Physical Sciences, Biology, Business/Management, Criminal Justice, Elementary Education, English, Humanities/Social Sciences, Liberal/General Studies, Mathematics, Military Science, Personnel Management, Philosophy, Psychology, Public Administration, Religion, Religious Education, Social Psychology, Social Work, Sociology.
Special: Double majors. Independent study. Accelerated study. Internships. Cooperative education programs. ROTC.
STUDENT LIFE. Housing: Coed dorms.
Services and counseling/handicapped student services: Health service. Personal counseling. Career guidance services. Learning disabled services.
Campus organizations: NAACP. Undergraduate student government. Student newspaper. Yearbook. Concert band, dance, drama, music ensembles, choral groups.
Foreign student organizations: International Student Organization.
ATHLETICS. Physical education requirements: None.

Intercollegiate competition: 10% of students participate. Baseball (M), basketball (M), cross-country (M), track (outdoor) (W), track and field (indoor) (M), track and field (outdoor) (M). Member of Eastern Intercollegiate Athletic Conference, NAIA.

Intramural and club sports: 30% of students participate. Intramural basketball, soccer, softball, tennis, volleyball. Men's club soccer.

ADMISSIONS. Requirements: Graduation from secondary school is recommended; GED is not accepted. No specific distribution of secondary school units required.

Procedure: Application deadline is August 31. Notification of admission on rolling basis. Freshmen accepted for fall terms only.

Special programs: Admission may be deferred.

FINANCIAL AID. Supporting data/closing dates: FAFSA: Accepted on rolling basis. Notification of awards on rolling basis.

Elizabeth City State University

Elizabeth City, NC 27909   919 335-3230

Undergraduate profile. 73% Black, .5% Asian-American, .3% Hispanic, .3% Native American, 25.3% White, .6% Non-resident aliens. 88% are state residents; 25% are transfers. Average age of undergraduates is 23.

Enrollment. Undergraduates: 739 men, 1,197 women (full-time). Freshman class: 1,106 applicants, 807 accepted, 461 enrolled.

Faculty. 109 full-time, 27 part-time; 79 Black, 36 White, 21 Other. 66% of faculty holds doctoral degree. Student/faculty ratio: 13 to 1.

Test score averages/ranges. Average SAT I scores: 371 verbal, 416 math.

1995-96 Costs. Tuition: $1,562. Room & board: $3,264. Fees, books, misc. academic expenses (school's estimate): $914.

PROFILE. Elizabeth City State, founded in 1891, is a comprehensive, public university. Its 87-acre campus is located in Elizabeth City, near the Pasquotank River.

Accreditation: SACS. Professionally accredited by the National Council for Accreditation of Teacher Education.

Religious orientation: Elizabeth City State University is nonsectarian; no religious requirements.

Library: Collections totaling 136,973 volumes, 1,628 periodical subscriptions, and 434,574 microform items.

Special facilities/museums: Lab school, planetarium, science complex, music engineering station.

Athletic facilities: Football stadium, basketball center, intramural sports hall, all-purpose outdoor activity fields, tennis and outdoor basketball courts.

STUDENT BODY. Freshman profile: 1% of freshmen who took SAT I scored 600 or over on verbal, 1% scored 600 or over on math; 9% scored 500 or over on verbal, 8% scored 500 or over on math; 37% scored 400 or over on verbal, 42% scored 400 or over on math; 88% scored 300 or over on verbal, 90% scored 300 or over on math. 100% of accepted applicants took SAT I. 99% of freshmen come from public schools.

Undergraduate achievement: 32% of entering class graduates. 10% of students who complete a degree program go on to graduate study within five years.

Foreign students: 13 students are from out of the country. Countries represented include Canada, Kuwait, Lebanon, Namibia, Nigeria, and South Africa; eight in all.

PROGRAMS OF STUDY. Degrees: B.A., B.S., B.S.Ed.

Majors: Accounting, Applied Mathematics, Art, Basic Business Education, Biology, Business Administration, Chemistry, Comprehensive Business Education, Computer/Information Science, Criminal Justice, Elementary Education, English, Geology, History, Industrial Technology, Mathematics, Music, Music Industry Studies, Physical Education/Health, Physics, Political Science, Psychology, Social Work Curriculum, Sociology, Special Education, Technology Education.

Distribution of degrees: The majors with the highest enrollments are business administration, criminal justice, and elementary education; music, technology education, and physics have the lowest.

Requirements: General education requirement.

Academic regulations: Minimum 2.0 GPA must be maintained.

Special: Minors offered in many majors and in airway science, American history, applied mathematics, athletic coaching, Black studies, correctional recreation, corrections, electronics, environmental science, geology, juvenile justice, mechanical technology, modern languages, music merchandising, professional middle grades education, professional secondary education, speech/drama, statistics, and studio art. Independent study. Internships. Cooperative education programs. Preprofessional programs in medicine, dentistry, and speech pathology. Certification in specific subject areas. ROTC.

Honors: Honors program. Honor societies.

Academic Assistance: Remedial reading, writing, math, and study skills.

STUDENT LIFE. Housing: Students may live on or off campus. Women's and men's dorms. School-owned/operated apartments. 48% of students live in college housing.

Services and counseling/handicapped student services: Placement services. Health service. Personal counseling. Career and academic guidance services.

Campus organizations: Undergraduate student government. Student newspaper (Compass, published twice/semester). Literary magazine. Yearbook. Radio station. NAACP. Marching and concert bands, university choir, gospel choir, art guild, dance group, cheering squad, commuter student club, departmental, social, and special-interest groups, 61 organizations in all. Four fraternities, no chapter houses; four sororities, no chapter houses. 10% of men join a fraternity. 10% of women join a sorority.

Religious organizations: United Campus Religious Fellowship.

ATHLETICS. Physical education requirements: Three semesters of physical education required.

Intercollegiate competition: 2% of students participate. Baseball (M), basketball (M,W), cheerleading (M,W), cross-country (M,W), football (M), softball (W), track (indoor) (M,W), track (outdoor) (M,W), track and field (indoor) (M,W), track and field (outdoor) (M,W), volleyball (W). Member of Central Intercollegiate Athletic Conference, NCAA Division II.

Intramural and club sports: 1% of students participate. Intramural basketball, billiards, flag football, roller skating, softball, swimming, table tennis, volleyball.

ADMISSIONS. Academic basis for candidate selection (in order of priority): Secondary school record, standardized test scores, class rank, school's recommendation, essay.

Nonacademic basis for candidate selection: Character and personality, extracurricular participation, particular talent or ability, geographical distribution, and alumni/ae relationship are considered.

Requirements: Graduation from secondary school is recommended; GED is accepted. 20 units and the following program of study are required: 4 units of English, 3 units of math, 3 units of science including 1 unit of lab, 1 unit of social studies, 8 units of electives including 4 units of academic electives, 1 unit of U.S. history. 2 units of foreign language recommended. Minimum combined SAT I score of 600 and minimum 2.0 GPA required of in-state applicants. Minimum combined SAT I score of 700 and minimum 2.0 GPA required of out-of-state applicants. Higher test scores, rank in top half of secondary class, and minimum 2.0 GPA recommended. Minimum 2.5 GPA required of education program applicants. Portfolio required of art program applicants. Audition required of music program applicants. SAT I is required; ACT may be substituted. PSAT is recommended. SAT II recommended. Campus visit and interview recommended. Off-campus interviews available with admissions and alumni representatives.

Procedure: Take SAT I by October of 12th year. Take SAT II by October of 12th year. Visit college for interview by March of 12th year. Suggest filing application by January 1. Application deadline is July 15. Notification of admission on rolling basis. Reply is required by July 15. Tuition deposit of $680 (in-state) or $2,917 (out-of-state), refundable until August 19. $100 room deposit, refundable until July 15. Freshmen accepted for all terms.

Special programs: Admission may be deferred one year. Credit and/or placement may be granted through CEEB Advanced Placement exams for scores of 3 or higher. Credit may be granted through CLEP general and subject exams. Credit may be granted for military experience. Credit and placement may be granted through DANTES exams.

Transfer students: Transfer students accepted for all terms. In fall 1993, 25% of all new students were transfers into all classes. 244 transfer applications were received, 221 were accepted. Application deadline is July 15 for fall; December 1 for spring. Minimum 2.0 GPA required. Lowest course grade accepted is "C." Maximum number of transferable credits is 90 semester hours. At least 30 semester hours must be completed at the university to receive degree.

Admissions contact: Erthel Hines, M.Soc.Work, Director of Admissions. 919 335-3305.

FINANCIAL AID. Available aid: Pell grants, SEOG, state scholarships and grants, school scholarships, private scholarships, ROTC scholarships, academic merit scholarships, and athletic scholarships. Incentive Scholarship Program. Perkins Loans (NDSL), PLUS, Stafford Loans (GSL), and state loans. AMS.

Financial aid statistics: In 1993-94, 91% of all undergraduate aid applicants received aid; 96% of freshman aid applicants. Average amounts of aid awarded freshmen: Scholarships and grants, $2,150; loans, $1,920.

Supporting data/closing dates: FAFSA: Accepted on rolling basis. School's own aid application. Notification of awards on rolling basis.

Financial aid contact: James E. Swimpson, Director of Financial Aid. 919 335-3283.

STUDENT EMPLOYMENT. Federal Work-Study Program. 72% of full-time undergraduates work on campus during school year. Students may expect to earn an average of $700 during school year. Off-campus part-time employment opportunities rated "poor."

COMPUTER FACILITIES. 250 IBM/IBM-compatible, Apple/Macintosh, and RISC-/UNIX-based microcomputers. Students may access Digital, SUN minicomputer/mainframe systems, BITNET, Internet. Client/LAN operating systems include Apple/Macintosh, DOS, UNIX/XENIX/AIX, LocalTalk/AppleTalk. Computer facilities are available to all students.

Fees: Computer fee is included in tuition/fees.

Hours: 9 AM-midn. (M-Th); 9 AM-6 PM (F); 6 PM-midn. (Su).

GRADUATE CAREER DATA. Graduate school percentages: 2% enter law school. 2% enter medical school. 1% enter dental school. 3% enter graduate business programs. 23% enter graduate arts and sciences programs. 1% enter theological school/seminary. Highest graduate school enrollments: East Carolina U, Norfolk State U, North Carolina Central U, Old Dominion U, U of North Carolina at Chapel Hill.

PROMINENT ALUMNI/AE. Dr. Jimmy R. Jenkins, chancellor, Elizabeth City State U; Mary E. Sharpe, president, General Alumni Association, Elizabeth City State U, retired educator; Edna G. Randolph, secretary, board of trustees, Elizabeth City State U, retired educator.

Fayetteville State University

Fayetteville, NC 28301   **910 486-1133**

Undergraduate profile. 67% Black, 1% Asian-American, 2% Hispanic, 1% Native American, 29% White. 93% are state residents. Average age of undergraduates is 25.

Enrollment. Undergraduates: 976 men, 1,656 women (full-time). Freshman class: 1,455 applicants, 1,064 accepted, 452 enrolled. Graduate enrollment: 233 men, 550 women.

Faculty. 192 full-time, 48 part-time; 123 Black, 81 White, 36 Other. 74% of faculty holds doctoral degree. Student/faculty ratio: 15 to 1.

Test score averages/ranges. Average SAT I scores: 390 verbal, 426 math.

1995-96 Costs. Tuition: $814 (state residents), $7,486 (out-of-state). Room & board: $2,550. Fees, books, misc. academic expenses (school's estimate): $636.

PROFILE. Fayetteville State, founded in 1867, is a public university. Programs are offered through the College of Arts and Sciences and the Schools of Business and Economics, and Education and Human Development. Its 136-acre campus is located in Fayetteville.

Accreditation: SACS. Professionally accredited by the National Council for Accreditation of Teacher Education.

Religious orientation: Fayetteville State University is nonsectarian; no religious requirements.

Library: Collections totaling 179,643 volumes, 1,874 periodical subscriptions, and 469,944 microform items.

Special facilities/museums: Planetarium.

Athletic facilities: Gymnasiums, swimming pool, football and softball fields, tennis courts, track, stadium.

STUDENT BODY. Freshman profile: 1% of freshmen who took SAT I scored 600 or over on verbal, 2% scored 600 or over on math; 12% scored 500 or over on verbal, 20% scored 500 or over on math; 43% scored 400 or over on verbal, 61% scored 400 or over on math; 92% scored 300 or over on verbal, 98% scored 300 or over on math. 100% of accepted applicants took SAT I.

Undergraduate achievement: 11% of entering class graduates. 10% of students who complete a degree program immediately go on to graduate study.

Foreign students: Countries represented include Nigeria.

PROGRAMS OF STUDY. Degrees: B.A., B.S., B.S.Med.Tech., B.S.Nurs.

Majors: Accounting, Biology, Business Administration, Business Education, Chemistry, Computer Science, Criminal Justice, Early Childhood Education, Economics, English Language/Literature, Geography, Health Education, History, Intermediate Education, Marketing, Mathematics, Medical Technology, Middle Grade Education, Music, Music Education, Nursing, Office Administration, Physical Education, Political Science, Psychology, Secondary Education/Social Sciences, Sociology, Spanish, Speech/Theatre, Visual Arts.

Distribution of degrees: The majors with the highest enrollments are business administration, sociology, and education; chemistry, medical technology, and music have the lowest.

Requirements: General education requirement.

Academic regulations: Freshmen must maintain minimum 1.0 GPA; sophomores, 1.6 GPA; juniors, 1.85 GPA; seniors, 1.99 GPA.

Special: Minors offered in all majors and in art education and recreation. Associate degrees offered. Double majors. Independent study. Internships. Cooperative education programs. 2-2 programs in applied math, conservation, engineering, natural resource/recreation management, physics, pulp/paper science, recreation/park administration, textile chemistry, and textiles technology with North Carolina State U. Teacher certification in early childhood, elementary, secondary, and special education. Certification in specific subject areas. AFROTC.

Honors: Honors program. Honor societies.

Academic Assistance: Remedial reading, writing, and math. Nonremedial tutoring.

STUDENT LIFE. Housing: Students may live on or off campus. Women's and men's dorms. 31% of students live in college housing.

Social atmosphere: Students gather at the student center, the SBE Lounge, and the Taylor Science Annex Lounge. Popular campus events include Homecoming, Martin Luther King celebrations, and the Lyceum lecture series. According to the student newspaper, "Fayetteville State is one of the most culturally diverse universities in the North Carolina system. Students and faculty reach for the best in education while trying to learn and accept each culture's qualities. This leads to large groups of students interacting in numerous activities both on and off campus."

Services and counseling/handicapped student services: Placement services. Health service. Day care. Counseling services for military and veteran students. Personal counseling. Career and academic guidance services.

Campus organizations: Undergraduate student government. Student newspaper (Broncos' Voice, published bimonthly). Yearbook. Radio and TV stations. Afro-American Society. Choir, band, pep club, marching dance group, class organizations, special-interest groups. Four fraternities, no chapter houses; four sororities, no chapter houses. 3% of men join a fraternity. 3% of women join a sorority.

Religious organizations: Baptist Student Union, Fellowship of Christian Students.

ATHLETICS. Physical education requirements: One semester of physical education required.
Intercollegiate competition: 4% of students participate. Basketball (M,W), cheerleading (M,W), cross-country (M,W), football (M), golf (M), softball (W), volleyball (W). Member of Central Intercollegiate Athletic Association, NCAA Division II.
Intramural and club sports: 10% of students participate. Intramural basketball, bowling, flag football, powderpuff football, softball, tennis, track, volleyball.

ADMISSIONS. Academic basis for candidate selection (in order of priority): Standardized test scores, secondary school record, class rank, school's recommendation.
Nonacademic basis for candidate selection: Character and personality are important. Extracurricular participation, particular talent or ability, and geographical distribution are considered.
Requirements: Graduation from secondary school is recommended; GED is accepted. 18 units and the following program of study are required: 4 units of English, 3 units of math, 3 units of science including 1 unit of lab, 1 unit of social studies, 1 unit of history, 6 units of academic electives. 2 units of foreign language recommended. SAT I is required; ACT may be substituted. PSAT is recommended.
Procedure: Notification of admission on rolling basis. $75 refundable room deposit. Freshmen accepted for all terms.
Special programs: Admission may be deferred one year. Credit and/or placement may be granted through CEEB Advanced Placement exams for scores of 3 or higher. Credit may be granted through CLEP general and subject exams. Credit may be granted through DANTES exams and for military experience. Early entrance/early admission program. Concurrent enrollment program.
Transfer students: Transfer students accepted for all terms. In fall 1993, 713 transfer applications were received, 631 were accepted. Application deadline is August 1 for fall; December 1 for spring. Minimum 2.0 GPA required. Lowest course grade accepted is "C." Maximum number of transferable credits is 60 semester hours from a two-year school and 90 semester hours from a four-year school. At least 30 semester hours must be completed at the university to receive degree.
Admissions contact: James Scurry, M.Ed., Director of Enrollment Management. 910 486-1371.

FINANCIAL AID. Available aid: Pell grants, SEOG, Federal Nursing Student Scholarships, state scholarships and grants, school scholarships, private scholarships and grants, ROTC scholarships, academic merit scholarships, athletic scholarships, and aid for undergraduate foreign students. American Indian Student Legislative Program. Perkins Loans (NDSL), PLUS, Stafford Loans (GSL), and NSL. Deferred payment plan.
Financial aid statistics: Average amounts of aid awarded freshmen: Loans, $928.
Supporting data/closing dates: Notification of awards on rolling basis.
Financial aid contact: Mae Graves, Director of Financial Aid. 910 486-1325.

STUDENT EMPLOYMENT. Federal Work-Study Program. Institutional employment. 22% of full-time undergraduates work on campus during school year. Students may expect to earn an average of $650 during school year. Off-campus part-time employment opportunities rated "fair."

COMPUTER FACILITIES. 250 IBM/IBM-compatible and Apple/Macintosh microcomputers; all are networked. Students may access Digital, Sequent minicomputer/mainframe systems, Internet. Client/LAN operating systems include DOS, Windows NT, Novell. Computer facilities are available to all students.
Fees: None.
Hours: 8 AM-midn.

GRADUATE CAREER DATA. Highest graduate school enrollments: Fayetteville State U. 12% of graduates choose careers in business and industry. Companies and businesses that hire graduates: Bell, Monsanto, IBM.

PROMINENT ALUMNI/AE. Dr. Jesse Williams, director, Cumberland County Health Department; Dr. Willis McCloud, superintendent, Northampton County Schools; Dr. Jessica Daniels, clinical psychologist, Baker Guidance Center, Boston, Mass.; James Ivery, assistant to deputy undersecretary, U.S. Department of Health and Human Services.

Fisk University

Nashville, TN 37208   **615 329-8500**

Undergraduate profile. N/A.

Enrollment. Freshman class: 982 applicants, 812 accepted, 242 enrolled.

Faculty. 60 full-time, 29 part-time; 27 Black, 30 White, 3 Other. 75% of faculty holds doctoral degree. Student/faculty ratio: 13 to 1.

Test score averages/ranges. N/A.

1995-96 Costs. Tuition: $6,740. Room: $2,266. Board: $1,682. Fees, books, misc. academic expenses (school's estimate): $750.

PROFILE. Fisk, founded in 1867, is a church-affiliated, liberal arts university. Its 40-acre campus, listed with the National Register of Historical Landmarks, is located on a hill overlooking downtown Nashville.

Accreditation: SACS. Professionally accredited by the National Association of Schools of Music.

Religious orientation: Fisk University is a nondenominational Christian school; no religious requirements.

Library: Collections totaling 186,174 volumes, 595 periodical subscriptions, and 4,270 microform items.

Special facilities/museums: Speech and language labs.

Athletic facilities: Gymnasium, weight room, recreation room, football and softball fields.

STUDENT BODY. Freshman profile: 90% of freshmen come from public schools.

Undergraduate achievement: 90% of fall 1993 freshmen returned for fall 1994 term. 42% of entering class graduates. 45% of students who complete a degree program immediately go on to graduate study.

PROGRAMS OF STUDY. Degrees: B.A., B.Mus., B.S.

Majors: Accounting, Art, Biology, Chemistry, Computer Science, Dramatics/Speech, Economics, English, Finance, French, History, Management, Mathematics, Music, Music Education, Physics, Political Science, Psychology, Religious/Philosophical Studies, Sociology, Spanish.

Distribution of degrees: The majors with the highest enrollments are biology, psychology, and English; music, Spanish, and sociology have the lowest.

Requirements: General education requirement.

Academic regulations: Freshmen must maintain minimum 1.5 GPA; sophomores, 1.8 GPA; juniors, 2.0 GPA; seniors, 2.0 GPA.

Special: Self-designed majors. Double majors. Independent study. Pass/fail grading option. Internships. Graduate school at which qualified undergraduates may take graduate-level courses. Preprofessional programs in law, medicine, pharmacy, dentistry, mass communication media, and theological studies. 2-2 medical technology and nursing programs with Rush-Presbyterian-St.Luke's Medical Center (Chicago). Five-year B.A./M.B.A. management program and five-year B.A./B.S. or B.A./B.Eng. science/engineering program with Vanderbilt U. Dual-degree pharmacy program with Howard U. Nashville area college consortium offers cross-registration at Meharry Medical Coll, Scarritt Coll for Christian Workers, and Vanderbilt U. Oak Ridge Science Semester (Tennessee). Exchange programs with numerous colleges. Teacher certification in secondary education. Study abroad in England. ROTC and NROTC at Vanderbilt U. AFROTC at Tennessee State U.

Honors: Phi Beta Kappa. Honors program.

Academic Assistance: Remedial reading, writing, and math. Nonremedial tutoring.

STUDENT LIFE. Housing: All students, except those from Nashville, must live on campus. Women's and men's dorms. 67% of students live in college housing.

Services and counseling/handicapped student services: Placement services. Health service. One-semester orientation course for new students. Birth control, personal, and psychological counseling. Career and academic guidance services.

Campus organizations: Undergraduate student government. Student newspaper. Literary magazine. Yearbook. Radio station. Stagecrafters, university choir, Modern Mass Choir, Jubilee Singers, jazz ensemble, Orchesis Dance Club, departmental and special-interest groups. Four fraternities, no chapter houses; four sororities, no chapter houses.

Religious organizations: Several religious groups.

Foreign student organizations: Foreign student club, International Student Association.

ATHLETICS. Physical education requirements: None.

Intercollegiate competition: 9% of students participate. Baseball (M), basketball (M,W), cross-country (M,W), tennis (M,W), track (indoor) (W), track (outdoor) (W), track and field (indoor) (M), track and field (outdoor) (M), volleyball (W). Member of NCAA Division III, WIAC.

Intramural and club sports: 3% of students participate. Intramural badminton, basketball, golf, softball, table tennis, tennis, volleyball.

ADMISSIONS. Academic basis for candidate selection (in order of priority): Secondary school record, class rank, standardized test scores, school's recommendation, essay.

Nonacademic basis for candidate selection: Character and personality are important. Extracurricular participation, particular talent or ability, and alumni/ae relationship are considered.

Requirements: Graduation from secondary school is required; GED is accepted. 15 units and the following program of study are recommended: 4 units of English, 2 units of math, 1 unit of science, 1 unit of foreign language, 1 unit of history, 6 units of electives. Electives should be in fields relating to intended major. Math units must include algebra and plane geometry. SAT II is considered; English composition exam recommended. Several years of applied music (preferably piano) and participation (as performer and listener) in various musical activities required of music program applicants. SAT I or ACT is required. Campus visit recommended.

Procedure: Take SAT I or ACT by December of 12th year. Application deadline is June 15. Notification of admission on rolling basis. $100 nonrefundable tuition deposit. Freshmen accepted for all terms.

Special programs: Credit and/or placement may be granted through CEEB Advanced Placement exams for scores of 4 or higher. Credit and/or placement may be granted through CLEP general and subject exams. Early entrance/early admission program.

Transfer students: Transfer students accepted for all terms. Application deadline is June 15 for fall; November 1 for spring. Minimum 2.0 GPA required. Lowest course grade accepted is "C."

Admissions contact: Harrison F. DeShields, M.A., Director of Admissions. 615 329-8666.

FINANCIAL AID. Available aid: Pell grants, SEOG, state grants, school scholarships and grants, academic merit scholarships, and United Negro College Fund. Perkins Loans (NDSL), PLUS, and Stafford Loans (GSL).

Financial aid statistics: In 1993-94, 89% of all undergraduate aid applicants received aid; 85% of freshman aid applicants. Average amounts of aid awarded freshmen: Scholarships and grants, $2,000; loans, $4,000.

Supporting data/closing dates: FAFSA. FAF: Deadline is April 1. Student Eligibility Report. Notification of awards on rolling basis.

Financial aid contact: Annette Miller, Director of Financial Aid. 615 329-8735.

STUDENT EMPLOYMENT. Federal Work-Study Program. Off-campus part-time employment opportunities rated "good."

GRADUATE CAREER DATA. Graduate school percentages: 10% enter law school. 15% enter medical school. 5% enter dental school. 10% enter graduate business programs. 15% enter graduate arts and sciences programs. 2% enter theological school/seminary. Highest graduate school enrollments: Emory U, Marshall U, Vanderbilt U. 27% of graduates choose careers in business and industry. Companies and businesses that hire graduates: Caterpillar, IBM.

PROMINENT ALUMNI/AE. Dr. John Hope Franklin, educator, author; Hazel O'Leary, secretary, U.S. Department of Energy.

Florida Agricultural and Mechanical University

Tallahassee, FL 32307   904 599-3000

Undergraduate profile. 89% Black, 1% Asian-American, 1% Hispanic, 7% White, 2% Other. 72% are state residents; 46% are transfers. Average age of undergraduates is 23.

Enrollment. Undergraduates: 3,454 men, 4,620 women (full-time). Freshman class: 4,968 applicants, 3,077 accepted, 1,653 enrolled. Graduate enrollment: 218 men, 325 women.

Faculty. 610 full-time, 6 part-time. 51% of faculty holds doctoral degree. Student/faculty ratio: 13 to 1.

Test score averages/ranges. Average SAT I scores: 409 verbal, 440 math. Average ACT scores: 14 English, 16 math, 21 composite.

1995-96 Costs. Tuition: $1,908 (state residents), $7,200 (out-of-state). Room & board: $2,884. Fees, books, misc. academic expenses (school's estimate): $300.

PROFILE. Florida Agricultural and Mechanical University, founded in 1887, is a public, historically Black university. Programs are offered through the Colleges of Arts and Sciences; Education; Engineering Sciences, Technology, and Agriculture; Pharmacy and Pharmaceutical Sciences and the Schools of Allied Health Sciences; Architecture; Business and Industry; General Studies; Journalism, Media, and Graphic Arts; Nursing; and Graduate Studies, Research, and Continuing Education. Its 419-acre campus is located in Tallahassee.

Accreditation: SACS. Professionally accredited by the Accreditation Board for Engineering and Technology, Inc., the Accrediting Council on Education in Journalism and Mass Communication, the National Architecture Accrediting Board, the National Council for Accreditation of Teacher Education.

Religious orientation: Florida Agricultural and Mechanical University is nonsectarian; no religious requirements.

Library: Collections totaling 485,985 volumes, 3,300 periodical subscriptions, and 82,000 microform items.

Athletic facilities: Gymnasium, baseball and softball fields, track, swimming pool, tennis courts.

STUDENT BODY. Freshman profile: 1% of freshmen who took SAT I scored 700 or over on verbal, 2% scored 700 or over on math; 6% scored 600 or over on verbal, 12% scored 600 or over on math; 22% scored 500 or over on verbal, 41% scored 500 or over on math; 64% scored 400 or over on verbal, 78% scored 400 or over on math; 95% scored 300 or over on verbal, 98% scored 300 or over on math. 1% of freshmen who took ACT scored 30 or over on English, 1% scored 30 or over on math; 13% scored 24 or over on English, 10% scored 24 or over on math, 9% scored 24 or over on composite; 59% scored 18 or over on English, 56% scored 18 or over on math, 66% scored 18 or over on composite; 97% scored 12 or over on English, 99% scored 12 or over on math, 100% scored 12 or over on composite; 100% scored 6 or over on English, 100% scored 6 or over on math. Majority of accepted applicants took ACT. 85% of freshmen come from public schools.

Foreign students: 156 students are from out of the country. Countries represented include the Bahamas, Bermuda, China, Haiti, Jamaica, and Nigeria; 84 in all.

PROGRAMS OF STUDY. Degrees: B.A., B.S., B.Tech.

Majors: Accounting, Agricultural Business, Animal Science, Architecture, Art Education, Biology, Broadcast Journalism, Business Administration, Business/Commerce/Distributive Education, Chemical Engineering, Chemistry, Civil Engineering, Civil Engineering Technology, Computer Information Science, Construction Engineering Technology, Criminal Justice/Corrections, Dramatic Arts/Theatre, Economics, Electrical Engineering, Electronic Engineering Technology, Elementary Education, English, English Education, Fine Arts, Graphic Arts Technology, Graphic Design, Health Care Administration, History, Industrial Arts Vocational/Technical Education, Industrial Engineering, Journalism, Magazine Production, Mathematics, Mathematics Education, Mechanical Engineering, Medical Records Administration, Music, Music Composition, Music Education,

Music Performance, Music Theory, Newspaper Journalism, Nursing, Occupational Therapy, Ornamental Horticulture/Landscape Design, Pharmacy, Philosophy/Religion, Photography, Physical Education, Physical Therapy, Physics, Political Science/Public Management, Printing Management, Psychology, Public Relations, Religious Studies, Respiratory Therapy, Science Education, Secondary Education, Social Studies Education, Social Welfare, Sociology.

Distribution of degrees: The majors with the highest enrollments are business administration and health professions; animal science, chemistry, and physics have the lowest.

Requirements: General education requirement.

Academic regulations: Minimum 2.0 GPA must be maintained.

Special: Double majors. Independent study. Pass/fail grading option. Internships. Graduate school at which qualified undergraduates may take graduate-level courses. Preprofessional programs in law, medicine, and dentistry. Washington Semester. Architecture Semester (Virginia). Teacher certification in early childhood, elementary, secondary, and special education. Study abroad in England, Italy, and Japan. ROTC and NROTC. AFROTC at Florida State U.

Honors: Honors program. Honor societies.

Academic Assistance: Remedial reading and math. Nonremedial tutoring.

STUDENT LIFE. Housing: All freshmen must live on campus unless living with family. Women's and men's dorms. On-campus married-student housing. 28% of students live in college housing.

Services and counseling/handicapped student services: Placement services. Health service. Day care. Counseling services for military, veteran, and older students. Birth control, personal, and psychological counseling. Career and academic guidance services. Religious counseling. Physically disabled student services. Learning disabled services. Notetaking services. Tape recorders. Tutors. Reader services for the blind.

Campus organizations: Undergraduate student government. Student newspaper (Famuan, published once/week). Yearbook. Radio and TV stations. NAACP, Pan-African Cultural Club. Music and drama groups, literary guild, cheerleaders, departmental, political, service, and special-interest groups. Four fraternities, three chapter houses; four sororities, two chapter houses.

Religious organizations: Bahai Fellowship, Baptist Campus Ministry, Canterbury Club, Council of Religious Activities, Methodist Student Organization.

Foreign student organizations: International Student Association, Bilalian Student Alliance, Nigerian Student Alliance.

ATHLETICS. Physical education requirements: None.

Intercollegiate competition: 3% of students participate. Baseball (M), basketball (M,W), cross-country (M,W), diving (M,W), football (M), golf (M), softball (W), swimming (M,W), tennis (M,W), track and field (indoor) (M,W), track and field (outdoor) (M,W), volleyball (W). Member of Mid Eastern Athletic Conference, NCAA Division I, NCAA Division I-AA for football, New South Women's Athletic Conference.

Intramural and club sports: 34% of students participate. Intramural basketball, flag football, soccer, softball, tennis, track, volleyball.

ADMISSIONS. Academic basis for candidate selection (in order of priority): Secondary school record, standardized test scores, school's recommendation, class rank, essay.

Nonacademic basis for candidate selection: Character and personality are important. Alumni/ae relationship is considered.

Requirements: Graduation from secondary school is required; GED is accepted. 19 units and the following program of study are required: 4 units of English, 3 units of math, 3 units of science including 2 units of lab, 2 units of foreign language, 3 units of social studies, 4 units of electives. Minimum combined SAT I score of 900 (composite ACT score of 21) and minimum 2.5 GPA required. SAT I or ACT is required. Campus visit recommended. No off-campus interviews.

Procedure: Take SAT I or ACT by December 1 of 12th year. Suggest filing application by February 1. Application deadline is May 1. Notification of admission on rolling basis. $350 room deposit refundable until August 1. Freshmen accepted for all terms.

Special programs: Admission may be deferred one year. Credit may be granted through CEEB Advanced Placement for scores of 3 or higher. Credit may be granted through CLEP general and subject exams. Credit may be granted for military and life experience. Early entrance/early admission program. Concurrent enrollment program.

Transfer students: Transfer students accepted for all terms. In fall 1994, 46% of all new students were transfers into all classes. 2,273 transfer applications were received, 1,005 were accepted. Application deadline is May 1 for fall; November 1 for spring. Minimum 2.0 GPA required. Lowest course grade accepted is "C." Maximum number of transferable credits is 90 semester hours. At least 30 semester hours must be completed at the university to receive degree.

Admissions contact: Barbara Cox, Assistant Registrar for Admissions. 904 599-3796.

FINANCIAL AID. Available aid: Pell grants, SEOG, state scholarships and grants, school scholarships and grants, private scholarships and grants, ROTC scholarships, academic merit scholarships, and athletic scholarships. Perkins Loans (NDSL), PLUS, Stafford Loans (GSL), state loans, school loans, and private loans.

Financial aid statistics: 40% of aid is not need-based. In 1994-95, 72% of all undergraduate aid applicants received aid; 80% of freshman aid applicants. Average amounts of aid awarded freshmen: Scholarships and grants, $969; loans, $1,000.

Supporting data/closing dates: FAFSA: Priority filing date is April 1; accepted on rolling basis. Notification of awards begins in May.

Financial aid contact: Alton W. Royal, M.A., Director of Financial Aid. 904 599-3730.

STUDENT EMPLOYMENT. Federal Work-Study Program. 10% of full-time undergraduates work on campus during school year. Students may expect to earn an average of $1,360 during school year. Off-campus part-time employment opportunities rated "good."

COMPUTER FACILITIES. 100 IBM/IBM-compatible and Apple/Macintosh microcomputers. Students may access IBM minicomputer/mainframe systems. Computer facilities are available to all students.

Fees: None.

GRADUATE CAREER DATA. 35% of graduates choose careers in business and industry. Companies and businesses that hire graduates: federal government agencies, banking and accounting firms, retail companies.

PROMINENT ALUMNI/AE. Dr. Lasalle Lefall, cancer researcher; Andre Dawson and Vince Coleman, athletes; Maj. Gen. Eugene Cromartie, U.S. Army; Davidson Hepburn, UN ambassador, the Bahamas.

Florida Memorial College

Miami, FL 33054   **800 822-1362**

Undergraduate profile. 87% Black, 6% Hispanic, 2% White, 5% Other. 80% are state residents.

Enrollment. Undergraduates: 440 men, 765 women (full-time). Freshman class: 2,100 applicants, 1,567 accepted, 523 enrolled.

Faculty. 56 full-time, 58 part-time; 36 Black, 14 White, 6 Other. 37% of faculty holds doctoral degree. Student/faculty ratio: 15 to 1.

Test score averages/ranges. Range of ACT scores of middle 50%: 21-32 composite.

1995-96 Costs. Tuition: $4,160. Room: $1,680. Board: $1,510. Fees, books, misc. academic expenses (school's estimate): $1,280.

PROFILE. Florida Memorial, founded in 1897, is a church-affiliated college. Its 50-acre campus is located in Miami.

Accreditation: SACS.

Religious orientation: Florida Memorial College is affiliated with the Baptist Church; eight semester hours of religion required.

Special facilities/museums: Reading and study skills labs.

Athletic facilities: Gymnasium, swimming pool, tennis court.

STUDENT BODY. Freshman profile: 30% of accepted applicants took ACT. 100% of freshmen come from public schools.

PROGRAMS OF STUDY. Degrees: B.A., B.S.

Majors: Accounting, Air Traffic Control, Airway Science, Aviation Computer Science, Aviation Management, Biology, Business Administration/Management, Computer/Information Sciences, Criminal Justice Studies, Data Processing, Elementary Education, English, Mathematics, Medical Laboratory Technologies, Physical Education, Political Science/Government, Psychology, Public Administration, Religion, Sociology.

Distribution of degrees: The majors with the highest enrollments are elementary education, business administration, and criminal justice studies; medical laboratory technology and mathematics have the lowest.

Requirements: General education requirement.

Academic regulations: Minimum 2.0 GPA required for graduation.

Special: Double majors. Dual degrees. Internships. Cooperative education programs. 3-1 hospitality management program. 3-2 engineering program. New York semester. Teacher certification in elementary education. Certification in specific subject areas.

Honors: Honors program.

Academic Assistance: Remedial reading, writing, math, and study skills.

STUDENT LIFE. Housing: Women's and men's dorms. 40% of students live in college housing.

Services and counseling/handicapped student services: Placement services. Health service. Chaplain. Career and academic guidance services.

Campus organizations: Undergraduate student government. Student newspaper. Yearbook. Choir, band, athletic, departmental, service, and special-interest groups. Four fraternities, no chapter houses; four sororities, no chapter houses.

Religious organizations: Several religious organizations.

ATHLETICS. Physical education requirements: Four semester hours of physical education required.

Intercollegiate competition: 7% of students participate. Baseball (M), basketball (M,W), cheerleading (W), track and field (outdoor) (M,W), volleyball (W). Member of NAIA, NAIA Florida Sun Conference.

Intramural and club sports: 15% of students participate. Intramural basketball, social games, softball, swimming, tennis, track. Men's club soccer.

ADMISSIONS. Academic basis for candidate selection (in order of priority): Secondary school record, school's recommendation, class rank.

Nonacademic basis for candidate selection: Character and personality are emphasized. Extracurricular participation is considered.

Requirements: Graduation from secondary school is required; GED is accepted. 15 units and the following program of study are recommended: 4 units of English, 4 units of math, 3 units of science, 2 units of foreign language, 2 units of social studies. Minimum 2.0 GPA required. SAT I or ACT is required. Admissions interview recommended. No off-campus interviews.

Procedure: Take SAT I or ACT by May of 12th year. Suggest filing application by April 1. Application deadline is July 1. Notification of admission on rolling basis. Reply is required by August 1. $50 nonrefundable room deposit. Freshmen accepted for all terms.

Special programs: Credit and placement may be granted through challenge exams. Concurrent enrollment program.

Transfer students: Transfer students accepted for all terms. Lowest course grade accepted is "C." Maximum number of transferable credits is 62 semester hours from a two-year school and 90 semester hours from a four-year school. At least 30 semester hours must be completed at the college to receive degree.

Admissions contact: Peggy Kelly, Director of Admissions. 305 626-3750.

FINANCIAL AID. Available aid: Pell grants, SEOG, state grants, private scholarships, athletic scholarships, and United Negro College Fund. PLUS, Stafford Loans (GSL), and unsubsidized Stafford loans. Tuition Plan Inc., Tuition Management Systems, and deferred payment plan.

Financial aid statistics: Average amounts of aid awarded freshmen: Scholarships and grants, $2,250; loans, $2,500.

Supporting data/closing dates: FAFSA: Accepted on rolling basis; deadline is April 1. Notification of awards on rolling basis.

Financial aid contact: Brian Phillip, Director of Financial Aid. 305 626-3741.

STUDENT EMPLOYMENT. Federal Work-Study Program. 60% of full-time undergraduates work on campus during school year. Students may expect to earn an average of $1,200 during school year. Off-campus part-time employment opportunities rated "excellent."

COMPUTER FACILITIES. IBM/IBM-compatible and Apple/Macintosh microcomputers. Client/LAN operating systems include Apple/Macintosh, DOS, OS/2, Windows NT, Novell. Computer facilities are available to all students.

Fees: None.

GRADUATE CAREER DATA. Graduate school percentages: 2% enter law school. 1% enter medical school. 4% enter graduate business programs. 10% enter graduate arts and sciences programs. Companies and businesses that hire graduates: Dade County Public Schools.

Fort Valley State College

Fort Valley, GA 31030   912 825-6211

Undergraduate profile. N/A.

Enrollment. Freshman class: 2,506 applicants, 1,438 accepted, 715 enrolled.

Faculty. 55% of faculty holds highest degree in specific field.

Test score averages/ranges. N/A.

1995-96 Costs. Tuition: $1,920 (state residents), $5,130 (out-of-state). Room: $1,365. Board: $1,410.

PROFILE. Fort Valley, founded in 1902, is a public, multipurpose college. Programs are offered through the Schools of Agriculture, Home Economics, and Allied Programs; Arts and Sciences; and Education, Graduate, and Special Academic Programs. Continuing Education and External Degree Programs are also offered. Its 630-acre campus is located in Fort Valley, 20 miles southeast of Macon.

Accreditation: SACS. Professionally accredited by the Accreditation Board for Engineering and Technology, Inc., the American Home Economics Association, the American Veterinary Medical Association, the National Council for Accreditation of Teacher Education.

Religious orientation: Fort Valley State College is nonsectarian; no religious requirements.

Library: Collections totaling 190,062 volumes and 1,213 periodical subscriptions.

Special facilities/museums: Experimental agricultural plots cover most of campus.

Athletic facilities: All-weather track, gymnasium, nautilus center, weight room, indoor pool.

STUDENT BODY. Undergraduate achievement: 88% of fall 1993 freshmen returned for fall 1994 term.

PROGRAMS OF STUDY. Degrees: B.A., B.Bus.Admin., B.S., B.S.Agri., B.S.Bus.Ed., B.S.Ed., B.S.Elec.Eng., B.S.Home Econ., B.S.Mus.Ed.

Majors: Accounting, Agricultural Education, Animal Science, Biology, Chemistry, Comprehensive Business Education, Criminal Justice, Data Processing, Early Childhood Education, Economics, Electrical Engineering Technology, Elementary Education, English, Food/Nutrition, French, General Business, Geography, Health/Physical Education, History, Home Economics Education, Infant/Child Development, Management, Marketing, Mathematics, Music, Office Administration, Plant Science, Political Science, Psychology, Science, Social Science, Social Welfare, Sociology, Zoology.

Requirements: General education requirement.

Special: Minors offered in most majors and in library science for education majors. Associate degrees offered. Self-designed majors. Internships. Cooperative education programs. Graduate school at which qualified undergraduates may take graduate-level courses. Preprofessional programs in medicine, veterinary science, and dentistry. 3-2 dual degree programs in business administration, chemistry, natural sciences, social sciences, and other fields with Georgia Tech. Cooperative physics program with Howard U. Cooperative geo-physics programs with U of Nevada at Las Vegas, U of

Oklahoma. Teacher certification in early childhood, elementary, middle/junior high, and secondary education. Exchange program abroad in the Cayman Islands (International Coll of the Cayman Islands). ROTC.

Honors: Honors program. Honor societies.

Academic Assistance: Remedial reading, writing, math, and study skills.

STUDENT LIFE. Housing: All students must live on campus unless living with family. Women's and men's dorms. 69% of students live in college housing.

Services and counseling/handicapped student services: Health service. Testing service. Special Studies Program. Counseling services for veteran and older students. Personal counseling. Career and academic guidance services.

Campus organizations: Undergraduate student government. Student newspaper (Peachite, published once/month). Literary magazine. Yearbook. Radio and TV stations. Academic clubs, 70 organizations in all. Four fraternities, no chapter houses; four sororities, no chapter houses.

Religious organizations: Baptist Student Union Choir, Christian Fellowship Society.

ATHLETICS. Physical education requirements: Six quarters of physical education required.

Intercollegiate competition: 9% of students participate. Basketball (M,W), football (M), tennis (M,W), track and field (outdoor) (M,W), volleyball (W). Member of NCAA Division II, Southern Intercollegiate Athletic Conference.

Intramural and club sports: 30% of students participate. Intramural basketball, flag football, kickball, softball, track and field, volleyball. Women's club slow-pitch softball.

ADMISSIONS. Academic basis for candidate selection (in order of priority): Secondary school record, standardized test scores.

Requirements: Graduation from secondary school is required; GED is accepted. 21 units and the following program of study are required: 4 units of English, 3 units of math, 3 units of science including 2 units of lab, 2 units of foreign language, 3 units of social studies, 6 units of academic electives. Audition required of music program applicants. Conditional admission possible for applicants who do not meet standard requirements but are able to pass freshman entrance exams. SAT I or ACT is required.

Procedure: Take SAT I or ACT by June of 12th year. Application deadline is August 25. Notification of admission on rolling basis. $20 nonrefundable room deposit. Freshmen accepted for all terms.

Special programs: Credit and/or placement may be granted through CEEB Advanced Placement exams for scores of 3 or higher. Credit and/or placement may be granted through CLEP general and subject exams. Credit and placement may be granted through challenge exams. Early entrance/early admission program.

Transfer students: Transfer students accepted for all terms. Application deadline is ten days prior to start of quarter. Minimum 2.0 GPA required. Lowest course grade accepted is "C-."

Admissions contact: Myldred P. Hill, Ed.D., Dean of Admissions and Enrollment Management. 912 825-6307.

FINANCIAL AID. Available aid: Pell grants, SEOG, state grants, school scholarships and grants, private scholarships, ROTC scholarships, academic merit scholarships, and athletic scholarships. Perkins Loans (NDSL), Stafford Loans (GSL), state loans, and private loans.

Supporting data/closing dates: FAFSA: Priority filing date is April 1; deadline is May 15. Notification of awards on rolling basis.

Financial aid contact: Jeanette Huff, Director of Financial Aid. 912 825-6363.

STUDENT EMPLOYMENT. Federal Work-Study Program. Institutional employment. Off-campus part-time employment opportunities rated "good."

COMPUTER FACILITIES. Apple/Macintosh microcomputers. Client/LAN operating systems include Apple/Macintosh. Computer facilities are available to all students.

Fees: None.

GRADUATE CAREER DATA. Graduate school percentages: 3% enter medical school. 7% enter graduate business programs. 15% enter graduate arts and sciences programs.

Grambling State University

Grambling, LA 71245

318 274-2000

Undergraduate profile. 94% Black, 3% White, 3% Other. 52% are state residents; 23% are transfers. Average age of undergraduates is 20.

Enrollment. Undergraduates: 3,268 men, 4,565 women (full-time). Freshman class: 5,428 applicants, 3,526 accepted, 1,390 enrolled. Graduate enrollment: 172 men, 417 women.

Faculty. 262 full-time, 20 part-time. 50% of faculty holds doctoral degree. Student/faculty ratio: 21 to 1.

Test score averages/ranges. Average ACT scores: 16 English, 15 math, 15 composite.

1995-96 Costs. Tuition: $2,500 (state residents), $3,500 (out-of-state). Room & board: $3,012. Fees, books, misc. academic expenses (school's estimate): $1,300.

PROFILE. Grambling, founded in 1901, is a public university. Programs are offered through the Colleges of Business, Education, Liberal Arts, and Sciences and Technology; and the School of Nursing. Its 360-acre campus is located in Grambling, 36 miles from Monroe.

Accreditation: SACS. Professionally accredited by the National Council for Accreditation of Teacher Education.

Religious orientation: Grambling State University is nonsectarian; no religious requirements.

Library: Collections totaling over 227,000 volumes.

Special facilities/museums: Audiovisual and TV center, lab schools.

STUDENT BODY. Freshman profile: 90% of freshmen come from public schools.

Undergraduate achievement: 55% of fall 1993 freshmen returned for fall 1994 term. 15% of students who complete a degree program immediately go on to graduate study.

Foreign students: 103 students are from out of the country. Countries represented include India, Japan, Mexico, Nigeria, and West Indies; 21 in all.

PROGRAMS OF STUDY. Degrees: B.A., B.Pub.Admin., B.S., B.S. Nurs., B.Soc.Work.

Majors: Accounting, Afro-American Study, Anthropology, Applied Mathematics, Applied Music, Art, Art Education, Automotive Technology, Biology, Biology Education, Building Construction Technology, Business Administration, Business Education, Cardiopulmonary Science, Chemistry, Chemistry Education, Computer Science, Criminal Justice, Cytotechnology, Drafting Technology, Early Childhood Education, Electrical Technology, Elementary Education, English, English Education, French, French Education, Geography, Health/Physical Education, History, Home Economics Education, Industrial Arts Education, Industrial Technology, Information Systems, Institutional Management, Institutional Management/Production, Journalism, Management, Marketing, Mathematics, Mathematics Education, Medical Technology, Music, Music Education, Music Theory, Nursing, Occupational Therapy, Philosophy, Physical Therapy, Physics, Political Science, Psychology, Public Administration, Radio/Television, Recreation, Rehabilitative Counseling, Secondary Education, Social Science, Social Science Education, Sociology, Spanish, Spanish Education, Special Education, Speech/Language/Hearing Specialist, Speech Pathology, Theatre, Theatre Education, Urban Studies.

Distribution of degrees: The majors with the highest enrollments are business administration, criminal justice, and nursing.

Requirements: General education requirement.

Academic regulations: Minimum 2.0 GPA must be maintained.

Special: Double majors. Dual degrees. Independent study. Pass/fail grading option. Internships. Cooperative education programs. Graduate school at which qualified undergraduates may take graduate-level courses. Preprofessional programs in law, medicine, veterinary science, dentistry, and engineering. 3-2 engineering/engineering technology program. Cooperative program with Louisiana Tech U; agriculture departments share facilities and staff. Member of National Student Exchange (NSE). Teacher certification in early childhood, elementary, secondary, and special education. Study abroad in China, India, Japan, and Mexico. ROTC and AFROTC.

Honors: Phi Beta Kappa. Honors program.

Academic Assistance: Remedial reading, writing, math, and study skills.

STUDENT LIFE. Housing: Freshmen must live on campus if space is available unless living with family. Women's and men's dorms. 40% of students live in college housing.

Social atmosphere: Students meet at the student union and the Renaissance. Greeks and Voice of Faith, a religious group, influence life on campus. Football games, Homecoming, Springfest, and job fairs are popular events on campus. "Campus life at Grambling prepares you for a real world full of different people," comments the student newspaper.

Services and counseling/handicapped student services: Placement services. Health service. Communicative Study and Skills Center. Counseling services for veteran students. Birth control and personal counseling. Career and academic guidance services. Learning disabled services.

Campus organizations: Undergraduate student government. Student newspaper (Gramblinite, published once/week). Yearbook. Radio and TV stations. Choir, women's choral, orchestra, string ensemble, opera workshop, several bands, Student Activities Committee, Debating Symposium, Little Theatre Guild, Associated Women Students, Men's Dormitory Council, athletic groups, special-interest groups. Four fraternities, no chapter houses; five sororities, no chapter houses. 5% of men join a fraternity. 5% of women join a sorority.

Religious organizations: Some religious groups.

ATHLETICS. Physical education requirements: Four semesters of physical education required. **Intercollegiate competition:** Baseball (M), basketball (M,W), football (M), golf (M), tennis (M,W), track and field (indoor) (M,W), track and field (outdoor) (M,W), volleyball (W). Member of NCAA Division I, NCAA Division I-AA for football, Southwestern Athletic Conference.

ADMISSIONS. Academic basis for candidate selection (in order of priority): Secondary school record, standardized test scores.

Nonacademic basis for candidate selection: Character and personality, particular talent or ability, and alumni/ae relationship are important. Extracurricular participation is considered.

Requirements: Graduation from secondary school is required; GED is accepted. 23 units and the following program of study are required: 3 units of English, 3 units of math, 2 units of science, 2 units of social studies, 2 units of history, 11 units of electives. 4 units of English, 1 unit of lab science, and 1 unit of foreign language recommended. Minimum 2.0 GPA required of out-of-state applicants; minimum composite ACT score of 16 recommended. Two years of pre-nursing program, minimum 2.5 GPA, and written recommendation required of nursing program applicants. Portfolio required of art program applicants. Audition required of music program applicants. Conditional admission possible for applicants not meeting standard requirements. ACT is required; SAT I may be substituted. Campus visit recommended. No off-campus interviews.

Procedure: Take SAT I or ACT by January of 12th year. Suggest filing application by April 15. Application deadline is July 15. Notification of admission on rolling basis. $50 refundable room deposit. Freshmen accepted for all terms.

Special programs: Admission may be deferred one year. Credit may be granted through CLEP general and subject exams. Credit may be granted for military experience. Credit and placement may be granted through challenge exams. Early decision program. In fall 1994, 10 applied for early decision and 2 were accepted. Deadline for applying for early decision is May 30. Early entrance/early admission program. Concurrent enrollment program.

Transfer students: Transfer students accepted for all terms. In fall 1994, 23% of all new students were transfers into all classes. 742 transfer applications were received, 501 were accepted. Application deadline is July 15 for fall; November 30 for spring. Minimum 2.0 GPA recommended. Lowest course grade accepted is "C." Maximum number of transferable credits is 60 semester hours from a two-year school and 90 semester hours from a four-year school. At least 30 semester hours must be completed at the university to receive degree.

Admissions contact: Nora D. Bingaman, M.Ed., Acting Director of Admissions. 318 274-2435.

FINANCIAL AID. Available aid: Pell grants, SEOG, state scholarships and grants, school scholarships and grants, private scholarships and grants, ROTC scholarships, academic merit scholarships, and athletic scholarships. Thurgood Marshall Scholarship. Dial Corporation Scholarship. Perkins Loans (NDSL), PLUS, Stafford Loans (GSL), NSL, state loans, and unsubsidized Stafford Loans.

Financial aid statistics: 5% of aid is not need-based. In 1994-95, 90% of all undergraduate aid applicants received aid; 90% of freshman aid applicants. Average amounts of aid awarded freshmen: Scholarships and grants, $750.

Supporting data/closing dates: FAFSA/FAF: Priority filing date is April 15. School's own aid application: Deadline is June 15. State aid form: Priority filing date is April 15. Notification of awards begins April 15.

STUDENT EMPLOYMENT. Federal Work-Study Program. 40% of full-time undergraduates work on campus during school year. Students may expect to earn an average of $460 during school year. Off-campus part-time employment opportunities rated "good."

COMPUTER FACILITIES. IBM/IBM-compatible, Apple/Macintosh, and RISC-/UNIX-based microcomputers. Students may access Digital, SUN minicomputer/mainframe systems, Internet. Residence halls may be equipped with networked microcomputers. Client/LAN operating systems include Apple/Macintosh, DOS, OS/2, UNIX/XENIX/AIX, Windows NT, DEC, Novell.
Fees: None.

GRADUATE CAREER DATA. 50% of graduates choose careers in business and industry. Companies and businesses that hire graduates: General Motors, IBM, Oscar Meyer, State Farm Insurance.

Hampton University

Hampton, VA 23368

804 727-5000

Undergraduate profile. 90% Black, 9% White, 1% Other. 18% are state residents.

Enrollment. Undergraduates: 1,808 men, 2,748 women (full-time). Freshman class: 7,178 applicants, 3,755 accepted, 1,433 enrolled. Graduate enrollment: 396.

Faculty. 291 full-time, 99 part-time. 60% of faculty holds doctoral degree. Student/faculty ratio: 18 to 1.

Test score averages/ranges. Average SAT I scores: 925 combined.

1995-96 Costs. Tuition: $7,662. Room: $1,930. Board: $1,764. Fees, books, misc. academic expenses (school's estimate): $1,300.

PROFILE. Hampton, founded in 1868, is a private university. Programs are offered through the Schools of Arts and Letters, Business, Education, Nursing, and Pure and Applied Sciences. Its 204-acre campus, including buildings listed with the National Register of Historic Places, is located within 40 miles of Jamestown, Yorktown, and Williamsburg.

Accreditation: SACS. Professionally accredited by the Accreditation Board for Engineering and Technology, Inc., the National Architecture Accrediting Board, the National Association of Schools of Music, the National Council for Accreditation of Teacher Education, the National League for Nursing.

Religious orientation: Hampton University is nonsectarian; no religious requirements.

Library: Collections totaling over 235,000 volumes, 1,200 periodical subscriptions, and 35,000 microform items.

Special facilities/museums: African, Native American, and oceanic museums, gallery, laboratory elementary school.

Athletic facilities: Gymnasium, swimming pools, tennis courts, athletic fields.

STUDENT BODY. Freshman profile: Majority of accepted applicants took SAT I.

Undergraduate achievement: 60% of entering class graduates. 25% of students who complete a degree program immediately go on to graduate study.

Foreign students: 42 students are from out of the country.

PROGRAMS OF STUDY. Degrees: B.A., B.Arch., B.S., B.S.Nurs.

Majors: Accounting, Airway Science, Architecture, Art, Biology, Building Construction Technology, Business, Business Education, Chemical Engineering, Chemistry, Communication Disorders, Community Service Education, Computer Science, Early Childhood, Economics, Education, Electrical Engineering, Elementary Education, Engineering, English, Environmental Analysis, Finance, Health/Physical Education, History, Interior Design, Management, Marine Biology, Marketing, Mass Media Arts, Mathematics, Mechanical Engineering, Music, Music Education, Nursing, Physical Education, Physics, Political Science, Professional Tennis Management, Psychology, Recreation, Secondary Education, Sociology, Spanish, Special Education, Speech/Drama.

Distribution of degrees: The majors with the highest enrollments are accounting, biology, and psychology; special education and speech/drama have the lowest.

Requirements: General education requirement.

Academic regulations: Minimum 2.0 GPA must be maintained.

Special: Independent study. Internships. Cooperative education programs. Graduate school at which qualified undergraduates may take graduate-level courses. Preprofessional programs in law, medicine, veterinary science, pharmacy, and dentistry. Teacher certification in early childhood, elementary, secondary, and special education. Study abroad possible. ROTC and NROTC.

Honors: Phi Beta Kappa. Honors program. Honor societies.

Academic Assistance: Remedial reading, writing, math, and study skills. Nonremedial tutoring.

STUDENT LIFE. Housing: Students may live on or off campus. Coed, women's, and men's dorms. 50% of students live in college housing.

Social atmosphere: On campus, students gather at the student union and the library; off campus, Ogden Circle and Hampden Harbor are popular hangouts. The Student Government Association, the Student Christian Association, and the Greek community are among the groups that have a widespread influence on campus life. Popular annual events include Homecoming, the Black Family Conference, the Mass Media Arts Symposium, and Career Day. "The social and cultural atmosphere of the Hampton University community is one characterized by African-American unity. In addition, Hampton encourages academic as well as social development and the importance of reaching out to the community surrounding the campus."

Services and counseling/handicapped student services: Placement services. Health service. Personal counseling. Career and academic guidance services. Physically disabled student services. Learning disabled services. Tutors.

Campus organizations: Undergraduate student government. Student newspaper (Hampton Script, published once/two weeks). Yearbook. Radio station. Band, choir, orchestra, University Players, debating, athletic, departmental, service, and special-interest groups, 70 organizations in all. Five fraternities, no chapter houses; three sororities, no chapter houses.

Religious organizations: Student Christian Association.

Foreign student organizations: International Student Club.

ATHLETICS. Physical education requirements: Two semesters of physical education required.

Intercollegiate competition: 3% of students participate. Basketball (M,W), cheerleading (M,W), cross-country (M,W), football (M), golf (M), softball (W), tennis (M), track (indoor) (M,W), track (outdoor) (M,W), track and field (indoor) (M,W), track and field (outdoor) (M,W), volleyball (W). Member of Central Intercollegiate Athletic Association, NCAA Division II.

Intramural and club sports: 1% of students participate. Intramural archery, basketball, bowling, flag football, softball, swimming, tennis.

ADMISSIONS. Academic basis for candidate selection (in order of priority): Secondary school record, standardized test scores, essay, school's recommendation, class rank.

Nonacademic basis for candidate selection: Character and personality, extracurricular participation, particular talent or ability, geographical distribution, and alumni/ae relationship are considered.

Requirements: Graduation from secondary school is recommended; GED is accepted. 17 units and the following program of study are required: 4 units of English, 3 units of math, 2 units of science, 2 units of history, 6 units of academic electives. Minimum combined SAT I score of 800, rank in top half of secondary school class, and minimum 2.0 GPA required. Conditional admission possible for applicants not meeting standard requirements. SAT I or ACT is required. Campus visit recommended.

Procedure: Take SAT I or ACT by September 15 of 12th year. Suggest filing application by September 1. Application deadline is March 15. Notification of admission on rolling basis. $600 tuition deposit, refundable until June 7. $100 room deposit, refundable until June 1. Freshmen accepted for all terms.

Special programs: Admission may be deferred one year. Credit and/or placement may be granted through CEEB Advanced Placement exams for scores of 3 or higher. Credit and placement may be granted for military and life experience. Early decision program. Early entrance/early admission program. Concurrent enrollment program.

Transfer students: Transfer students accepted for all terms. In fall 1993, 832 transfer applications were received, 292 were accepted. Application deadline is March 15 for fall; December 15 for spring. Minimum 2.3 GPA required. Lowest course grade accepted is "C." At least 30 semester hours must be completed at the university to receive degree.

Admissions contact: Dr. Ollie M. Bowman, Dean of Admissions. 800 624-3328, 804 727-5328.

FINANCIAL AID. Available aid: Pell grants, SEOG, state grants, school scholarships and grants, private scholarships and grants, ROTC scholarships, academic merit scholarships, athletic scholarships, and aid for undergraduate foreign students. Perkins Loans (NDSL), PLUS, Stafford Loans (GSL), NSL, state loans, and private loans. Tuition Plan Inc. and deferred payment plan.

Supporting data/closing dates: FAFSA/FAF: Priority filing date is March 31. School's own aid application: Priority filing date is March 31. State aid form: Accepted on rolling basis. Notification of awards on rolling basis.

Financial aid contact: Delores Davis, Director of Financial Aid. 800 624-3341, 804 727-5332.

STUDENT EMPLOYMENT. Federal Work-Study Program. Off-campus part-time employment opportunities rated "good."

COMPUTER FACILITIES. IBM/IBM-compatible microcomputers.

Fees: None.

GRADUATE CAREER DATA. Graduate school percentages: 3% enter law school. 1% enter medical school. 4% enter graduate business programs. 17% enter graduate arts and sciences programs.

PROMINENT ALUMNI/AE. Booker T. Washington, national leader and founder, Tuskegee Institute; Sarah Collins Fernandis; Susan La Flesche, first Native American woman to receive the degree of doctor of medicine.

Harris-Stowe State College

St. Louis, MO 63103

314 533-3366

Undergraduate profile: 65% Black, 1% Hispanic, 31% White, 3% Other. 99% are state residents. Average age of undergraduates is 25.

Enrollment. Undergraduates: 300 men, 550 women (full-time).

Faculty. 43 full-time. 61% of faculty holds doctoral degree. Student/faculty ratio: 16 to 1.

Test score averages/ranges. N/A.

1995-96 Costs. Tuition: $2,070 (state residents), $4,140 (out-of-state). Housing: None. Fees, books, misc. academic expenses (school's estimate): $815.

PROFILE. Harris-Stowe, founded in 1857, is a public college for educational studies. Its urban campus is located in St. Louis.

Accreditation: NCACS. Professionally accredited by the National Council for Accreditation of Teacher Education.

Religious orientation: Harris-Stowe State College is nonsectarian; no religious requirements.

Library: Collections totaling over 60,000 volumes.

Special facilities/museums: Education resource center, urban education specialist/multicultural education collection, juvenile literature collection, audiovisual lab.

Athletic facilities: Gymnasiums, athletic fields, swimming pool.

PROGRAMS OF STUDY. Degrees: B.S.Ed., B.S.Urban Ed.

Majors: Early Childhood Education, Elementary School Education, Middle School/Junior High Education, Urban Education.

Distribution of degrees: The major with the highest enrollment is elementary school education.

Special: Teacher education curricula consist of general education requirements, professional education, teaching methodologies, and clinical experiences. Accelerated study. Graduate school at which qualified undergraduates may take graduate-level courses. Cross-registration with St. Louis U and U of Missouri at St. Louis. Teacher certification in early childhood, elementary, and secondary education. ROTC and AFROTC.

Academic Assistance: Nonremedial tutoring.

STUDENT LIFE. Housing: Commuter campus; no student housing.

Services and counseling/handicapped student services: Placement services. Health service. Counseling services for military and veteran students. Personal and psychological counseling. Career and academic guidance services.

Campus organizations: Undergraduate student government. Student newspaper. Literary magazine. Yearbook. Concert chorale, Harris-Stowe Dancers, Pep Club, pom-pom squad, cheerleaders, Childhood Education International.

ATHLETICS. Physical education requirements: None.

Intercollegiate competition: 5% of students participate. Baseball (M), basketball (M,W), soccer (M), track and field (indoor) (W), track and field (outdoor) (W), volleyball (W). Member of American Midwest Conference, NAIA.

Intramural and club sports: 5% of students participate. Intramural basketball, softball, tennis, touch football, volleyball.

ADMISSIONS. Requirements: Graduation from secondary school is required; GED is accepted. 11 secondary school units in English, math, social studies, and science required. Rank in top half of secondary school class recommended. Conditional admission possible for applicants not meeting standard requirements. SAT I or ACT is required. Campus visit and interview recommended. No off-campus interviews.

Procedure: Freshmen accepted in terms other than fall.

Special programs: Admission may be deferred. Credit and/or placement may be granted through CEEB Advanced Placement exams. Credit and/or placement may be granted through CLEP general and subject exams. Credit and placement may be granted for military experience. Concurrent enrollment program.

Transfer students: Transfer students accepted for all terms. Lowest course grade accepted is "C." Maximum number of transferable credits is 64 semester hours from two-year schools.

Admissions contact: Valerie A. Beeson, M.A., Director of Admissions.

FINANCIAL AID. Available aid: Pell grants, SEOG, state grants, school scholarships and grants, ROTC scholarships, and aid for undergraduate foreign students. Perkins Loans (NDSL) and Stafford Loans (GSL). Deferred payment plan.

Supporting data/closing dates: FAFSA/FAF: Deadline is May 1. School's own aid application: Accepted on rolling basis.

STUDENT EMPLOYMENT. Federal Work-Study Program. Institutional employment.

Howard University

Washington, DC 20059   202 806-6100

Undergraduate profile. 87% Black, 2% Asian-American, 1% Hispanic, 2% White, 8% Other. 20% are state residents; 36% are transfers. Average age of undergraduates is 20.

Enrollment. Undergraduates: 2,293 men, 3,981 women (full-time). Freshman class: 6,532 applicants, 1,743 accepted, 1,549 enrolled. Graduate enrollment: 1,950 men, 3,419 women.

Faculty. 1,352 full-time, 819 part-time; 1,509 Black, 424 White, 238 Other. Student/faculty ratio: 6 to 1.

Test score averages/ranges. Average SAT I scores: 426 verbal, 452 math. Average ACT scores: 20 English, 19 math, 20 composite.

1995-96 Costs. Tuition: $8,105. Room: $2,955. Board: $1,800. Fees, books, misc. academic expenses (school's estimate): $1,025.

PROFILE. Howard, founded in 1867, is a private, comprehensive, historically Black university. Programs are offered through the Divisions of Academic Affairs and Health Affairs. Its 89-acre main campus is located in central Washington; its 22-acre West Campus is located near Rock Creek Park in northwest Washington.

Accreditation: MSACS.

Religious orientation: Howard University is nonsectarian; no religious requirements.

Library: Collections totaling 1,900,000 volumes, 19,400 periodical subscriptions, and 2,266,115 microform items.

Special facilities/museums: Three art galleries, language labs, hospital. Research center with comprehensive collection on Africa and persons of African descent.

Athletic facilities: Gymnasiums, weight room, basketball, tennis, and volleyball courts, swimming pool, track, baseball, football, intramural, and soccer fields, tae kwon do/judo room.

STUDENT BODY. Freshman profile: 3% of freshmen who took SAT I scored 600 or over on verbal, 5% scored 600 or over on math; 17% scored 500 or over on verbal, 28% scored 500 or over on math; 60% scored 400 or over on verbal, 69% scored 400 or over on math; 96% scored 300 or over on verbal, 97% scored 300 or over on math. 1% of freshmen who took ACT scored 30 or over on English, 1% scored 30 or over on composite; 16% scored 24 or over on English, 9% scored 24 or over on math, 10% scored 24 or over on composite; 58% scored 18 or over on English, 51% scored 18 or over on math, 62% scored 18 or over on composite; 81% scored 12 or over on English, 81% scored 12 or over on math, 76% scored 12 or over on composite; 87% scored 6 or over on English, 83% scored 6 or over on math, 77% scored 6 or over on composite. 95% of accepted applicants took SAT I; 5% took ACT. 80% of freshmen come from public schools.

Undergraduate achievement: 75% of 1993 freshmen returned for fall 1994 term. 23% of entering class graduates. 40% of students who complete a degree program immediately go on to graduate study.

Foreign students: Countries represented include the Bahamas, Bermuda, Canada, Jamaica, Nigeria, and Trinidad/Tobago; 110 in all.

PROGRAMS OF STUDY. Degrees: B.A., B.Arch., B.Bus.Admin., B.F.A., B.Mus., B.Mus.Ed., B.S., B.S.Arch., B.S.Chem.Eng., B.S.Civil Eng., B.S.Comp.Sys.Eng., B.S.Elec.Eng., B.S.Eng., B.S.Mech.Eng., B.S.Med.Tech., B.S.Nurs., B.S.Occup.Ther., B.S.Radiol.Tech.

Majors: Accounting, Administration of Justice, Afro-American Study, Anthropology, Applied Music, Architecture, Art, Art Education, Art History, Astronomy, Biology, Broadcast Management, Broadcast Production, Ceramics, Chemical Engineering, Chemistry, Civil Engineering, Classics, Communication Sciences/Disorders, Composition, Computer Information Systems, Computer System Engineering, Consumer Affairs Management, Design, Drama, Economics, Electrical Engineering, Elementary Education, English, Environmental Sciences, Experimental Studio, Fashion Fundamentals, Film Directing, Finance, French, Geography, Geology, German, Graphic Art, History, Hotel/Motel Management, Human Communication Studies, Human Development, Insurance, Interior Design, International Business, Jazz Studies, Journalism, Management, Marketing, Mathematics, Mechanical Engineering, Medical Technology, Military Science, Music History/Literature, Music Therapy, Musical Theatre, Nursing, Nutritional Sciences, Occupational Therapy, Painting, Pharmacy, Philosophy, Photography, Physical Education/Recreation, Physical Therapy, Physician's Assistant, Physics, Political Science, Printmaking, Psychology, Russian, Sculpture, Sociology, Spanish, Theatre/Speech Education.

Distribution of degrees: The majors with the highest enrollments are electrical engineering, business administration, and communications; German, classics, and Afro-American studies have the lowest.

Requirements: General education requirement.

Academic regulations: Minimum 2.0 GPA must be maintained.

Special: Dual degrees. Independent study. Accelerated study. Pass/fail grading option. Internships. Graduate school at which qualified undergraduates may take graduate-level courses. Preprofessional programs in medicine, veterinary science, pharmacy, dentistry, optometry, allied health, medicine, osteopathy, and podiatry. J.D./M.B.A., B.S./M.D., B.S./D.D.S., B.S./Doc. Podiatric Med., and M.D./Ph.D. programs. Member of Consortium of Universities of the Washington, D.C., Metropolitan Area. Exchange programs with Duke U, Harvard U, Mills Coll, Reed Coll, Smith Coll, Stanford U, Tufts U, U of California at Berkeley, U of Southern California, and Vassar Coll. Teacher certification in early childhood, elementary, and secondary education. Certification in specific subject areas. Member of International Student Exchange Program (ISEP). ROTC and AFROTC.

Honors: Phi Beta Kappa. Honors program.

Academic Assistance: Remedial reading, math, vocabulary, writing, and study skills.

STUDENT LIFE. Housing: All freshmen and transfer students must live on campus. Coed, women's, and men's dorms. School-owned/operated apartments. Both on-campus and off-campus married-student housing. 38% of students live in college housing.

Services and counseling/handicapped student services: Placement services. Health service. Day care. Counseling services for veteran students. Personal and psychological counseling. Career and academic guidance services. Physically disabled student services. Notetaking services. Reader services for the blind.

Campus organizations: Undergraduate student government. Student newspaper (Hilltop, published once/week). Yearbook. Radio and TV stations. African Cultural Ensemble, Caribbean Student Association, Pan-African Association. Gospel choir, string ensemble, band, jazz society, dance group, drama groups, debating, state and city geographical clubs, professional clubs. Four fraternities, no chapter houses; four sororities, no chapter houses. 1% of men join a fraternity. 1% of women join a sorority.

Religious organizations: Absalom Jones Student Association, Adventist Community, Baptist Student Union, Methodist Fellowship.

ATHLETICS. Physical education requirements: Four semesters of physical education required. **Intercollegiate competition:** 1% of students participate. Baseball (M), basketball (M,W), cross-country (M,W), diving (M,W), football (M), soccer (M), swimming (M,W), tennis (M,W), track (indoor) (M,W), track and field (indoor) (M,W), track and field (outdoor) (M,W), volleyball (W), wrestling (M). Member of Mid Eastern Athletic Conference, NCAA Division I, NCAA Division I-AA for football.

Intramural and club sports: 10% of students participate. Intramural badminton, basketball, bowling, handball, lacrosse, soccer, softball, swimming, table tennis, tennis, touch football, weight lifting. Men's club basketball, cheerleading, football, lacrosse, soccer, swimming, tennis, wrestling. Women's club basketball, cheerleading, soccer, swimming, tennis.

ADMISSIONS. Academic basis for candidate selection (in order of priority): Class rank, secondary school record, standardized test scores, school's recommendation.

Nonacademic basis for candidate selection: Extracurricular participation, particular talent or ability, and alumni/ae relationship are considered.

Requirements: Graduation from secondary school is required; GED is accepted. 16 units and the following program of study are required: 4 units of English, 2 units of math, 2 units of science, 2 units of foreign language, 4 units of academic electives. Audition, tape, or portfolio required of College of Fine Arts program applicants. Center for Academic Reinforcement for applicants not normally admissible. SAT I or ACT is required. Campus visit recommended.

Procedure: Take SAT I or ACT by December of 12th year. Suggest filing application by November 1. Application deadline is April 15. Notification of admission on rolling basis, within five days of receipt of completed application. $150 nonrefundable tuition deposit. $100 nonrefundable room deposit. Freshmen accepted for all terms.

Special programs: Admission may be deferred one semester. Credit and/or placement may be granted through CEEB Advanced Placement exams for scores of 3 or higher. Early entrance/early admission program. Concurrent enrollment program.

Transfer students: Transfer students accepted for all terms. Application deadline is April 1 for fall; November 1 for spring. Minimum 2.5 GPA. Lowest course grade accepted is "C." At least 30 semester hours must be completed at the university to receive degree.

Admissions contact: Rochetta Johnson, Assistant Director, Admissions. 202 806-2752.

FINANCIAL AID. Available aid: Pell grants, SEOG, Federal Nursing Student Scholarships, state scholarships and grants, school scholarships and grants, private scholarships and grants, ROTC scholarships, academic merit scholarships, athletic scholarships, and aid for undergraduate foreign students. Perkins Loans (NDSL), PLUS, Stafford Loans (GSL), and Health Professions Loans. Deferred payment plan.

Supporting data/closing dates: FAFSA: Priority filing date is April 1. FAF. Notification of awards on rolling basis.

Financial aid contact: Mr. Avon Dennis, Assistant Director, Financial Aid. 202 806-2800.

STUDENT EMPLOYMENT. Federal Work-Study Program. Institutional employment. 6% of full-time undergraduates work on campus during school year. Students may expect to earn an average of $200 during school year. Freshmen are discouraged from working during their first term. Off-campus part-time employment opportunities rated "good."

COMPUTER FACILITIES. 300 IBM/IBM-compatible, Apple/Macintosh, and PowerPC-based microcomputers. Students may access AT&T, Digital, Hewlett-Packard, IBM, NCR, SUN, and UNISYS minicomputer/mainframe systems, BITNET, CompuServe, and Internet. Client/LAN operating systems include Apple/Macintosh, DOS, UNIX/XENIX/AIX, X-windows, DEC, Local-Talk/AppleTalk, and Novell. Computer facilities are available to all students.

Fees: None.

GRADUATE CAREER DATA. Graduate school percentages: 10% enter law school. 12% enter medical school. 9% enter dental school. 4% enter graduate business programs. 15% enter graduate arts and sciences programs. 3% enter theological school/seminary. Highest graduate school enrollments: American U, Howard U, U of Maryland. 14% of graduates choose careers in business and industry. Companies and businesses that hire graduates: AT&T, IBM, ITT.

PROMINENT ALUMNI/AE. Thurgood Marshall, former U.S. Supreme Court justice; Edward W. Brooke, former U.S. senator; Phyllicia Ayers-Allen/Rashad, actress; Kenneth Clark, psychologist; Sirjang Lai Tandon, computer entrepreneur; Andrew Young, former mayor of Atlanta.

Huston-Tillotson College

Austin, TX 78702   **512 505-3000**

Undergraduate profile. 77% Black, 8% Hispanic, 3% White, 12% Other. 88% are state residents; 21% are transfers. Average age of undergraduates is 21.

Enrollment. Undergraduates: 244 men, 262 women (full-time). Freshman class: 190 applicants, 180 accepted, 152 enrolled.

Faculty. 38 full-time, 12 part-time; 24 Black, 17 White, 9 Other. 42% of faculty holds doctoral degree. Student/faculty ratio: 13 to 1.

Test score averages/ranges. Average SAT I scores: 691 combined. Average ACT scores: 15 composite.

1995-96 Costs. Tuition: $4,816. Room & board: $3,814. Fees, books, misc. academic expenses (school's estimate): $1,408.

PROFILE. Huston-Tillotson is a church-affiliated college. It was formed by the 1952 merger of Tillotson College (founded in 1877) and Samuel Huston College (founded in 1876). Its 23-acre campus is located one mile from downtown Austin.

Accreditation: SACS.

Religious orientation: Huston-Tillotson College is an interdenominational Christian school. Attendance is mandatory for chapel once/week.

Library: Collections totaling 80,406 volumes, 320 periodical subscriptions, and 73,011 microform items.

Athletic facilities: Gymnasium, tennis court, athletic field.

STUDENT BODY.

Freshman profile: Majority of accepted applicants took SAT I. 85% of freshmen come from public schools.

Undergraduate achievement: 18% of students who complete a degree program immediately go on to graduate study.

Foreign students: 74 students are from out of the country. Countries represented include Bahrain, Indonesia, Iran, Morocco, Nigeria, and Saudi Arabia; 16 in all.

PROGRAMS OF STUDY. Degrees: B.A., B.S.

Majors: Accounting, Biology, Business Administration, Chemistry, Computer Science, English, Government, Marketing, Mass Communication, Mathematics, Music, Physical Education/Recreation, Sociology, Teacher Education.

Distribution of degrees: The majors with the highest enrollments are business administration and sociology; mathematics has the lowest.

Requirements: General education requirement.

Academic regulations: Freshmen must maintain minimum 1.5 GPA; sophomores, 1.65 GPA; juniors, 1.75 GPA; seniors, 1.90 GPA.

Special: Minors offered in all majors. Courses offered in African-American studies, economics, finance, hospitality management, history, international studies, philosophy, psychology, and religion. Double majors. Independent study. Internships. Cooperative education programs. Preprofessional programs in law, medicine, dentistry, and nursing. 2-2 allied health program with Texas Tech U. 3-2 engineering program with Prairie View A&M U. Semester-away programs possible. Teacher certification in early childhood, elementary, secondary, and special education. Study abroad possible.

Honors: Honors program. Honor societies.

Academic Assistance: Remedial reading, writing, math, and study skills. Nonremedial tutoring.

STUDENT LIFE. Housing: All unmarried students must live on campus unless living with family. Coed dorms. 40% of students live in college housing.

Services and counseling/handicapped student services: Placement services. Health service. Counseling services for older students. Personal and psychological counseling. Career and academic guidance services. Religious counseling. Learning disabled services.

Campus organizations: Undergraduate student government. Student newspaper. Yearbook. Black Journalists Association. Choir, ensemble, educators club, physical education club, soccer club, Distinguished Brothers, Angels of Elegance, Gems Club, Prelaw Society, social groups. Four fraternities, no chapter houses; four sororities, no chapter houses. 1% of men join a fraternity. 1% of women join a sorority.

Religious organizations: Fellowship Hour Organization, Canterbury Club.

ATHLETICS. Physical education requirements: Four semesters of physical education required.

Intercollegiate competition: 3% of students participate. Baseball (M), basketball (M,W), tennis (M,W), volleyball (W). Member of Big State Conference, NAIA, SAIAW, TAIAW.

Intramural and club sports: 1% of students participate.

ADMISSIONS. Academic basis for candidate selection (in order of priority): Standardized test scores, secondary school record, class rank, school's recommendation, essay.

Nonacademic basis for candidate selection: Alumni/ae relationship is important. Character and personality, extracurricular participation, and particular talent or ability are considered.

Requirements: Graduation from secondary school is required; GED is accepted. 18 units and the following program of study are required: 4 units of English, 3 units of math, 2 units of lab science, 2 units of social studies, 6 units of electives. Minimum combined SAT I score of 700 recommended. Audition required of music program scholarship applicants. SAT I or ACT is required. Campus visit and interview recommended. Off-campus interviews available with admissions and alumni representatives.

Procedure: Application deadline is March 1. Notification of admission on rolling basis. $125 room deposit, refundable upon leaving the college. Freshmen accepted for all terms.

Special programs: Admission may be deferred two semesters. Credit may be granted through CEEB Advanced Placement. Credit may be granted through CLEP subject exams. Early entrance/early admission program. Concurrent enrollment program.

Transfer students: Transfer students accepted for all terms. In fall 1994, 21% of all new students were transfers into all classes. 107 transfer applications were received, 95 were accepted. Application deadline is March 1 for fall; December 1 for spring. Minimum 2.0 GPA required. Lowest course grade accepted is "C." Maximum number of transferable credits is 66 semester hours from a two-year school and 96 semester hours from a four-year school. At least 30 semester hours must be completed at the college to receive degree.

Admissions contact: Donnie J. Scott, Director of Admissions. 512 505-3027, extensions 3028, 3029.

FINANCIAL AID. Available aid: Pell grants, SEOG, state grants, school scholarships, academic merit scholarships, aid for undergraduate foreign students, and United Negro College Fund. Perkins Loans (NDSL), PLUS, Stafford Loans (GSL), and school loans. AMS, Tuition Management Systems, and deferred payment plan.

Financial aid statistics: In 1993-94, 88% of all undergraduate aid applicants received aid; 95% of freshman aid applicants. Average amounts of aid awarded freshmen: Loans, $2,625.

Supporting data/closing dates: FAFSA/FAF: Priority filing date is May 1. School's own aid application: Priority filing date is May 1. State aid form: Priority filing date is May 1. Income tax forms: Priority filing date is May 1. Notification of awards on rolling basis.

Financial aid contact: Jackie Wilson, Director of Financial Aid. 512 505-3030, extensions 3026, 3031.

STUDENT EMPLOYMENT. Federal Work-Study Program. Institutional employment. 20% of full-time undergraduates work on campus during school year. Students may expect to earn an average of $1,620 during school year. Freshmen are discouraged from working during their first term. Off-campus part-time employment opportunities rated "good."

COMPUTER FACILITIES. 67 IBM/IBM-compatible microcomputers. Computers are available only to students enrolled in computer courses.

Fees: None.

Hours: 8 AM-10 PM.

GRADUATE CAREER DATA. Highest graduate school enrollments: St. Edwards U, Southwest Texas State U. Companies and businesses that hire graduates: IBM, State Farm, IRS.

PROMINENT ALUMNI/AE. Dr. Hubert G. Lovelady, inventor; Azie Taylor Morton, former U.S. treasurer.

Jackson State University

Jackson, MS 39217   **601 968-2121**

Undergraduate profile. 95% Black, .5% Asian-American, 4% White, .5% Other. 67% are state residents; 4% are transfers. Average age of undergraduates is 20.

Enrollment. Undergraduates: 2,071 men, 2,623 women (full-time). Graduate enrollment: 320 men, 654 women.

Faculty. 320 full-time, 57 part-time; 201 Black, 72 White, 47 Other. 65% of faculty holds doctoral degree. Student/faculty ratio: 17 to 1.

Test score averages/ranges. Average ACT scores: 17 English, 17 math, 17 composite. Range of ACT scores of middle 50%: 10-26 English, 11-23 math.

1995-96 Costs. Tuition: $2,380 (state residents), $4,974 (out-of-state). Room: $1,706. Board: $1,114-$1,282.

PROFILE. Jackson State, founded in 1877, is a public university. Programs are offered through the Schools of Business, Education, Industrial and Technical Studies, and Liberal Studies. Its 128-acre campus is located in Jackson.

Accreditation: SACS. Professionally accredited by the Accrediting Council on Education in Journalism and Mass Communication, the Council on Social Work Education, the National Association of Schools of Music, the National Council for Accreditation of Teacher Education.

Religious orientation: Jackson State University is nonsectarian; no religious requirements.

Library: Collections totaling over 371,200 volumes, and 2,715 periodical subscriptions.

Special facilities/museums: Research center.

Athletic facilities: Swimming pools, track and field, bowling lanes, baseball, football, practice, and soccer fields, martial arts and weight rooms, basketball and tennis courts, ballet, dance studios.

STUDENT BODY. Freshman profile: 6% of freshmen who took ACT scored 24 or over on English, 2% scored 24 or over on math, 3% scored 24 or over on composite; 37% scored 18 or over on English, 32% scored 18 or over on math, 36% scored 18 or over on composite; 93% scored 12 or over on English, 98% scored 12 or over on math, 99% scored 12 or over on composite; 100% scored 6 or over on English, 100% scored 6 or over on math, 100% scored 6 or over on composite. 3% of accepted applicants took SAT I; 97% took ACT.

Undergraduate achievement: 48% of students who complete a degree program go on to graduate study within five years.

Foreign students: 217 students are from out of the country. Countries represented include China, India, Iran, Kuwait, Nigeria, and Rumania; 29 in all.

PROGRAMS OF STUDY. Degrees: B.A., B.Bus.Admin., B.Mus., B.Mus.Ed., B.S., B.S.Ed., B.Soc.Work.

Majors: Accounting, Art, Biology, Business Administration, Business Education, Chemistry, Computer Science, Criminal Justice/Correctional Services, Economics, Elementary Education, English, English Literature, Finance, Health/Physical Education/Recreation, History, Industrial Arts Education, Industrial Technology, Management, Marketing, Mass Communications, Mathematics, Mathematics Education, Meteorology, Music Education, Music/Piano Performance, Office Administration, Physics, Political Science, Psychology, Secondary Education, Social Science Education, Social Work, Sociology, Spanish, Special Education, Speech, Urban Studies.

Distribution of degrees: The majors with the highest enrollments are business administration, accounting, and elementary education; economics, physics, and Spanish have the lowest.

Requirements: General education requirement.

Academic regulations: Minimum 2.0 GPA must be maintained.

Special: Minors offered. Courses offered in early childhood education, environmental studies, historical preservation, library science, marine science, and reading. Double majors. Independent study. Internships. Cooperative education programs. Graduate school at which qualified undergraduates may take graduate-level courses. Preprofessional programs in law, medicine, veterinary science, and dentistry. Combined-degree programs in math and chemistry with Caltech, Georgia Tech, and Mississippi State U. Medical technology/medical record administration concentration with U of Mississippi Medical Center. Research semester at Lawrence Berkeley Lab. Member of National Student Exchange (NSE). Teacher certification in elementary, secondary, and special education. Certification in specific subject areas. ROTC.

Honors: Phi Beta Kappa. Honors program. Honor societies.

Academic Assistance: Remedial reading, writing, math, and study skills.

STUDENT LIFE. Housing: All student athletes must live on campus. Women's and men's dorms. School-owned/operated apartments. Athletic dorm (men's). 44% of students live in college housing.

Social atmosphere: Favorite gathering spots include the Campus Union, JSU Gibbs/Green Memorial Plaza, the cafeteria, and off campus, the Jackson Metrocenter Mall. The Student Government Association, Panhellenic Council, NAACP chapter, the Baptist Student Union, Campus Crusade for Christ, and Student Advisory Councils are influential groups on campus. Students enjoy the African-American Harvest Bazaar, African-American history festivals and celebrations, Homecoming activities, the campus-wide Mardi Gras, the Soul Bowl (JSU vs. Alcorn State football game), and Greek Week. "JSU's social and cultural life is enriched by over 125 student organizations. All of the organizations facilitate the growth and community service projects JSU performs as part of its urban mission," reports the student newspaper.

Services and counseling/handicapped student services: Placement services. Health service. Day care. Counseling services for military, veteran, and older students. Birth control, personal, and psychological counseling. Career and academic guidance services. Physically disabled student services. Learning disabled services. Notetaking services. Tape recorders. Tutors.

Campus organizations: Undergraduate student government. Student newspaper (Blue and White Flash, published once/week). Yearbook. Radio station. Band, orchestra, choirs, Dramatic Guild, 60 organizations in all. Four fraternities, no chapter houses; four sororities, no chapter houses.

Religious organizations: Bahai Club, Baptist Student Union, Campus Crusade for Christ, COGIC Collegiate, Emmanuel Club, Newman Club, Wesley Foundation.

Foreign student organizations: Foreign Student Association, International Student Association.

ATHLETICS. Physical education requirements: Two semesters of physical education required.

Intercollegiate competition: 5% of students participate. Baseball (M), basketball (M,W), cheer-leading (M,W), cross-country (M,W), football (M), golf (M,W), tennis (M,W), track (indoor) (M,W), track (outdoor) (M,W), track and field (indoor) (M,W), track and field (outdoor) (M,W), volleyball (W). Member of NCAA Division I, NCAA Division I-AA for football, Southwestern Athletic Conference.

Intramural and club sports: 62% of students participate. Intramural aerobics, basketball, karate, softball, swimming, tennis. Men's club bowling, gymnastics, martial arts, rifle, softball, swimming, weight lifting. Women's club bowling, gymnastics, martial arts, rifle, softball, swimming, weight lifting.

ADMISSIONS. Academic basis for candidate selection (in order of priority): Standardized test scores, secondary school record, school's recommendation, class rank.

Nonacademic basis for candidate selection: Character and personality, extracurricular participation, and particular talent or ability are important. Alumni/ae relationship is considered.

Requirements: Graduation from secondary school is recommended; GED is accepted. 15 units and the following program of study are required: 4 units of English, 3 units of math, 3 units of lab science, 3 units of social studies, 2 units of academic electives. Minimum 2.0 GPA required of all applicants. Minimum combined SAT I score of 580 (composite ACT score of 15) required of in-state applicants; minimum combined SAT I score of 630 (composite ACT score of 16) required of out-of-state applicants. Automatic admission with combined SAT I score of 720 or composite ACT score of 18. ACT is required; SAT I may be substituted. Off-campus interviews available with admissions and alumni representatives.

Procedure: Take SAT I or ACT by December of 12th year. Application deadline is August 15. Notification of admission on rolling basis. $25 nonrefundable room deposit. Freshmen accepted for all terms.

Special programs: Admission may be deferred one year. Credit may be granted through CLEP general and subject exams. Early decision program. Early entrance/early admission program. Concurrent enrollment program.

Transfer students: Transfer students accepted for all terms. In fall 1993, 4% of all new students were transfers into all classes. Application deadline is August 15 for fall; December 15 for spring. Minimum 2.0 GPA required. Lowest course grade accepted is "C." Maximum number of transferable credits is 64 semester hours from a two-year school and 98 semester hours from a four-year school. At least 30 semester hours must be completed at the university to receive degree.

Admissions contact: Stephanie Chatman, Director of Admissions. 601 968-2100.

FINANCIAL AID. Available aid: Pell grants, SEOG, state scholarships and grants, school scholarships and grants, private scholarships and grants, ROTC scholarships, academic merit scholarships, and athletic scholarships. Perkins Loans (NDSL), PLUS, Stafford Loans (GSL), school loans, and private loans.

Financial aid statistics: 15% of aid is not need-based. In 1994-95, 94% of all undergraduate aid applicants received aid; 90% of freshman aid applicants.

Supporting data/closing dates: School's own aid application: Deadline is April 1. Notification of awards on rolling basis.

Financial aid contact: Gene Blakely, Ph.D., Director of Financial Aid. 601 968-2227.

STUDENT EMPLOYMENT. Federal Work-Study Program. Institutional employment. 23% of full-time undergraduates work on campus during school year. Students may expect to earn an average of $2,000 during school year. Freshmen are discouraged from working during their first term. Off-campus part-time employment opportunities rated "good."

COMPUTER FACILITIES. 300 IBM/IBM-compatible and Apple/Macintosh microcomputers; 150 are networked. Students may access AT&T, Data General, Digital, IBM, NCR, SUN minicomputer/mainframe systems, BITNET, Internet. Computer facilities are available to all students.
Fees: None.
Hours: 8 AM-11 PM.

GRADUATE CAREER DATA. Graduate school percentages: 10% enter medical school. 9% enter graduate business programs. 16% enter graduate arts and sciences programs. Highest graduate school enrollments: U Medical Center, Jackson; U of Southern Mississippi. Companies and businesses that hire graduates: AT&T, IBM.

PROMINENT ALUMNI/AE. Joseph Jackson, president, National Baptist Convention; Robert Clark, state legislator; John Peoples, former president, Jackson State U; Charles Moore, contractor/entrepreneur; Walter Payton, professional athlete.

Jarvis Christian College

Hawkins, TX 75765   **903 769-5700**

Undergraduate profile. 99% Black, 1% White. 79% are state residents. Average age of undergraduates is 18.

Enrollment. Undergraduates: 203 men, 278 women (full-time). Freshman class: 248 applicants, 148 accepted, 85 enrolled.

Faculty. 35 full-time, 7 part-time; 27 Black, 8 White, 7 Other. 60% of faculty holds doctoral degree. Student/faculty ratio: 14 to 1.

Test score averages/ranges. Average SAT I scores: 290 verbal, 327 math. Average ACT scores: 10 English, 7 math, 14 composite.

1995-96 Costs. Tuition: $4,200. Room & board: $3,485. Fees, books, misc. academic expenses (school's estimate): $885.

PROFILE. Jarvis Christian, founded in 1912, is a church-affiliated, liberal arts college. Its 250-acre campus is located in Hawkins, 100 miles southeast of Dallas.

Accreditation: SACS.

Religious orientation: Jarvis Christian College is affiliated with the Disciples of Christ Church; two semesters of religion required.

Library: Collections totaling 80,000 volumes, 472 periodical subscriptions, and 2,598 microform items.

Special facilities/museums: Language lab, media center, observatory, electron microscope.

Athletic facilities: Gymnasium, fitness lab, swimming pool, baseball and softball fields, weight room, tennis courts.

STUDENT BODY. Freshman profile: 23% of accepted applicants took SAT I; 36% took ACT. 100% of freshmen come from public schools.

Undergraduate achievement: 22% of entering class graduates. 10% of students who complete a degree program go on to graduate study within one year.

PROGRAMS OF STUDY. Degrees: B.A., B.Bus.Admin., B.S.

Majors: Biology, Business Administration, Chemistry, English, History, Human Performance, Mathematics, Music, Reading, Religion, Sociology, Special Education.

Distribution of degrees: The majors with the highest enrollments are accounting, management, and history; chemistry and biology have the lowest.

Requirements: General education requirement.

Academic regulations: Minimum 2.0 GPA must be maintained.

Special: Minors offered in all majors and in accounting, art, computer science, management, marketing, political science, psychology, and speech. Double majors. Dual degrees. Accelerated study. Cooperative education programs. Preprofessional programs in law and medicine. 3-2 law program with St. John's Sch of Law. 3-2 engineering program with U of Texas at Arlington. Member of Black Executive Exchange Program. UNCF Premedical Summer Program with Fisk U. Biomedical Sciences Program of Meharry Medical Coll. Brookhaven Semester Program in New York. Teacher certification in elementary and secondary education.

Honors: Phi Beta Kappa. Honors program. Honor societies.

Academic Assistance: Remedial reading, writing, math, and study skills. Nonremedial tutoring.

STUDENT LIFE. Housing: All unmarried students under age 21 must live on campus unless living near campus with relatives. Women's and men's dorms. On-campus married-student housing. On-campus single parent housing. 87% of students live in college housing.

Services and counseling/handicapped student services: Placement services. Health service. Day care. Testing service. Counseling services for older students. Birth control and personal counseling. Career and academic guidance services. Religious counseling. Learning disabled services.

Campus organizations: Undergraduate student government. Student newspaper (Expression). Yearbook. Women's and men's senates, dorm councils, Panhellenic Council, Student Activities Council, gospel and concert choirs, Students in Free Enterprise, NABA, social groups, 22 organizations in all. Four fraternities, no chapter houses; three sororities, no chapter houses.

Religious organizations: Student Ministers Association, United Campus Christian Fellowship.

ATHLETICS. Physical education requirements: Two semesters of physical education required.
Intercollegiate competition: 50% of students participate. Baseball (M), basketball (M,W), cheerleading (M,W), softball (W), track and field (indoor) (M,W), track and field (outdoor) (M,W), volleyball (M,W). Member of IAC, NSCAA.

Intramural and club sports: 1% of students participate. Intramural badminton, basketball, flag football, softball, swimming, tennis, volleyball.

ADMISSIONS. Academic basis for candidate selection (in order of priority): Secondary school record, standardized test scores, school's recommendation, class rank, essay.

Nonacademic basis for candidate selection: Character and personality are emphasized. Particular talent or ability and alumni/ae relationship are important. Extracurricular participation is considered.

Requirements: Graduation from secondary school is recommended; GED is accepted. 16 units and the following program of study are required: 3 units of English, 2 units of math, 1 unit of science, 3 units of social studies, 7 units of academic electives. Open admissions policy. Satisfactory score on TASP Skills Test required of education program applicants. ACT is required; SAT I may be substituted. Campus visit and interview recommended. Off-campus interviews available with an admissions representative.

Procedure: Take SAT I or ACT by May 1 of 12th year. Visit college for interview by August of 12th year. Suggest filing application by April 1. Application deadline is August 1. Notification of admission on rolling basis. Reply is required by August 1. $30 room deposit, refundable until August 15. Freshmen accepted for all terms.

Special programs: Admission may be deferred three semesters. Credit may be granted through CLEP general and subject exams. Credit may be granted for military experience. Placement may be granted through challenge exams.

Transfer students: Transfer students accepted for all terms. Application deadline is August 1 for fall; December 1 for spring. Minimum 2.0 GPA recommended. Maximum number of transferable credits is 65 semester hours. At least 59 semester hours must be completed at the college to receive degree.

Admissions contact: Anetha Francis, Director of Admissions. 903 769-5700, extension 733.

FINANCIAL AID. Available aid: Pell grants, SEOG, state scholarships and grants, school scholarships, private scholarships, and United Negro College Fund. Vocational Rehabilitation Grants. Perkins Loans (NDSL), PLUS, and Stafford Loans (GSL). Deferred payment plan.

Financial aid statistics: In 1993-94, 98% of all undergraduate aid applicants received aid; 98% of freshman aid applicants. Average amounts of aid awarded freshmen: Scholarships and grants, $1,000; loans, $2,250.

Supporting data/closing dates: FAFSA: Priority filing date is April 15; deadline is July 1. School's own aid application: Priority filing date is April 15; deadline is August 1. Income tax forms: Priority filing date is April 15; accepted on rolling basis; deadline is July 1. Notification of awards on rolling basis.

Financial aid contact: Harold Abney, Director of Financial Aid. 903 769-5700, extension 741.

STUDENT EMPLOYMENT. Federal Work-Study Program. Institutional employment. 2% of full-time undergraduates work on campus during school year. Students may expect to earn an average of $600 during school year. Freshmen are discouraged from working during their first term. Off-campus part-time employment opportunities rated "good."

COMPUTER FACILITIES. IBM/IBM-compatible and Apple/Macintosh microcomputers. Client/LAN operating systems include Apple/Macintosh, DOS, Windows NT. Computer facilities are available to all students.

Fees: Computer fee is included in tuition/fees.

Hours: 8 AM-9 PM (M-F).

GRADUATE CAREER DATA. 90% of graduates choose careers in business and industry. Companies and businesses that hire graduates: American Food Management, Dallas ISD, Ford Motor Credit, General Service Administration, Jarvis Christian Coll, K mart, Longview ISD, U.S. Census Bureau.

PROMINENT ALUMNI/AE. Dr. E.W. Rand and Dr. C.A. Berry, college presidents; Dianne Curry, fashion model; Jerome Towns, principal of school district, Kilgore, Tex.; John Kendrick, General Foods.

Johnson C. Smith University

Charlotte, NC 28216   **704 378-1000**

Undergraduate profile. 99% Black, .5% Asian-American, .5% Native American. 25% are state residents; 7% are transfers. Average age of undergraduates is 20.

Enrollment. Undergraduates: 539 men, 770 women (full-time). Freshman class: 2,045 applicants, 1,320 accepted, 404 enrolled.

Faculty. 79 full-time; 41 Black, 37 White, 8 Other. 78% of faculty holds highest degree in specific field. Student/faculty ratio: 17 to 1.

Test score averages/ranges. Average SAT I scores: 339 verbal, 372 math.

1995-96 Costs. Tuition: $7,128. Room: $1,646. Board: $1,394. Fees, books, misc. academic expenses (school's estimate): $650.

PROFILE. Johnson C. Smith University is a private, liberal arts institution. Programs are offered through the Divisions of Education and Psychology, Humanities, Mathematics and Sciences, and Social Sciences. Its 105-acre campus, located near downtown Charlotte, includes buildings of traditional and modern design.

Accreditation: SACS. Professionally accredited by the National Council for Accreditation of Teacher Education.

Religious orientation: Johnson C. Smith University is nonsectarian; three semester hours of philosophy or religion required.

Library: Collections totaling 115,226 volumes, 800 periodical subscriptions, and 24,069 microform items.

Special facilities/museums: Language lab, honors college, banking and finance center.

Athletic facilities: Gymnasium, tennis courts, swimming pool.

STUDENT BODY. Freshman profile: 92% of accepted applicants took SAT I.

Undergraduate achievement: 77% of fall 1993 freshmen returned for fall 1994 term. 20% of entering class graduates.

Foreign students: One student is from out of the country.

PROGRAMS OF STUDY. Degrees: B.A., B.S., B.Soc.Work.

Majors: Accounting, Banking/Finance, Biology, Business Administration, Chemistry, Communication Arts, Computer Science, Early Childhood Education, Economics, Education, Elementary Education, English, Health Education, History, Marketing, Mathematics, Mathematics/Physics, Music, Music Business, Music Education, Physical Education, Political Science, Psychology, Secondary Education, Social Work, Sociology, Urban Studies.

Distribution of degrees: The majors with the highest enrollments are business administration, communication arts, and social work; health education, music business, and mathematics have the lowest.

Requirements: General education requirement.

Academic regulations: Minimum 2.0 GPA required for graduation.

Special: Double majors. Independent study. Accelerated study. Internships. Cooperative education programs. Preprofessional programs in law, medicine, pharmacy, and dentistry. 3-2 engineering and education programs with U of North Carolina at Charlotte. Member of Charlotte Area Educational Consortium. Teacher certification in early childhood, elementary, secondary, and special education. Study abroad in European countries, Australia, Canada, Japan, Mexico, and Russia. ROTC and AFROTC at U of North Carolina at Charlotte.

Honors: Phi Beta Kappa. Honors program.

Academic Assistance: Remedial reading, writing, math, and study skills. Nonremedial tutoring.

STUDENT LIFE. Housing: Students may live on or off campus. Coed, women's, and men's dorms. Honors College Center accommodates 15 students. 75% of students live in college housing.

Services and counseling/handicapped student services: Placement services. Health service. Day care. Counseling services for veteran students. Birth control and personal counseling. Career and academic guidance services. Religious counseling. Learning disabled services.

Campus organizations: Undergraduate student government. Student newspaper (Student News, published twice/year). Yearbook. Radio station. NAACP. Band, choir, Shaki/Shaki dance club, drama club, political science club, special-interest groups. Four fraternities, no chapter houses; four sororities, no chapter houses. 20% of men join a fraternity. 25% of women join a sorority.

Religious organizations: Spiritual Choir, Student Christian Association.

ATHLETICS. Physical education requirements: Two semester hours of physical education required.

Intercollegiate competition: 3% of students participate. Baseball (M), basketball (M,W), cross-country (M,W), football (M), golf (M), softball (W), tennis (M), track and field (indoor) (M,W), track and field (outdoor) (M,W), volleyball (W). Member of Central Intercollegiate Athletic Association, NCAA Division II.

Intramural and club sports: 1% of students participate. Intramural badminton, basketball, swimming, volleyball.

ADMISSIONS. Academic basis for candidate selection (in order of priority): Secondary school record, standardized test scores, school's recommendation, class rank.

Nonacademic basis for candidate selection: Character and personality are important. Extracurricular participation, particular talent or ability, and alumni/ae relationship are considered.

Requirements: Graduation from secondary school is required; GED is accepted. 16 units and the following program of study are required: 4 units of English, 2 units of math, 1 unit of lab science, 2 units of social studies, 7 units of academic electives. Minimum combined SAT I score of 600, rank in top two-thirds of secondary school class, and minimum 2.0 GPA required. SAT I is required; ACT may be substituted. Campus visit and interview recommended. Off-campus interviews available with admissions and alumni representatives.

Procedure: Take SAT I or ACT by February of 12th year. Visit college for interview by February of 12th year. Suggest filing application by April 15. Application deadline is August 1. Notification of admission on rolling basis. Tuition deposit equal to 75% of total tuition, refundable until eight weeks after start of classes. $100 nonrefundable room deposit. Freshmen accepted for all terms.

Special programs: Admission may be deferred two years. Credit and/or placement may be granted through CEEB Advanced Placement exams for scores of 3 or higher. Early decision program.

Transfer students: Transfer students accepted for all terms. In fall 1994, 7% of all new students were transfers into all classes. 123 transfer applications were received, 83 were accepted. Application deadline is August 1 for fall; November 1 for spring. Minimum 2.0 GPA required. Lowest course grade accepted is "C." Maximum number of transferable credits is 64 semester hours. At least 32 semester hours must be completed at the university to receive degree.

Admissions contact: Michael Jackson, Director of Admissions. 800 782-7303.

FINANCIAL AID. Available aid: Pell grants, SEOG, state scholarships and grants, school scholarships, private scholarships, academic merit scholarships, athletic scholarships, and United Negro College Fund. Perkins Loans (NDSL), PLUS, Stafford Loans (GSL), private loans, and unsubsidized Stafford Loans. Tuition Plan Inc., Tuition Management Systems, and deferred payment plan.

Kentucky State University **79**

Financial aid statistics: 15% of aid is not need-based. In 1994-95, 76% of all undergraduate aid applicants received aid; 95% of freshman aid applicants. Average amounts of aid awarded freshmen: Scholarships and grants, $3,095; loans, $2,625.
Supporting data/closing dates: FAFSA/FAF: Priority filing date is April 15. State aid form. Notification of awards begins April 16.
Financial aid contact: Carolyn Smith, Director of Financial Aid. 704 378-1034.
STUDENT EMPLOYMENT. Federal Work-Study Program. Institutional employment. 23% of full-time undergraduates work on campus during school year. Students may expect to earn an average of $2,000 during school year. Off-campus part-time employment opportunities rated "fair."
COMPUTER FACILITIES. 100 IBM/IBM-compatible, Apple/Macintosh, and RISC-/UNIX-based microcomputers. Students may access IBM minicomputer/mainframe systems, Internet. Residence halls may be equipped with stand-alone microcomputers, networked microcomputers. Client/LAN operating systems include Apple/Macintosh, DOS, UNIX/XENIX/AIX, LocalTalk/AppleTalk, Novell. Computer facilities are available to all students.
Fees: None.
GRADUATE CAREER DATA. Highest graduate school enrollments: Duke U, Emory U, Florida State U, Georgia Tech, Howard U, North Carolina A&T State U, North Carolina Central U, Ohio State U, U of North Carolina, U of Pittsburgh. Companies and businesses that hire graduates: First Union, Nations Bank, Wachovia, Price Waterhouse, BB&T.
PROMINENT ALUMNI/AE. Eva Clayton, U.S. congresswoman; Darryl Roberts, movie director/producer; Argie Knox Johnson, general superintendent, Chicago public schools.

Kentucky State University

Frankfort, KY 40601   502 227-6000

Undergraduate profile. 48% Black, 51% White, 1% Other. 78% are state residents; 7% are transfers. Average age of undergraduates is 26.
Enrollment. Undergraduates: 776 men, 859 women (full-time). Freshman class: 1,763 applicants, 947 accepted, 747 enrolled. Graduate enrollment: 29 men, 38 women.
Faculty. 126 full-time; 35 part-time. 70% of faculty holds doctoral degree. Student/faculty ratio: 15 to 1.
Test score averages/ranges. Average ACT scores: 18 composite.
1995-96 Costs. Tuition: $1,680 (state residents), $5,040 (out-of-state). Room: $1,364. Board: $1,620. Fees, books, misc. academic expenses (school's estimate): $900.

PROFILE. Kentucky State, founded in 1886, is a public university of liberal studies. Programs are offered through the Colleges of Applied Sciences, Arts and Sciences, and Leadership Studies; the Community College; the Graduate Center/the School of Public Affairs; and the School of Business. Its 309-acre campus is located in Frankfort, 25 miles from Lexington.
Accreditation: SACS. Professionally accredited by the Council on Social Work Education, the National Association of Schools of Music, the National Council for Accreditation of Teacher Education, the National League for Nursing.
Religious orientation: Kentucky State University is nonsectarian. No religious requirements.
Library: Collections totaling over 300,000 volumes.
Special facilities/museums: Art gallery, school for early childhood education, nutrition lab, agriculture research building, research farm, fish hatchery, electron microscope.
Athletic facilities: Gymnasium, tennis courts, weight room, track, baseball and football stadiums, intramural field, swimming pool.
STUDENT BODY. Undergraduate achievement: 62% of fall 1993 freshmen returned for fall 1994 term. 22% of entering class graduates. 10% of students who complete a degree program go on to graduate study within five years.
Foreign students: 19 students are from out of the country. Countries represented include Canada, Gambia, Honduras, India, and Thailand.

PROGRAMS OF STUDY. Degrees: B.A., B.Mus., B.S.

Majors: Accounting, Applied Mathematics/Engineering, Art Education, Biology, Biology Education, Business Administration, Chemistry, Child Development/Family Relations, Computer Science, Criminal Justice, Early Elementary Education, Economics, English, English Education, History, History Education, Liberal Studies, Management, Marketing, Mathematics, Mathematics Education, Medical Technology, Microcomputers, Music Education, Music Performance, Physical Education, Political Science, Psychology, Public Administration, Social Studies Education, Social Work, Sociology, Studio Art, Textiles/Clothing/Merchandising.

Distribution of degrees: The majors with the highest enrollments are business administration, computer science, and criminal justice.

Requirements: General education requirement.

Academic regulations: Freshmen must maintain minimum 1.8 GPA; sophomores, juniors, seniors, 2.0 GPA.

Special: Minor is required of some for graduation. Minors offered in many majors and in African-American studies, athletic training, fashion merchandising, finance, French, gerontology, philosophy, physics, recreation, Spanish, speech/theatre, and sports management. Associate degrees offered. Self-designed majors. Dual degrees. Independent study. Pass/fail grading option. Internships. Cooperative education programs. Preprofessional programs in law, medicine, veterinary science, pharmacy, dentistry, optometry, community health, cytotechnology, engineering, medical technology, and physical therapy. Dual-degree engineering programs with U of Kentucky and U of Maryland. Member of Kentucky Educational Television consortium. Exchange program with Berea Coll. Teacher certification in elementary and secondary education. Certification in specific subject areas. Exchange programs abroad in England (U of London, Oxford U). ROTC and AFROTC at U of Kentucky.

Honors: Honors program.

Academic Assistance: Remedial reading, writing, math, and study skills. Nonremedial tutoring.

STUDENT LIFE. Housing: All unmarried, nonveteran students under age 21 must live on campus unless living with family. Women's and men's dorms. School-owned/operated apartments. 31% of students live in college housing.

Services and counseling/handicapped student services: Placement services. Health service. Counseling services for military and veteran students. Birth control, personal, and psychological counseling. Career and academic guidance services. Physically disabled student services.

Campus organizations: Undergraduate student government. Student newspaper (Thorobred News). Literary magazine. Yearbook. Black Student Union. Jazz ensemble, Kentucky Players, intercollegiate debating, departmental and special-interest groups. Four fraternities, no chapter houses; four sororities, no chapter houses.

Religious organizations: Bahai Club, Baptist Student Union, Wesley Foundation.

Foreign student organizations: International Student Association.

ATHLETICS. Physical education requirements: Two semester hours of physical education required.

Intercollegiate competition: 10% of students participate. Baseball (M), basketball (M,W), cross-country (M,W), football (M), golf (M), softball (W), tennis (M,W), track (indoor) (M,W), track (outdoor) (M,W), track and field (indoor) (M,W), track and field (outdoor) (M,W), volleyball (W). Member of Great Lakes Valley Conference, NCAA Division II.

Intramural and club sports: 70% of students participate. Intramural basketball, softball, tennis, touch football, volleyball. Women's club cheerleading.

ADMISSIONS. Academic basis for candidate selection (in order of priority): Secondary school record, standardized test scores.

Requirements: Graduation from secondary school is required; GED is accepted. 21 units and the following program of study are required: 4 units of English, 3 units of math, 2 units of science, 1 unit of social studies, 1 unit of history, 8 units of electives. Minimum combined SAT I score of 720 (composite ACT score of 18) and minimum 2.5 GPA required. ACT is required; SAT I may be substituted. Campus visit recommended.

Procedure: Take SAT I or ACT by October of 12th year. Notification of admission on rolling basis. $85 room deposit, refundable until August 1. Freshmen accepted for all terms.

Special programs: Credit and/or placement may be granted through CEEB Advanced Placement exams for scores of 3 or higher. Credit may be granted through CLEP general and subject exams. Credit and placement may be granted through ACT PEP and DANTES exams and for military and life experience. Early entrance/early admission program. Concurrent enrollment program.

Transfer students: Transfer students accepted for all terms. In fall 1994, 7% of all new students were transfers into all classes. 297 transfer applications were received, 177 were accepted. Lowest course grade accepted is "C." Maximum number of transferable credits is 65 semester hours. At least 32 semester hours must be completed at the university to receive degree.

Admissions contact: Lyman R. Dale, M.S., Director of Records, Registration, Admissions, and Community Programs. 800 633-9415 (in-state), 800 325-1716 (out-of-state), 502 227-6813.

FINANCIAL AID. Available aid: Pell grants, SEOG, state grants, school scholarships, private scholarships and grants, academic merit scholarships, and athletic scholarships. SSIG. Perkins Loans (NDSL), PLUS, and Stafford Loans (GSL). Tuition Management Systems and deferred payment plan.

Financial aid statistics: 5% of aid is not need-based. In 1994-95, 85% of all undergraduate aid applicants received aid; 75% of freshman aid applicants. Average amounts of aid awarded freshmen: Scholarships and grants, $2,216; loans, $1,800.

Supporting data/closing dates: FAFSA/FAF: Priority filing date is April 15; deadline is in May. Notification of awards on rolling basis.

Financial aid contact: Carmella Conner, M.S.Ed., Director of Financial Aid. 502 227-5960.

STUDENT EMPLOYMENT. Federal Work-Study Program. Institutional employment. 32% of full-time undergraduates work on campus during school year. Students may expect to earn an average of $1,000 during school year. Off-campus part-time employment opportunities rated "good."

COMPUTER FACILITIES. 600 IBM/IBM-compatible and Apple/Macintosh microcomputers; 200 are networked. Students may access IBM minicomputer/mainframe systems. Residence halls may be equipped with networked terminals, modems. Client/LAN operating systems include DOS, Novell. Computer facilities are available to all students.

Fees: $10 computer fee per semester.

Hours: 8 AM-9 PM (M-F); 10 AM-4 PM (Sa).

GRADUATE CAREER DATA. Highest graduate school enrollments: Jackson State U, U of Kentucky, U of Louisville. 47% of graduates choose careers in business and industry. Companies and businesses that hire graduates: Ashland Oil, AT&T, Darcom, Department of Defense, Humana, Internal Revenue Service, Kroger, McDonnell Douglas.

PROMINENT ALUMNI/AE. Patricia Russel McCloud, attorney; Moneta Sleet, Pulitzer prize-winning photographer; Dr. Bailus Walker, Jr., Commissioner of Public Health, Massachusetts; Harrison B. Wilson, president, Norfolk State U; George Wilson, secretary, Corrections Cabinet, Kentucky.

Knoxville College

Knoxville, TN 37921   **615 524-6500**

Undergraduate profile. 98.9% Black, .1% Asian-American, 1% White. 23% are state residents. Average age of undergraduates is 19.

Enrollment. Undergraduates: 548 men, 298 women (full-time). Freshman class: 503 applicants, 403 accepted, 293 enrolled.

Faculty. 59 full-time, 15 part-time; 20 Black, 25 White, 14 Other. 46% of faculty holds highest degree in specific field. Student/faculty ratio: 20 to 1.

Test score averages/ranges. N/A.

1995-96 Costs. Tuition: $5,400. Room & board: $4,082. Fees, books, misc. academic expenses (school's estimate): $1,092.

PROFILE. Knoxville College, founded in 1875, is a church-affiliated institution. Programs are offered through the Divisions of Business, Humanities, Natural Sciences and Mathematics, and Social Sciences and Education. Its 39-acre campus is located in northeast Knoxville.

Accreditation: SACS.

Religious orientation: Knoxville College is affiliated with the United Presbyterian Church; two semesters of religion required.

Library: Collections totaling 85,563 volumes, 166 periodical subscriptions, 5,687 microform items, and three CD-ROMs.

Special facilities/museums: Language lab.

Athletic facilities: Gymnasium.

STUDENT BODY. Freshman profile: 90% of freshmen come from public schools.

Undergraduate achievement: 50% of fall 1993 freshmen returned for fall 1994 term. 80% of entering class graduates. 18% of students who complete a degree program go on to graduate study within five years.

Foreign students: Countries represented include Iran, Kenya, and Nigeria.

PROGRAMS OF STUDY. Degrees: B.A., B.S.

Majors: Accounting, Biology, Business, Chemistry, Communications, Economics, Education, Elementary Education, English, English Literature, Exercise Science, Health/Physical Education, History, Hotel/Motel/Restaurant Management, Humanities/Social Sciences, Junior High Education, Leisure Studies, Liberal/General Studies, Mathematics, Music, Physics, Political Science/Government, Pre-Law, Psychology, Recreation/Community Services, Secondary Education, Secretarial/Related Programs, Sociology, Zoology.

Distribution of degrees: The majors with the highest enrollments are business, leisure studies, and sociology; education, chemistry, and mathematics have the lowest.

Requirements: General education requirement.

Academic regulations: Freshmen must maintain minimum 1.4 GPA; sophomores, 1.8 GPA; juniors, 2.0 GPA; seniors, 2.0 GPA.

Special: Minors offered in general studies and in secretarial studies (general, legal, medical). Double majors. Dual degrees. Independent study. Accelerated study. Internships. Cooperative education programs. Preprofessional programs in law, medicine, nursing, and social work. ROTC at U of Tennessee.

Honors: Honors program.

Academic Assistance: Remedial reading, writing, math, and study skills. Nonremedial tutoring.

STUDENT LIFE. Housing: Students must live on campus unless living with family. Women's and men's dorms. 80% of students live in college housing.

Social atmosphere: Popular gathering spots for students include the College Center, the Strip, and the Canteen. The Christian Fellowship, fraternities, and athletes are the most influential groups on campus. The most popular events on campus are Homecoming, the Gator Bowl, Freak Nick, the Kuumba Festival, and Kwaanza. According to the student newspaper, Knoxville College maintains strong ties to the Presbyterian Church, and students are actively involved in cultural activities both on and off campus.

Services and counseling/handicapped student services: Placement services. Counseling services. Personal counseling. Career and academic guidance services. Religious counseling. Physically disabled student services. Notetaking services. Tape recorders. Tutors. Reader services for the blind.

Campus organizations: Undergraduate student government. Student newspaper (Campus Communicator, published once/month). Black Awareness Organization. Concert and college choirs, concert, marching, and jazz bands, brass choir, opera workshop, drama club, departmental groups, special-interest groups. Five fraternities, no chapter houses; five sororities, no chapter houses. 16% of men join a fraternity. 18% of women join a sorority.

Religious organizations: Christian Fellowship Society.

ATHLETICS. Physical education requirements: Two semesters of physical education required. **Intercollegiate competition:** 4% of students participate. Baseball (M), basketball (M,W), cheerleading (M,W), football (M), tennis (M,W), track (outdoor) (M,W), volleyball (W). Member of NCAA Division II.

Intramural and club sports: 2% of students participate. Intramural basketball, flag football, softball.

ADMISSIONS. Academic basis for candidate selection (in order of priority): Secondary school record, class rank, school's recommendation, standardized test scores.

Nonacademic basis for candidate selection: Character and personality are emphasized. Extracurricular participation and alumni/ae relationship are important. Particular talent or ability is considered.

Requirements: Graduation from secondary school is recommended; GED is accepted. 15 units and the following program of study are required: 4 units of English, 2 units of math, 2 units of science including 1 unit of lab, 2 units of social studies, 4 units of electives including 3 units of academic electives. 3 units of math and 5 units of academic electives recommended. Audition required of music program applicants. SAT I or ACT is required. Campus visit and interview recommended. Off-campus interviews available with admissions and alumni representatives.

Procedure: Take SAT I or ACT by November of 12th year. Application deadline is in May. Notification of admission on rolling basis. $50 refundable room deposit. Freshmen accepted for all terms.

Special programs: Admission may be deferred one year. Credit may be granted through CEEB Advanced Placement for scores of 3 or higher. Early decision program.

Transfer students: Transfer students accepted for all terms. In fall 1993, less than 1% of all new students were transfers into all classes. Application deadline is July 1 for fall; November 15 for spring. Minimum 2.0 GPA required. Lowest course grade accepted is "C." Maximum number of transferable credits is 60 semester hours from a two-year school and 90 semester hours from a four-year school.

Admissions contact: Robert Thomas, Director of Enrollment Services. 615 524-6568, 800 743-5669.

FINANCIAL AID. Available aid: Pell grants, SEOG, state grants, school scholarships and grants, private scholarships, and United Negro College Fund. PLUS and Stafford Loans (GSL), and unsubsidized Stafford Loans. Deferred payment plan.

Financial aid statistics: 11% of aid is not need-based. In 1993-94, 99% of all undergraduate aid applicants received aid. Average amounts of aid awarded freshmen: Scholarships and grants, $3,250; loans, $2,625.

Supporting data/closing dates: FAFSA: Priority filing date is June 1; deadline is July 1. School's own aid application: Priority filing date is June 1; deadline is July 1. State aid form: Priority filing date is January 1. Income tax forms: Priority filing date is June 1. Notification of awards on rolling basis.

Financial aid contact: Robert Thomas, Director of Enrollment Services. 615 524-6525.

STUDENT EMPLOYMENT. Federal Work-Study Program. Institutional employment. 46% of full-time undergraduates work on campus during school year. Students may expect to earn an average of $1,500 during school year. Freshmen are discouraged from working during their first term. Off-campus part-time employment opportunities rated "fair."

COMPUTER FACILITIES. 100 IBM/IBM-compatible and Apple/Macintosh microcomputers; 28 are networked. Students may access IBM, SUN minicomputer/mainframe systems, Internet. Residence halls may be equipped with stand-alone microcomputers. Client/LAN operating systems include Apple/Macintosh, DOS, UNIX/XENIX/AIX, LocalTalk/AppleTalk, Novell. Computer facilities are available to all students. **Fees:** None.

GRADUATE CAREER DATA. Highest graduate school enrollments: U of Tennessee. Companies and businesses that hire graduates: City government, Martin Marietta, TVA.

PROMINENT ALUMNI/AE. William (Bud) Blaky, attorney, Washington, D.C.; George Curry, journalist, Chicago; Dr. Edith Irby Jones, physician, Houston, Tex.

Lane College

Jackson, TN 38301   **901 426-7500**

Undergraduate profile. 100% Black. 57% are state residents; 15% are transfers. Average age of undergraduates is 19.

Enrollment. Undergraduates: 333 men, 323 women (full-time). Freshman class: 447 applicants, 357 accepted, 186 enrolled.

Faculty. 32 full-time, 5 part-time; 17 Black, 4 White, 16 Other. 33% of faculty holds doctoral degree. Student/faculty ratio: 16 to 1.

Test score averages/ranges. Average ACT scores: 15 English, 15 math, 15 composite.

1995-96 Costs. Tuition: $4,769. Room & board: $3,202. Fees, books, misc. academic expenses (school's estimate): $750.

PROFILE. Lane, founded in 1882, is a church-affiliated, liberal arts college. Its 17-acre campus is located in Jackson, in western Tennessee.

Accreditation: SACS.

Religious orientation: Lane College is affiliated with the Christian Methodist Episcopal Church; attendance at religious activities recommended.

Library: Collections totaling 67,131 volumes, 246 periodical subscriptions, and 12,501 microform items.

Athletic facilities: Field house, swimming pool, weight room, track, baseball and football fields.

STUDENT BODY. Freshman profile: 29% of freshmen who took ACT scored 18 or over on composite; 65% scored 12 or over on composite; 100% scored 6 or over on composite. 77% of accepted applicants took ACT. 97% of freshmen come from public schools.

Undergraduate achievement: 60% of fall 1993 freshmen returned for fall 1994 term. 11% of entering class graduates. 25% of students who complete a degree program immediately go on to graduate study.

PROGRAMS OF STUDY. Degrees: B.A., B.S.

Majors: Administration, Biology, Business, Chemistry, Communications, Computer Science, Criminal Justice, Elementary Education, Engineering, English, History, International Studies, Mathematics, Music, Physical Education/Health, Religion, Social Justice, Sociology.

Distribution of degrees: The majors with the highest enrollments are business, elementary education, and communications; music, religion, and history have the lowest.

Academic regulations: Freshmen must maintain minimum 1.25 GPA; sophomores, 1.5 GPA; juniors, 1.75 GPA; seniors, 2.0 GPA.

Special: Minors offered in most majors. Courses offered in art, art appreciation, drama, economics, French, geography, music appreciation, professional education, psychology, political science, reading, secondary education, science, social welfare, and speech. Undergraduate Program Examination required of all seniors. Cooperative education programs. Graduate school at which qualified undergraduates may take graduate-level courses. Preprofessional programs in law and medicine. 2-3 engineering program with Tennessee State U. Teacher certification in elementary and secondary education. Certification in specific subject areas.

Academic Assistance: Remedial reading, writing, math, and study skills. Nonremedial tutoring.

STUDENT LIFE. Housing: Students may live on or off campus. Women's and men's dorms. 61% of students live in college housing.

Social atmosphere: Groups with a strong influence on student social life include Greeks, athletes, and Christian groups. Homecoming, Religious Emphasis Week, and the mid-week chapel service are some of the more popular social events.

Services and counseling/handicapped student services: Placement services. Health service. Testing service. Special services program. Reading and writing labs. Chaplain. Personal counseling. Career and academic guidance services.

Campus organizations: Undergraduate student government. Student newspaper (Lane Inquirer, published once/month). Yearbook. Marching, concert, and jazz bands, departmental clubs. Four fraternities, no chapter houses; four sororities, no chapter houses. 10% of men join a fraternity. 12% of women join a sorority.

ATHLETICS. Physical education requirements: Two semester hours of physical education required.

Intercollegiate competition: 25% of students participate. Baseball (M), basketball (M,W), cheerleading (M,W), cross-country (M,W), football (M), lightweight football (M), tennis (M,W), track and field (outdoor) (M,W), volleyball (W). Member of NCAA Division II.

Intramural and club sports: 30% of students participate. Intramural basketball, flag football, softball, table tennis. Men's physical education club, all-sports athletic club. Women's physical education club, all-sports athletic club.

ADMISSIONS. Academic basis for candidate selection (in order of priority): Secondary school record, standardized test scores, school's recommendation, class rank.

Nonacademic basis for candidate selection: Character and personality are emphasized. Extracurricular participation, particular talent or ability, and alumni/ae relationship are considered.

Requirements: Graduation from secondary school is required; GED is accepted. 15 units and the following program of study are required: 4 units of English, 2 units of math, 2 units of science, 1 unit of foreign language, 2 units of social studies. 2 units of foreign language are recommended. Center for Academic Skills Development for applicants not normally admissible. ACT is required; SAT I may be substituted. Campus visit recommended. No off-campus interviews.

Procedure: Take SAT I or ACT by December of 12th year. Suggest filing application by May 15. Application deadline is August 1. Notification of admission on rolling basis. Reply is required by June 15. $50 refundable room deposit. Freshmen accepted for all terms.

Special programs: Admission may be deferred one year. Credit and/or placement may be granted through CEEB Advanced Placement exams for scores of 3 or higher. Credit and/or placement may be granted through CLEP general and subject exams. Credit may be granted for military experience. Placement may be granted through challenge exams.

Transfer students: Transfer students accepted for all terms. In fall 1994, 15% of all new students were transfers into all classes. 109 transfer applications were received, 55 were accepted. Application deadline is August 1 for fall; December 15 for spring. Lowest course grade accepted is "C." Maximum number of transferable credits is 68 semester hours from a two-year school and 92 semester hours from a four-year school. At least 30 semester hours must be completed at the college to receive degree.

Admissions contact: Ruth Maddox, M.B.A., Director of Admissions. 901 426-4532, 800 960-7533.

FINANCIAL AID. Available aid: Pell grants, SEOG, state grants, school scholarships, private scholarships, academic merit scholarships, athletic scholarships, and United Negro College Fund. Perkins Loans (NDSL), PLUS, Stafford Loans (GSL), and unsubsidized Stafford Loans. Deferred payment plan.

Financial aid statistics: 5% of aid is not need-based. In 1994-95, 100% of all undergraduate aid applicants received aid; 95% of freshman aid applicants. Average amounts of aid awarded freshmen: Scholarships and grants, $2,150; loans, $2,000.

Supporting data/closing dates: FAFSA: Priority filing date is July 1. FAF: Deadline is July 1. Income tax forms: Accepted on rolling basis. Notification of awards on rolling basis.

Financial aid contact: Ursula Singleton, M.B.A., Director of Financial Aid. 901 426-7537.

STUDENT EMPLOYMENT. Federal Work-Study Program. Institutional employment. 47% of full-time undergraduates work on campus during school year. Students may expect to earn an average of $1,300 during school year. Off-campus part-time employment opportunities rated "fair."

COMPUTER FACILITIES. 60 microcomputers. Students may access IBM minicomputer/mainframe systems. Client/LAN operating systems include DOS. Computer facilities are available to all students.

Fees: $25 computer fee per course.

Hours: 40 hours/week.

GRADUATE CAREER DATA. Graduate school percentages: 2% enter law school. 6% enter medical school. 2% enter dental school. 5% enter graduate business programs. 10% enter graduate arts and sciences programs. Highest graduate school enrollments: Tennessee State U, U of Memphis.

15% of graduates choose careers in business and industry. Companies and businesses that hire graduates: Proctor & Gamble, AT&T.

PROMINENT ALUMNI/AE. Nathan Mitchell, attorney; Yvonne Griggs Allen, educator; Frank Thomas, educator.

Langston University

Langston, OK 73050   405 466-2231

Undergraduate profile. 75% Black, 1% Asian-American, 1% Hispanic, 1% Native American, 22% White. 80% are state residents. Average age of undergraduates is 20.

Enrollment. Undergraduates: 921 men, 1,233 women (full-time). Freshman class: 1,400 applicants, 800 accepted, 480 enrolled. Graduate enrollment: 17 men, 20 women.

Faculty. 95 full-time; 117 part-time. 55% of faculty holds doctoral degree. Student/faculty ratio: 25 to 1.

Test score averages/ranges. Average SAT I scores: 760 combined. Average ACT scores: 17 composite.

1995-96 Costs. Tuition: $4,258 (state residents), $7,532 (out-of-state). Room & board: $2,560. Fees, books, misc. academic expenses (school's estimate): $837.

PROFILE. Langston, founded in 1897, is a public, multipurpose university. Programs are offered through the Divisions of Allied Health, Applied Science, Arts and Sciences, Business, and Education and Behavioral Sciences. Its 40-acre campus is located in Langston, 42 miles north of Oklahoma City.

Accreditation: NCACS. Professionally accredited by the National Council for Accreditation of Teacher Education, the National League for Nursing.

Religious orientation: Langston University is nonsectarian; no religious requirements.

Library: Collections totaling over 160,000 volumes, 680 periodical subscriptions, and 3,175 microform items.

Athletic facilities: Athletic center, basketball courts, weight rooms, track, football field, gymnasium, stadium.

STUDENT BODY. Freshman profile: 5% of freshmen who took ACT scored 30 or over on English, 4% scored 30 or over on math, 5% scored 30 or over on composite; 20% scored 24 or over on English, 17% scored 24 or over on math, 20% scored 24 or over on composite; 59% scored 18 or over on English, 54% scored 18 or over on math, 59% scored 18 or over on composite; 95% scored 12 or over on English, 94% scored 12 or over on math, 95% scored 12 or over on composite; 100% scored 6 or over on English, 100% scored 6 or over on math, 100% scored 6 or over on composite. 20% of accepted applicants took SAT I; 80% took ACT. 90% of freshmen come from public schools.

Undergraduate achievement: 18% of students who complete a degree program immediately go on to graduate study.

Foreign students: 34 students are from out of the country. Countries represented include the Bahamas, Ethiopia, Japan, Somalia, South Africa, and United Arab Emirates; seven in all.

PROGRAMS OF STUDY. Degrees: B.A., B.A.Ed., B.S., B.S.Ed., B.S.Nurs.

Majors: Accounting, Agricultural Economics, Animal Science/Husbandry, Biology, Business/Commerce, Business/Commerce/Distribution, Business Management/Administration, Chemistry, Communication Media/Film/Radio/TV, Computer Information Sciences, Corrections, Criminal Justice, Dietetics/Human Nutritional Services, Dramatics/Theatre Arts, Drawing, Economics, Elementary Education, English, Food/Nutrition/Dietetics, Gerontology, Health Care Administration, History, Home Economics, Home Economics Education, Industrial Arts, Liberal Arts/Sciences, Music/Liberal Arts, Nursing, Physical Education/Recreation, Physical Therapy, Pre-Professional Science, Psychology, Secondary Education, Social Science Education, Social Sciences, Sociology, Special Education, Urban Studies, Vocational Home Economics, Vocational-Technical Education.

Distribution of degrees: The majors with the highest enrollments are elementary education, nursing, and accounting; agricultural economics, mathematics, and administrative management have the lowest.

Requirements: General education requirement.
Academic regulations: Minimum 2.0 GPA required for graduation.
Special: Minors offered in all majors and in French, German, religion, and Spanish. Courses offered in philosophy and political science. Black studies program. Preprofessional programs in law, library science, and social work. Cooperative nursing program leads to B.S. after completion of work at Langston and approved school of nursing. Teacher certification in elementary and secondary education. ROTC at Central State U.
Academic Assistance: Remedial reading, writing, math, and study skills. Nonremedial tutoring.

STUDENT LIFE. Housing: Freshmen and sophomores must live on campus. Women's and men's dorms. School-owned/operated apartments. On-campus married-student housing. 50% of students live in college housing.
Services and counseling/handicapped student services: Placement services. Health service. Upward Bound. Freshman development program. Reading laboratory. Counseling services for veteran and older students. Personal counseling. Career and academic guidance services. Physically disabled student services. Notetaking services. Tape recorders. Tutors. Reader services for the blind.
Campus organizations: Undergraduate student government. Student newspaper (Gazette, published once/week). Yearbook. Radio and TV stations. Choir and concert choir, debating, marching and concert bands, political clubs, special-interest groups, theatre productions. Four fraternities, no chapter houses; four sororities, no chapter houses. 10% of men join a fraternity. 15% of women join a sorority.
Religious organizations: Several religious groups.

ATHLETICS. Physical education requirements: Four semester hours of physical education required.
Intercollegiate competition: 3% of students participate. Basketball (M,W), football (M), track (indoor) (M,W), track (outdoor) (M,W), track and field (outdoor) (W). Member of NAIA, Oklahoma Intercollegiate Conference.
Intramural and club sports: 40% of students participate. Intramural basketball, flag football, softball, table tennis, track, volleyball.

ADMISSIONS. Academic basis for candidate selection (in order of priority): Secondary school record, class rank, school's recommendation, standardized test scores, essay.
Requirements: Graduation from secondary school is required; GED is accepted. 11 units and the following program of study are required: 4 units of English, 3 units of math, 2 units of lab science, 2 units of history. Minimum composite ACT score of 19, rank in top three-quarters of secondary school class, or minimum 2.7 GPA required of state residents. Minimum composite ACT score of 19, rank in top half of secondary school class, or minimum 2.7 GPA required of out-of-state applicants. ACT is required; SAT I may be substituted.
Procedure: Take SAT I or ACT by May of 12th year. Application deadline is August 20. Notification of admission on rolling basis. Reply is required by May 1. Freshmen accepted for fall term only.
Special programs: Early entrance/early admission program. Concurrent enrollment program.
Transfer students: Transfer students accepted for all terms. In fall 1994, 350 transfer applications were received, 245 were accepted. Application deadline is August 10 for fall; January 10 for spring. Minimum 2.0 GPA recommended. Lowest course grade accepted is "D."
Admissions contact: Ronald K. Smith, M.A., Director of Admissions and Records. 405 466-2980, 405 466-3428.

FINANCIAL AID. Available aid: Pell grants, SEOG, state scholarships and grants, school scholarships and grants, private scholarships and grants, ROTC scholarships, academic merit scholarships, and athletic scholarships. Perkins Loans (NDSL), PLUS, Stafford Loans (GSL), unsubsidized Stafford Loans, and school loans. Deferred payment plan.
Financial aid statistics: 18% of aid is not need-based. In 1993-94, 43% of all undergraduate aid applicants received aid. Average amounts of aid awarded freshmen: Scholarships and grants, $750; loans, $1,500.
Supporting data/closing dates: FAFSA: Priority filing date is May; 1. School's own aid application: Priority filing date is May 1. Notification of awards begins July 15.

Financial aid contact: Yvonne Maxwell, M.S., Director of Financial Aid. 406 466-3282, 406 466-3289.

STUDENT EMPLOYMENT. Federal Work-Study Program. Institutional employment. Off-campus part-time employment opportunities rated "poor."

COMPUTER FACILITIES. 150 IBM/IBM-compatible and Apple/Macintosh microcomputers; 50 are networked. Students may access Digital, Prime minicomputer/mainframe systems. Client/LAN operating systems include Apple/Macintosh, DOS, UNIX/XENIX/AIX, Windows NT, Local-Talk/AppleTalk, Novell.

Fees: None.

GRADUATE CAREER DATA. Graduate school percentages: 1% enter law school. 1% enter medical school. 1% enter dental school. 1% enter graduate business programs. 1% enter graduate arts and sciences programs. 1% enter theological school/seminary. Highest graduate school enrollments: Howard U, Oklahoma State U, U of Central Oklahoma, U of Oklahoma. 35% of graduates choose careers in business and industry. Companies and businesses that hire graduates: Federal Aviation Administration, Tinker Air Force Base, Oklahoma City public schools.

LeMoyne-Owen College

Memphis, TN 38126   **901 774-9090**

Undergraduate profile. 96% Black, 1% White, 3% Other. 90% are state residents; 25% are transfers. Average age of undergraduates is 18.

Enrollment. Undergraduates: 480 men, 720 women (full-time). Freshman class: 1,043 applicants, 874 accepted, 401 enrolled. Graduate enrollment: 80 men, 70 women.

Faculty. 44 full-time; 8 part-time. 60% of faculty holds doctoral degree. Student/faculty ratio: 16 to 1.

Test score averages/ranges. N/A.

1995-96 Costs. Tuition: $6,000. Room & board: $2,000.

PROFILE. LeMoyne-Owen is a church-affiliated, liberal arts college. It is the product of the 1968 merger of two traditionally Black institutions. Its 15-acre campus is located in South Memphis.

Accreditation: SACS.

Religious orientation: LeMoyne-Owen College is affiliated with the United Church of Christ and Missionary Baptist Church; four semesters of religion required. Attendance is mandatory for chapel once/week.

Library: Collections totaling 90,231 volumes and 216 periodical subscriptions.

Special facilities/museums: Museum/gallery, language lab.

Athletic facilities: Gymnasium.

STUDENT BODY. Freshman profile: 10% of accepted applicants took SAT I; 90% took ACT. 95% of freshmen come from public schools.

Undergraduate achievement: 50% of entering class graduates. 35% of students who complete a degree program go on to graduate study within five years.

Foreign students: Countries represented include Iran and Nigeria.

PROGRAMS OF STUDY. Degrees: B.A., B.Bus.Admin., B.S.

Majors: Accounting, Art, Biochemistry, Business Administration, Chemistry, Computer Science, Economics, English, Health/Physical Education/Recreation, History, Humanities, Mathematics, Natural Science, Philosophy, Political Science, Pre-Dentistry, Pre-Medicine, Pre-Nursing, Pre-Physical Therapy, Social Work, Sociology.

Distribution of degrees: The majors with the highest enrollments are business administration and mathematics; English and history have the lowest.

Requirements: General education requirement.

Academic regulations: Minimum 2.0 GPA must be maintained.

Special: Self-designed majors. Double majors. Dual degrees. Independent study. Accelerated study. Internships. Graduate school at which qualified undergraduates may take graduate-level courses. Preprofessional programs in law, medicine, veterinary science, pharmacy, dentistry, and optometry. Dual degree program in English. 3-2 engineering program with Tuskegee U. Member of Greater Memphis Consortium; cross-registration possible. Teacher certification in elementary and secondary education. Certification in specific subject areas. Study abroad in Europe. ROTC, NROTC, and AFROTC at U of Memphis.

Honors: Honors program. Honor societies.

Academic Assistance: Remedial reading, writing, math, and study skills. Nonremedial tutoring.

STUDENT LIFE. Housing: Women's and men's dorms. Off-campus privately-owned housing. Off-campus married-student housing. 30% of students live in college housing.

Services and counseling/handicapped student services: Placement services. Health service. Day care. Counseling services for military, veteran, and older students. Personal counseling. Career and academic guidance services.

Campus organizations: Undergraduate student government. Student newspaper (Magician). Yearbook. Gospel and concert choirs, drama group, academic and special-interest groups. Four fraternities, no chapter houses; three sororities, no chapter houses. 35% of men join a fraternity. 55% of women join a sorority.

Religious organizations: Religious Life Committee.

ATHLETICS. Physical education requirements: Two semesters of physical education required.
Intercollegiate competition: 9% of students participate. Baseball (M), basketball (M,W), cross-country (M,W), track and field (indoor) (M,W), track and field (outdoor) (M,W), volleyball (W). Member of NCAA Division II, Southern Intercollegiate Athletic Conference.

Intramural and club sports: 20% of students participate. Intramural basketball, flag football, softball, swimming, table tennis, tennis, track and field, volleyball.

ADMISSIONS. Academic basis for candidate selection (in order of priority): Secondary school record, standardized test scores, school's recommendation, class rank.

Nonacademic basis for candidate selection: Character and personality and extracurricular participation are important. Particular talent or ability is considered.

Requirements: Graduation from secondary school is recommended; GED is accepted. 20 units are required. Special Services Program for applicants not normally admissible. ACT is required; SAT I may be substituted. Campus visit recommended. Off-campus interviews available with an alumni representative.

Procedure: Take SAT I or ACT by fall of 12th year. Visit college for interview by March 15 of 12th year. Application deadline is June 15. Notification of admission on rolling basis. $100 nonrefundable room deposit. Freshmen accepted for all terms.

Special programs: Credit and/or placement may be granted through CEEB Advanced Placement exams. Credit and/or placement may be granted through CLEP general and subject exams. Placement may be granted through challenge exams. Early decision program. In fall 1994, 45 applied for early decision and 40 were accepted. Deadline for applying for early decision is March 15. Early entrance/early admission program. Concurrent enrollment program.

Transfer students: Transfer students accepted for all terms. Minimum 2.0 GPA required. Lowest course grade accepted is "C." At least 30 semester hours must be completed at the college to receive degree.

Admissions contact: David Valentine, Interim Director of Admissions. 901 942-7302.

FINANCIAL AID. Available aid: Pell grants, SEOG, school scholarships, private scholarships, ROTC scholarships, academic merit scholarships, athletic scholarships, and United Negro College Fund. Perkins Loans (NDSL), Stafford Loans (GSL), school loans, and private loans. Deferred payment plan.

Supporting data/closing dates: FAFSA. FAF: Deadline is July 15. Notification of awards on rolling basis.

Financial aid contact: Stephanie Larry, M.A., Director of Financial Aid. 901 942-7313.

STUDENT EMPLOYMENT. Federal Work-Study Program. 70% of full-time undergraduates work on campus during school year. Students may expect to earn an average of $500 during school year. Off-campus part-time employment opportunities rated "excellent."

COMPUTER FACILITIES. 30 IBM/IBM-compatible and Apple/Macintosh microcomputers. Students may access IBM minicomputer/mainframe systems. Residence halls may be equipped with stand-alone microcomputers. Computer facilities are available to all students.
Fees: None.
Hours: 8:15 AM-10 PM.
GRADUATE CAREER DATA. Graduate school percentages: 2% enter law school. 2% enter medical school. 10% enter graduate business programs. 5% enter theological school/seminary. 40% of graduates choose careers in business and industry. Companies and businesses that hire graduates: Aetna Life, Army Corps of Engineers, DuPont, Federal Express, Holiday Inn, Plough, State Farm, Memphis and Shelby County Boards of Education.
PROMINENT ALUMNI/AE. Marion Barry, mayor, Washington, D.C.; Lila A. Robinson, chemical engineer, executive director, Peer Consultants; Jesse Turner, president, Tri-State Bank of Memphis, Tenn., and Shelby County commissioner; Willie W. Heverton, mayor of Memphis.

Lincoln University (Missouri)

Jefferson City, MO 65102-0029   314 681-5000

Undergraduate profile. 28% Black, 1% Asian-American, 1% Hispanic, 1% Native American, 68% White, 1% Other. 89% are state residents; 19% are transfers. Average age of undergraduates is 26.

Enrollment. Undergraduates: 902 men, 1,012 women (full-time). Freshman class: 504 applicants, 504 accepted, 459 enrolled. Graduate enrollment: 113 men, 250 women.

Faculty. 157 full-time, 94 part-time; 53 Black, 181 White, 17 Other. 53% of faculty holds doctoral degree. Student/faculty ratio: 14 to 1.

Test score averages/ranges. Average ACT scores: 18 composite. Range of ACT scores of middle 50%: 16-20 composite.

1995-96 Costs. Tuition: $2,016 (state residents), $4,032 (out-of-state). Room & board: $2,728. Fees, books, misc. academic expenses (school's estimate): $560.

PROFILE. Lincoln, founded in 1866, is a public university. Programs are offered through the Colleges of Arts and Sciences and Professional Studies. Its 137-acre campus is located in Jefferson City, midway between St. Louis and Kansas City.
Accreditation: NCACS. Professionally accredited by the American Assembly of Collegiate Schools of Business, the National Association of Schools of Music, the National Council for Accreditation of Teacher Education, the National League for Nursing.
Religious orientation: Lincoln University is nonsectarian; no religious requirements.
Library: Collections totaling over 143,573 volumes, 759 periodical subscriptions, 27,109 microform items, and 1,710 CD-ROMs.
Athletic facilities: Football stadium, track, baseball and soccer fields, gymnasium.
STUDENT BODY. Freshman profile: 78% of accepted applicants took ACT.
Undergraduate achievement: 49% of fall 1993 freshmen returned for fall 1994 term.
Foreign students: 37 students are from out of the country. Countries represented include Ethiopia, Kenya, Malawi, Nigeria, Sierra Leone, and Tanzania; 20 in all.
PROGRAMS OF STUDY. Degrees: B.A., B.Mus.Ed., B.S., B.S.Ed.
Majors: Accounting, Agriculture, Art, Biology, Building Engineering, Business Administration, Business Education, Chemistry, Computer Information Systems, Criminal Justice, Economics, Elementary Education, English, Fashion Merchandising, French, Health/Physical Education, History, Journalism, Marketing, Mathematics, Mechanical Technology, Medical Technology, Music, Philosophy, Physics, Political Science, Psychology, Public Administration, Radio/TV Broadcasting, Secretarial Science, Social Sciences Education, Sociology, Special Education.
Distribution of degrees: The majors with the highest enrollments are business administration, elementary education, and nursing; philosophy and physics have the lowest.
Requirements: General education requirement.

Academic regulations: Minimum 2.0 GPA must be maintained.

Special: Minors offered in most majors and in Afro-American studies, anthropology, clothing/textiles, computer science, German, military science, social work, Spanish, and speech/theatre. Courses offered in geography and urban planning. Interrrelated programs in agribusiness, animal science, natural resource management, and plant/soil sciences. Associate degrees offered. Double majors. Cooperative education programs. Graduate school at which qualified undergraduates may take graduate-level courses. Preprofessional programs in medicine, veterinary science, pharmacy, dentistry, optometry, podiatry, and engineering. Teacher certification in elementary, secondary, and special education. Certification in specific subject areas. ROTC.

Honors: Honors program.

Academic Assistance: Remedial reading, writing, math, and study skills. Nonremedial tutoring.

STUDENT LIFE. Housing: All unmarried, nonveteran students under age 21 with fewer than 60 semester hours must live on campus unless living with family. Women's and men's dorms. 10% of students live in college housing.

Services and counseling/handicapped student services: Placement services. Health service. Career and academic guidance services. Religious counseling. Physically disabled student services. Learning disabled program/services. Notetaking services. Tape recorders. Tutors. Reader services for the blind.

Campus organizations: Undergraduate student government. Student newspaper (Clarion). Yearbook. Radio and TV stations. Band, choir, jazz ensemble, orchestra, dance troupes, Stagecrafters, commuter students organization, academic and special-interest groups. Four fraternities, no chapter houses; four sororities, no chapter houses. 1% of women join a sorority.

Religious organizations: Baptist and Catholic groups.

Foreign student organizations: International Student Association.

ATHLETICS. Physical education requirements: Four semesters of physical education required.

Intercollegiate competition: 1% of students participate. Baseball (M), basketball (M,W), cross-country (W), golf (M), soccer (M), softball (W), tennis (W), track (indoor) (M,W), track (outdoor) (M,W), track and field (indoor) (M,W), track and field (outdoor) (M,W). Member of Mid-America Intercollegiate Athletics Association, NCAA Division II.

Intramural and club sports: 7% of students participate. Intramural basketball, football, softball.

ADMISSIONS.

Requirements: Graduation from secondary school is required; GED is accepted. 16 units and the following program of study are recommended: 4 units of English, 3 units of math, 2 units of science, 3 units of social studies, 4 units of electives including 3 units of academic electives. Open admissions policy for in-state residents; minimum 2.0 GPA required of out-of-state applicants. Admissions test required of nursing program applicants. ACT is required; SAT I may be substituted.

Procedure: Suggest filing application by April 1. Application deadline is August 1. Notification of admission on rolling basis. $125 refundable room deposit. Freshmen accepted for all terms.

Special programs: Admission may be deferred one year. Credit may be granted through CLEP general and subject exams. Credit and placement may be granted through challenge exams. Early decision program. Early entrance/early admission program. Concurrent enrollment program.

Transfer students: Transfer students accepted for all terms. In fall 1994, 19% of all new students were transfers into all classes. 145 transfer applications were received, 145 were accepted. Application deadline is July 15 for fall; December 15 for spring. Minimum 2.0 GPA required. Lowest course grade accepted is "C." Maximum number of transferable credits is 64 semester hours from a two-year school and 90 semester hours from a four-year school. At least 30 semester hours must be completed at the university to receive degree.

Admissions contact: Stanford Baddley, M.Ed., Executive Director of Enrollment Services. 314 681-5599.

FINANCIAL AID. Available aid: Pell grants, SEOG, state scholarships and grants, school scholarships, private scholarships, ROTC scholarships, academic merit scholarships, and athletic scholarships. Perkins Loans (NDSL), PLUS, and Stafford Loans (GSL). Deferred payment plan.

Financial aid statistics: 34% of aid is not need-based. In 1993-94, 70% of all undergraduate aid applicants received aid. Average amounts of aid awarded freshmen: Scholarships and grants, $2,300; loans, $2,625.

Supporting data/closing dates: FAFSA/FAF: Priority filing date is March 1. School's own aid application: Priority filing date is March 1. State aid form: Priority filing date is March 1. Income tax forms: Accepted on rolling basis. Notification of awards on rolling basis.

Financial aid contact: Stanford Baddley, M.Ed., Executive Director of Enrollment Services. 314 681-6156.

STUDENT EMPLOYMENT. Federal Work-Study Program. Institutional employment. 18% of full-time undergraduates work on campus during school year. Students may expect to earn an average of $1,000 during school year. Freshmen are discouraged from working during their first term. Off-campus part-time employment opportunities rated "excellent."

COMPUTER FACILITIES. 250 IBM/IBM-compatible and Apple/Macintosh microcomputers; 100 are networked. Students may access IBM, SUN, UNISYS minicomputer/mainframe systems, BITNET, Internet. Client/LAN operating systems include DOS, UNIX/XENIX/AIX, X-windows, Banyan, Microsoft, Novell. Computer facilities are available to all students.

Fees: Computer fee is included in tuition/fees.

Hours: 9 AM-9 PM (M-Th); 9 AM-5PM (F).

Lincoln University (Pennsylvania)

Lincoln University, PA 19352　　　　　　　　　　　　**610 932-8300**

Undergraduate profile. 94% Black, 1% Hispanic, 2% White, 3% Other. 51% are state residents. Average age of undergraduates is 19.

Enrollment. Undergraduates: 503 men, 708 women (full-time). Freshman class: 1,403 applicants, 890 accepted, 375 enrolled. Graduate enrollment: 53 men, 135 women.

Faculty. 90 full-time, 28 part-time; 55 Black, 44 White, 19 Other. 71% of faculty holds doctoral degree. Student/faculty ratio: 12 to 1.

Test score averages/ranges. Average SAT I scores: 362 verbal, 382 math. Range of SAT I scores of middle 50%: 310-360 verbal, 330-380 math.

1995-96 Costs. Tuition: $8,181 (comprehensive state residents), $10,369 (comprehensive out-of-state).

PROFILE. Lincoln University, founded in 1854, is a private, state-related institution. Undergraduate programs are offered through the Divisions of Humanities, Natural Sciences, and Social Sciences; graduate programs are also offered. Its 422-acre campus is located in southern Chester County, 45 miles southwest of Philadelphia.

Accreditation: MSACS.

Religious orientation: Lincoln University is nonsectarian; two semesters of religion required.

Library: Collections totaling 167,438 volumes, 752 periodical subscriptions, and 2,879 microform items.

Special facilities/museums: African museum, fine arts center, hall for life sciences, learning resource center.

STUDENT BODY. Freshman profile: 1% of freshmen who took SAT I scored 600 or over on verbal, 1% scored 600 or over on math; 4% scored 500 or over on verbal, 9% scored 500 or over on math; 33% scored 400 or over on verbal, 39% scored 400 or over on math; 86% scored 300 or over on verbal, 90% scored 300 or over on math.

Undergraduate achievement: 30% of entering class graduates. 20% of students who complete a degree program immediately go on to graduate study.

Foreign students: 31 students are from out of the country. Countries represented include Kenya, Namibia, Nigeria, South Africa, Zambia, and Zimbabwe; 12 in all.

PROGRAMS OF STUDY. Degrees: B.A., B.S.

Majors: Anthropology/Sociology, Biology, Black Studies, Business Administration, Chemistry, Classical Languages, Computer Science, Criminal Justice, Economics, Education, English, English/Education, Finance, French, Health/Physical Education, History, Human Services, Instrumental Music, International Public Service, Mathematics, Modern Language Education, Music, Music Education, Philosophy, Physics, Political Science, Psychology, Public Affairs, Recreational Leadership Studies, Religion, Science, Social Welfare, Sociology, Spanish, Therapeutic Recreation, Voice.

Distribution of degrees: The majors with the highest enrollments are business administration, criminal justice, and sociology; philosophy, mathematics, and international public service have the lowest.

Requirements: General education requirement.

Academic regulations: Minimum 2.0 GPA must be maintained.

Special: Courses offered in Chinese, Russian, and Swahili. Independent study. Pass/fail grading option. Internships. Cooperative education programs. Preprofessional programs in law, medicine, veterinary science, pharmacy, dentistry, theology, engineering, and nursing. 2-2 nursing program with West Chester U. 3-2 engineering programs with Lafayette Coll, New Jersey Inst of Tech, and Pennsylvania State U. 3-3 engineering program with Drexel U. Journalism program with Temple U. Exchange program with American U. Teacher certification in early childhood, elementary, and secondary education. Study abroad in Brazil, the Dominican Republic, France, Germany, Mexico, Russia, Spain, and Taiwan. ROTC and AFROTC at U of Delaware.

Honors: Honors program. Honor societies.

Academic Assistance: Remedial reading, writing, math, and study skills. Nonremedial tutoring.

STUDENT LIFE. Housing: All freshmen must live on campus. Coed, women's, and men's dorms. 89% of students live in college housing.

Services and counseling/handicapped student services: Placement services. Health service. Birth control, personal, and psychological counseling. Career and academic guidance services. Religious counseling.

Campus organizations: Undergraduate student government. Student newspaper (Lincolnian, published once/month). Yearbook. Radio station. Concert choir, gospel ensemble, concert band, jazz ensemble, drama group, dance company, law society, 15 organizations in all. Four fraternities, no chapter houses; four sororities, no chapter houses. 3% of men join a fraternity. 20% of women join a sorority.

Religious organizations: Militants for Christ, Islamic Association, Chapel Usher Board, Fellowship of Catholic Students.

Foreign student organizations: International Club.

ATHLETICS. Physical education requirements: Two semesters of physical education required.

Intercollegiate competition: 2% of students participate. Baseball (M), basketball (M,W), cross-country (M), soccer (M), tennis (M), track (indoor) (M), track (outdoor) (M), volleyball (W), wrestling (M). Member of ECAC, NAIA, NCAA Division III.

Intramural and club sports: 1% of students participate. Intramural badminton, basketball, bowling, softball, table tennis, tennis, touch football, track, volleyball.

ADMISSIONS. Academic basis for candidate selection (in order of priority): Secondary school record, standardized test scores, school's recommendation, class rank, essay.

Nonacademic basis for candidate selection: Character and personality, extracurricular participation, particular talent or ability, geographical distribution, and alumni/ae relationship are considered.

Requirements: Graduation from secondary school is required; GED is accepted. 21 units and the following program of study are required: 4 units of English, 3 units of math, 3 units of science, 3 units of social studies, 5 units of electives including 3 units of academic electives, 1 unit of health/physical education, 2 units of arts and humanities. Additional unit of math, foreign language, history, or social studies recommended in elective subjects. Freshman Studies Program for applicants not normally admissible. SAT I is required; ACT may be substituted. Campus visit and interview recommended. Off-campus interviews available with admissions and alumni representatives.

Procedure: Take SAT I or ACT by fall of 12th year. Notification of admission on rolling basis. $75 nonrefundable tuition deposit. $75 nonrefundable room deposit. Freshmen accepted for all terms.

Special programs: Admission may be deferred. Placement may be granted through CEEB Advanced Placement exams. Placement may be granted through CLEP general and subject exams. Placement may be granted through challenge exams. Early entrance/early admission program.

Transfer students: Transfer students accepted for all terms. Application deadline is rolling for fall; rolling for spring. Minimum 2.0 GPA required. Lowest course grade accepted is "C."

Admissions contact: Jimmy Arrington, M.A., Dean of Admissions. 610 932-8300, extension 206.

FINANCIAL AID. Available aid: Pell grants, SEOG, state grants, school scholarships, private scholarships, and academic merit scholarships. Perkins Loans (NDSL) and PLUS. Tuition Plan Inc.

Financial aid statistics: Average amounts of aid awarded freshmen: Loans, $2,000.

Supporting data/closing dates: FAFSA/FAF. State aid form. Income tax forms. Notification of awards on rolling basis.

Financial aid contact: Georgia Daniel, M.A., Director of Financial Aid. 610 932-8300.

STUDENT EMPLOYMENT. Federal Work-Study Program. Institutional employment. 30% of full-time undergraduates work on campus during school year. Freshmen are discouraged from working during their first term. Off-campus part-time employment opportunities rated "poor."

COMPUTER FACILITIES. 125 IBM/IBM-compatible and Apple/Macintosh microcomputers. Students may access Digital minicomputer/mainframe systems. Computer facilities are available to all students.

Fees: Computer fee is included in tuition/fees.

GRADUATE CAREER DATA. Graduate school percentages: 1% enter law school. 1% enter medical school. 10% enter graduate business programs. 2% enter graduate arts and sciences programs. Highest graduate school enrollments: Pennsylvania State U, Temple U, U of Pennsylvania. 10% of graduates choose careers in business and industry. Companies and businesses that hire graduates: AT&T, Internal Revenue Service, Nationwide Insurance, Xerox.

PROMINENT ALUMNI/AE. Thurgood Marshall, former justice, U.S. Supreme Court; Langston Hughes, poet; Hildras Poindexter, authority on tropical diseases.

Livingstone College

Salisbury, NC 28144

704 638-5500

Undergraduate profile. 90% Black, 5% White, 5% Other. 50% are state residents; 1% are transfers. Average age of undergraduates is 18.

Enrollment. Undergraduates: 442 men, 320 women (full-time). Freshman class: 854 applicants, 713 accepted, 324 enrolled. Graduate enrollment: 39 men, 19 women.

Faculty. 55 full-time; 9 part-time. 40 Black, 15 White, 9 Other. 34% of faculty holds doctoral degree. Student/faculty ratio: 10 to 1.

Test score averages/ranges. Average SAT I scores: 295 verbal, 322 math.

1995-96 Costs. Tuition: $9,200. Room & board: $3,400. Fees, books, misc. academic expenses (school's estimate): $1,450.

PROFILE. Livingstone, founded in 1879, is a church-affiliated college. Programs are offered through the College of Arts and Sciences and Hood Theological Seminary. Its 272-acre campus is located in Salisbury, 38 miles northeast of Charlotte.

Accreditation: SACS. Professionally accredited by the Council on Social Work Education.

Religious orientation: Livingstone College is affiliated with the African Methodist Episcopal Zion Church; four semesters of religion required.

Library: Collections totaling over 78,000 volumes, 245 periodical subscriptions, and 40,650 microform items.

Special facilities/museums: Learning center, museum.

Athletic facilities: Gymnasium, football and softball fields, track, tennis courts, weight room.

STUDENT BODY. Freshman profile: 1% of freshmen who took SAT I scored 500 or over on math; 5% scored 400 or over on verbal, 8% scored 400 or over on math; 40% scored 300 or over on verbal, 50% scored 300 or over on math. 90% of accepted applicants took SAT I; 10% took ACT. 95% of freshmen come from public schools.

Undergraduate achievement: 85% of fall 1993 freshmen returned for fall 1994 term. 60% of entering class graduates.

Foreign students: 15 students are from out of the country. Countries represented include Bermuda, Liberia, Nigeria, the Virgin Islands, and the West Indies.

PROGRAMS OF STUDY. Degrees: B.A., B.S., B.Soc.Work.

Majors: Accounting, Biology, Business Administration, Chemistry, Criminal Justice, Elementary Education, English, History, Mathematics, Music, Music Education, Physical Education, Political Science, Psychology, Social Studies, Social Welfare, Sociology.

Distribution of degrees: The majors with the highest enrollments are business administration and psychology; music, English, and biology have the lowest.

Requirements: General education requirement.

Special: Double majors. Dual degrees. Independent study. Internships. Cooperative education programs. Preprofessional programs in law, medicine, and pharmacy. Dual degree pharmacy program with Howard U. Dual degree law program with St. John's U. Dual degree engineering program with North Carolina A&T State U. Teacher certification in early childhood, elementary, and secondary education. ROTC at Davidson Coll.

Honors: Honors program.

Academic Assistance: Remedial reading, writing, math, and study skills.

STUDENT LIFE. Housing: Students may live off campus with permission. Women's and men's dorms. 92% of students live in college housing.

Services and counseling/handicapped student services: Health service. Personal counseling. Academic guidance services. Religious counseling. Learning disabled services.

Campus organizations: Undergraduate student government. Student newspaper (Stone). Yearbook. NAACP. Stage, marching, and jazz bands, concert choir, National Honor Society, PreAlumnus Council, Panhellenic Council, debating, social welfare action group, departmental and special-interest groups. Four fraternities, no chapter houses; four sororities, no chapter houses. 8% of men join a fraternity. 10% of women join a sorority.

Religious organizations: Pretheological Union, Prayer Meeting Choir.

ATHLETICS. Physical education requirements: Two semesters of physical education required.

Intercollegiate competition: 20% of students participate. Basketball (M,W), cross-country (M,W), football (M), softball (W), tennis (M), track and field (outdoor) (M,W), volleyball (W). Member of CIAA, NCAA Division II.

Intramural and club sports: 28% of students participate. Intramural basketball, flag football, softball, table tennis. Men's club track/field. Women's club track/field.

ADMISSIONS. Academic basis for candidate selection (in order of priority): Secondary school record, standardized test scores, class rank, school's recommendation.

Nonacademic basis for candidate selection: Character and personality and particular talent or ability are important. Extracurricular participation and geographical distribution are considered.

Requirements: Graduation from secondary school is required; GED is accepted. 20 units and the following program of study are required: 4 units of English, 2 units of math, 2 units of science including 1 unit of lab, 2 units of foreign language, 1 unit of social studies, 1 unit of history, 7 units of electives. Minimum 2.0 GPA recommended. Audition required of music program applicants. Conditional admission possible for applicants not meeting standard requirements. SAT I is required; ACT may be substituted. Campus visit recommended. Off-campus interviews available with an admissions representative.

Procedure: Take SAT I or ACT by June 1 of 12th year. Application deadline is July 15. Notification of admission on rolling basis. Reply is required by August 1. $50 room deposit, refundable until July 1. Freshmen accepted for all terms.

Special programs: Admission may be deferred one year. Credit and/or placement may be granted through CEEB Advanced Placement exams for scores of 3 or higher. Placement may be granted through challenge exams and for military experience.

Transfer students: Transfer students accepted for all terms. In fall 1994, 1% of all new students were transfers into all classes. 80 transfer applications were received, 66 were accepted. Application deadline is July 1 for fall; December 1 for spring. Minimum 2.0 GPA recommended. Lowest course grade accepted is "C." Maximum number of transferable credits is 64 semester hours. At least 45 semester hours must be completed at the college to receive degree.

Admissions contact: Bruce Murphy, Director of Admissions. 704 638-5502.

FINANCIAL AID. Available aid: Pell grants, SEOG, state scholarships and grants, school scholarships and grants, private scholarships, academic merit scholarships, athletic scholarships, aid for undergraduate foreign students, and United Negro College Fund. PLUS, Stafford Loans (GSL), and unsubsidized Stafford Loans. Deferred payment plan.

Financial aid statistics: 30% of aid is not need-based. In 1994-95, 98% of all undergraduate aid applicants received aid; 95% of freshman aid applicants. Average amounts of aid awarded freshmen: Scholarships and grants, $1,500; loans, $2,625.

Supporting data/closing dates: FAFSA: Priority filing date is March 31. FAF: Accepted on rolling basis. School's own aid application: Priority filing date is March 31. SINGLEFILE: Priority filing date is April 15. Notification of awards on rolling basis.

Financial aid contact: Wanda White, M.S., Director of Financial Aid. 704 638-5562.

STUDENT EMPLOYMENT. Federal Work-Study Program. Institutional employment. 50% of full-time undergraduates work on campus during school year. Students may expect to earn an average of $1,000 during school year. Off-campus part-time employment opportunities rated "good."

COMPUTER FACILITIES. 50 IBM/IBM-compatible and Apple/Macintosh microcomputers; 40 are networked. Computer facilities are available to all students.

Fees: None.

GRADUATE CAREER DATA. Highest graduate school enrollment: U of Delaware. 10% of graduates choose careers in business and industry.

PROMINENT ALUMNI/AE. Dr. Roy Hudson, vice president, Upjohn; Dr. George Battle, Jr., president, CHAR/MECK school board; Dr. James Gavin, Senior Officer Scientist, Hughes Medical Institute.

Martin University

Indianapolis, IN 46218
317 543-3238

Undergraduate profile. 87% Black, 1% Hispanic, 12% White.

Enrollment. Undergraduates: 72 men, 252 women (full-time). Freshman class: 287 applicants, 259 accepted, 259 enrolled. Graduate enrollment: 7 men, 20 women.

Faculty. 39 full-time, 7 part-time; 23 Black, 23 White. 50% of faculty holds highest degree in specific field. Student/faculty ratio: 11 to 1.

Test score averages/ranges. N/A.

1995-96 Costs. Tuition: $6,060. Housing: None. Fees, books, misc. academic expenses (school's estimate): $460.

PROFILE. Martin, founded in 1977, is a liberal arts university.

Accreditation: NCACS.

Religious orientation: Martin University is nonsectarian; no religious requirements.

Special facilities/museums: Specialized hematology laboratory (sickle cell anemia research).

STUDENT BODY. Undergraduate achievement: 90% of fall 1993 freshmen returned for fall 1994 term.

PROGRAMS OF STUDY. Degrees: B.A., B.S.

Majors: Accounting, Afro-American Studies, Art Education, Biology, Business Administration/Management, Business Education, Chemistry, Communications, Community Psychology, Computer/Information Sciences, Computer Programming, Counseling Psychology, Creative Writing, Education, Elementary Education, English, English Education, History, Humanities, Humanities/ Social Sciences, Information Sciences/Systems, Insurance/Risk Management, Journalism, Junior High Education, Marketing/Distribution, Mathematics, Mathematics Education, Medieval Studies, Music, Music Education, Physics, Political Science/Government, Psychology, Religion, Renewable Natural Resources, Science Education, Secondary Education, Social Science Education, Social Studies Education, Sociology, Speech/Communication/Theatre, Theological Studies, Urban Studies.

Requirements: General education requirement.

Academic regulations: Freshmen must maintain minimum 2.0 GPA.

Special: Self-designed majors. Double majors. Accelerated study. Internships. Program with U of Indianapolis in teacher education and nursing. Teacher certification in elementary and secondary education.

STUDENT LIFE. Housing: Commuter campus; no student housing.

Services and counseling/handicapped student services: Placement services. Health service. Counseling services for veteran and older students. Personal counseling. Career guidance services. Learning disabled services.

Campus organizations: Undergraduate student government. Student newspaper. Choral groups, dance, opera, GIFT of Brightwood (neighborhood youth services).

ATHLETICS. Physical education requirements: None.

ADMISSIONS.

Requirements: Graduation from secondary school is recommended; GED is accepted. No specific distribution of secondary school units required. Open admissions policy. Applicants tested with WRAT and Wonderlic. Admissions interview required.

Procedure: Application deadline is September 12. Notification of admission on rolling basis. Freshmen accepted for fall term only.

Special programs: Credit and/or placement may be granted through CLEP general and subject exams.

Transfer students: Lowest course grade accepted is "C."

Admissions contact: Bobbye Jean Craig, Director of Admissions.

FINANCIAL AID. Available aid: Pell grants, SEOG, and state grants. Stafford Loans (GSL).

Supporting data/closing dates: FAFSA: Priority filing date is March 1; accepted on rolling basis. Notification of awards on rolling basis.

Financial aid contact: Yvette Ellis, Vice President of Financial Aid. 317 543-3258.

STUDENT EMPLOYMENT. Federal Work-Study Program.

COMPUTER FACILITIES. 35 IBM/IBM-compatible microcomputers; 22 are networked. Client/LAN operating systems include DOS, Novell. Computer facilities are available to all students.

Fees: $20 computer fee per semester.

Hours: 8:30 AM-8:30 PM daily.

Marygrove College

Detroit, MI 48221-2599   **313 862-8000**

Undergraduate profile. 80% Black, 1% Asian-American, 1% Hispanic, 11% White, 7% Other. 99% are state residents; 52% are transfers. Average age of undergraduates is 31.

Enrollment. Undergraduates: 85 men, 466 women (full-time). Freshman class: 698 applicants, 376 accepted, 269 enrolled. Graduate enrollment: 19 men, 109 women.

Faculty. 59 full-time, 13 part-time; 13 Black, 55 White, 4 Other. 51% of faculty holds doctoral degree. Student/faculty ratio: 17 to 1.

Test score averages/ranges. N/A.

1995-96 Costs. Tuition: $8,496. Room & board: $4,160. Fees, books, misc. academic expenses (school's estimate): $50.

PROFILE. Marygrove, founded in 1910, is a church-affiliated college. Programs are offered through the Divisions of Education, Letters, Natural Science and Mathematics, Professional Studies, Social Science, and Visual and Performing Arts. Its 68-acre campus is located in Detroit. Campus architecture includes Tudor-Gothic style buildings.

Accreditation: NCACS. Professionally accredited by the American Medical Association (CA-HEA), the Council on Social Work Education, the National Council for Accreditation of Teacher Education.

Religious orientation: Marygrove College is affiliated with the Roman Catholic Church (Servants of the Immaculate Heart of Mary); one semester of religion, theology, or philosophy required.

Library: Collections totaling 195,573 volumes, 800 periodical subscriptions, 23,026 microform items, and 550 audiovisual items.

Special facilities/museums: Media center, production center.

Athletic facilities: Gymnasium and weight room.

STUDENT BODY. Freshman profile: 10% of accepted applicants took SAT I; 90% took ACT. 80% of freshmen come from public schools.

Undergraduate achievement: 70% of fall 1993 freshmen returned for fall 1994 term. 40% of entering class graduates. 40% of students who complete a degree program immediately go on to graduate study.

PROGRAMS OF STUDY. Degrees: B.A., B.Bus.Admin., B.Mus., B.S., B.Soc.Work.

Majors: Accounting, Allied Health Science, Applied Music, Art, Art History/Appreciation, Art Therapy, Biology, Business, Business Administration, Business Education, Ceramics, Chemistry, Clothing, Communication Studies, Computer Science, Dance, Design, Drawing, Economics, Education, English, Family/Consumer Studies, Food Sciences/Human Nutrition, French, General Human Ecology, German, Graphic Design, History, Human Ecology Education, Human Ecology/Home Economics, Humanities, Journalism, Language Arts, Management, Mathematics, Music, Natural Science, Organ, Painting, Philosophy, Piano, Political Science/Government, Printmaking, Psychology, Religious Studies, Sacred Music, Social Sciences, Social Studies, Social Work, Sociology, Spanish, Special Education, Theory, Translation, Voice.

Distribution of degrees: The majors with the highest enrollments are business, computer science, and psychology.

Requirements: General education requirement.

Academic regulations: Minimum 2.0 GPA must be maintained.

Special: Minors offered in most majors. Associate degrees offered. Self-designed majors. Double majors. Independent study. Pass/fail grading option. Internships. Cooperative education programs. Graduate school at which qualified undergraduates may take graduate-level courses. Preprofessional programs in law, medicine, and dentistry. Member of Detroit Area Catholic Higher Education Consortium; cross-registration possible. Teacher certification in early childhood, elementary, secondary, and special education.

Honors: Honor societies.

Academic Assistance: Remedial reading, writing, math, and study skills. Nonremedial tutoring.

STUDENT LIFE. Housing: Students may live on or off campus. Coed dorms. 5% of students live in college housing.

Services and counseling/handicapped student services: Placement services. Health service. Counseling services for older students. Personal and psychological counseling. Career and academic guidance services. Religious counseling.

Campus organizations: Undergraduate student government. Literary magazine. Black Social Work Students. Chamber singers, chorale, dance group, drama club, art club, opera workshop, ensembles, cardiovascular club, psychology club, business association, 16 organizations in all.

Religious organizations: Campus Ministry.

Foreign student organizations: Intercultural Club.

ATHLETICS. Physical education requirements: None.

ADMISSIONS. Academic basis for candidate selection (in order of priority): Secondary school record, school's recommendation, standardized test scores, class rank.

Nonacademic basis for candidate selection: Particular talent or ability is emphasized. Character and personality and alumni/ae relationship are important. Extracurricular participation is considered.

Requirements: Graduation from secondary school is required; GED is accepted. 25 units and the following program of study are recommended: 8 units of English, 4 units of math, 1 unit of science, 1 unit of foreign language, 4 units of social studies, 5 units of history. Minimum 2.7 GPA required. Separate requirements for allied health program applicants. Portfolio required of art program applicants. Audition required of music program applicants. Conditional admission possible for applicants not meeting standard requirements. Developmental Studies Program for applicants not normally admissible. ACT is required; SAT I may be substituted. PSAT is recommended. Campus visit and interview recommended. No off-campus interviews.

Procedure: Take SAT I or ACT by June of 12th year. Visit college for interview by March 15 of 12th year. Notification of admission on rolling basis. $50 nonrefundable room deposit. Freshmen accepted for all terms.

Special programs: Admission may be deferred one year. Credit and/or placement may be granted through CEEB Advanced Placement exams for scores of 3 or higher. Credit and/or placement may be granted through CLEP general and subject exams. Credit may be granted for military experience. Credit and placement may be granted through ACT PEP, DANTES, and challenge exams and for life experience. Early entrance/early admission program.

Transfer students: Transfer students accepted for all terms. In fall 1994, 52% of all new students were transfers into all classes. 392 transfer applications were received, 216 were accepted. Minimum 2.0 GPA required. Lowest course grade accepted is "C." Maximum number of transferable credits is 64 semester hours from a two-year school and 98 semester hours from a four-year school. At least 30 credits must be completed at the college to receive degree.

Admissions contact: Carla R. Stepp, M.A., Director of Admissions. 313 862-5200.

FINANCIAL AID. Available aid: Pell grants, SEOG, state scholarships and grants, school scholarships and grants, private scholarships and grants, academic merit scholarships, and aid for undergraduate foreign students. Perkins Loans (NDSL), PLUS, Stafford Loans (GSL), state loans, and private loans. Tuition Plan Inc., Education Plan Inc., deferred payment plan, and family tuition reduction.

Financial aid statistics: Average amounts of aid awarded freshmen: Scholarships and grants, $1,600; loans, $1,300.

Supporting data/closing dates: FAFSA/FAF: Priority filing date is February 1; accepted on rolling basis. School's own aid application: Priority filing date is February 1. State aid form: Priority filing date is April 15; deadline is August 30. Income tax forms: Accepted on rolling basis. Notification of awards begins May 1.

Financial aid contact: Donald Hurt, Director of Financial Aid. 313 862-8000.

STUDENT EMPLOYMENT. Federal Work-Study Program. 17% of full-time undergraduates work on campus during school year. Students may expect to earn an average of $1,200 during school year. Off-campus part-time employment opportunities rated "fair."

COMPUTER FACILITIES. 84 IBM/IBM-compatible and Apple/Macintosh microcomputers; 21 are networked. Client/LAN operating systems include Apple/Macintosh, DOS. Computer facilities are available to all students.

Fees: None.

Hours: 9 AM-9 PM (M-F); 9 AM-2 PM (Sa).

PROMINENT ALUMNI/AE. Nettie Seabrooks, deputy mayor, city of Detroit; Wendell Anthony, president, NAACP Detroit chapter.

Miles College

Fairfield, AL 35064

205 923-2771

Undergraduate profile. 93% Black, 2% White, 5% Other. 21% are state residents. Average age of undergraduates is 18.
Enrollment. Undergraduates: 445 men, 496 women (full-time). Freshman class: 416 enrolled.
Faculty. 41 full-time; 8 part-time. 43% of faculty holds highest degree in specific field. Student/faculty ratio: 22 to 1.
Test score averages/ranges. Average ACT scores: 11 English, 7 math, 9 composite.
1995-96 Costs. Tuition: $4,000. Room & board: $2,700. Fees, books, misc. academic expenses (school's estimate): $650.

PROFILE. Miles, founded in 1905, is a private, church-affiliated, liberal arts college. Its 35-acre campus is located in Fairfield, five miles south of Birmingham.
Accreditation: SACS.
Religious orientation: Miles College is affiliated with the Christian Methodist Episcopal Church; one semester of religion required. Attendance is mandatory for chapel 13 times/semester.
Library: Collections totaling over 180,000 volumes, 250 periodical subscriptions and 850 microform items.
Special facilities/museums: Afro-American materials center, media center.
Athletic facilities: Gymnasium, athletic, baseball, and football fields, track, weight room, tennis courts, indoor and outdoor basketball courts.
STUDENT BODY. Freshman profile: 90% of freshmen come from public schools.
Undergraduate achievement: 65% of fall 1993 freshmen returned for fall 1994 term. 20% of entering class graduates.
Foreign students: Countries represented include Nigeria.
PROGRAMS OF STUDY. Degrees: B.A., B.S.
Majors: Accounting, Biology, Business Administration/Management, Chemistry, Communications, Elementary Education, English, English Education, Mathematics, Mathematics Education, Music Performance, Secondary Education, Social Science Education, Social Sciences, Social Work, Sociology.
Distribution of degrees: The majors with the highest enrollments are business, social science, and communications; political science and elementary education have the lowest.
Requirements: General education requirement.
Academic regulations: Freshmen must maintain minimum 1.6 GPA; sophomores, 1.8 GPA; juniors, 2.0 GPA; seniors, 2.0 GPA.
Special: Minor required for social science majors only. Minors offered in some majors and in political science. Courses offered in art, dance, drama, economics, philosophy, and religion. English proficiency exam and senior comprehensive exam required for graduation. Double majors. Dual degrees. Independent study. Internships. Cooperative education programs. Cooperative programs in engineering, physics, and veterinary medicine with Tuskegee U and U of Alabama. Member of Alabama Center for Higher Education, NAEDHE, Positive Futures, Inc., and Teaching Learning Institute. Cross-registration with U of Alabama at Birmingham. Teacher certification in elementary and secondary education. Certification in specific subject areas. ROTC at U of Alabama at Birmingham. AFROTC at Samford U.
Honors: Honors program.
Academic Assistance: Remedial reading, writing, and math. Nonremedial tutoring.
STUDENT LIFE. Housing: Students may live on or off campus. Women's and men's dorms. School-owned/operated apartments. On-campus married-student housing. 52% of students live in college housing.
Services and counseling/handicapped student services: Placement services. Health service. Counseling services for military, veteran, and older students. Personal and psychological counseling. Career and academic guidance services.

Campus organizations: Undergraduate student government. Student newspaper (Milean, published once/quarter). Yearbook. Radio and TV stations. Concert and gospel choirs, mathematics and humanities clubs, program business club, political science and press clubs, special services clubs, Mummers and ACHE clubs, National Education Association, veterans tutorial assistance, library action committee, pre-alumni council. Four fraternities, no chapter houses; four sororities, no chapter houses. 20% of men join a fraternity. 25% of women join a sorority.
Religious organizations: Interdenominational association.
Foreign student organizations: International Intercultural Club.

ATHLETICS. Physical education requirements: Three semesters of physical education required.
Intercollegiate competition: 4% of students participate. Baseball (M), basketball (M,W), cross-country (M,W), track and field (indoor) (M,W), track and field (outdoor) (M,W), volleyball (W). Member of NCAA Division II, Southern Intercollegiate Athletic Conference.
Intramural and club sports: 3% of students participate. Intramural basketball, flag football, softball, table tennis, volleyball.

ADMISSIONS. Nonacademic basis for candidate selection: Particular talent or ability and alumni/ae relationship are emphasized. Character and personality and geographical distribution are important. Extracurricular participation is considered.
Requirements: Graduation from secondary school is required; GED is accepted. No specific distribution of secondary school units required. Open admissions policy. Minimum composite ACT score of 16 and 2.0 high school GPA required of education program applicants. 4 units of math and science required of natural science program applicants. ACT is required; SAT I may be substituted. Campus visit and interview recommended.
Procedure: Take SAT I or ACT by May of 12th year. Application deadline is July 15. Notification of admission on rolling basis. Reply is required by August 15. Tuition deposit refundable until three weeks prior to start of semester. $50 nonrefundable room deposit. Freshmen accepted for all terms.
Special programs: Admission may be deferred one year. Placement may be granted through challenge exams. Early decision program.
Transfer students: Transfer students accepted for all terms. Lowest course grade accepted is "D."
Admissions contact: Brenda Grant, Director of Admissions. 205 923-2771, extension 290.

FINANCIAL AID. Available aid: Pell grants, SEOG, state grants, school scholarships, private scholarships, and ROTC scholarships. Perkins Loans (NDSL), PLUS, and Stafford Loans (GSL). AMS and deferred payment plan.
Financial aid statistics: Average amounts of aid awarded freshmen: Loans, $1,000.
Supporting data/closing dates: FAFSA/FAF: Priority filing date is April 15; accepted on rolling basis. State aid form: Priority filing date is April 15; accepted on rolling basis. Notification of awards on rolling basis.
Financial aid contact: Betty Edwards, M.A., Director of Financial Aid. 205 923-2771, extension 222.

STUDENT EMPLOYMENT. Federal Work-Study Program. Institutional employment. 55% of full-time undergraduates work on campus during school year. Students may expect to earn an average of $1,000 during school year. Off-campus part-time employment opportunities rated "good."

COMPUTER FACILITIES. 40 IBM/IBM-compatible microcomputers. Computer facilities are available to all students.
Fees: None.
Hours: 9 AM-noon and 2-4 PM.

GRADUATE CAREER DATA. Graduate school percentages: 1% enter law school. 33% enter graduate arts and sciences programs. Highest graduate school enrollments: Alabama State U, Atlanta U, U of Alabama-Birmingham. 40% of graduates choose careers in business and industry. Companies and businesses that hire graduates: Atlanta Life Insurance, Mountain Bell, Bell South, Alabama Power, board of education, social security administration.

PROMINENT ALUMNI/AE. Dr. Richard Arrington, Jr., mayor of Birmingham; U.W. Clemons, federal court judge; Bernice Williams, Small Business Administration; Dr. Perry Ward, president, Lawson State Community College; Lewis White, assistant to mayor of Birmingham, Ala.; Nathaniel Pollard, president, Bowie State U.

Mississippi Valley State University

Itta Bena, MS 38941

601 254-9041

Undergraduate profile. 99% Black, .5% White, .5% Other. 86% are state residents; 5% are transfers. Average age of undergraduates is 21.

Enrollment. Undergraduates: 851 men, 1,109 women (full-time). Freshman class: 3,588 applicants, 1,045 accepted, 519 enrolled. Graduate enrollment: 3 men, 10 women.

Faculty. 112 full-time, 28 part-time; 121 Black, 19 Other. 46% of faculty holds doctoral degree. Student/faculty ratio: 20 to 1.

Test score averages/ranges. Average ACT scores: 17 composite. Range of ACT scores of middle 50%: 13-18 English, 14-17 math.

1995-96 Costs. Tuition: $2,278 (state residents), $4,420 (out-of-state). Room & board: $2,300. Fees, books, misc. academic expenses (school's estimate): $665.

PROFILE. Mississippi Valley State, founded in 1946, is a public university. Programs are offered through the Divisions of Arts and Sciences, Business, and Education. Its 450-acre campus is located in Itta Bena, 35 miles east of Greenwood.

Accreditation: SACS. Professionally accredited by the Council on Social Work Education, the National Association of Schools of Art and Design, the National Association of Schools of Music, the National Council for Accreditation of Teacher Education.

Religious orientation: Mississippi Valley State University is nonsectarian; no religious requirements.

Library: Collections totaling over 122,000 volumes, 700 periodical subscriptions, and 275,580 microform items.

STUDENT BODY. Freshman profile: 3% of freshmen who took ACT scored 24 or over on composite; 29% scored 18 or over on composite; 100% scored 12 or over on composite. 97% of accepted applicants took ACT. 97% of freshmen come from public schools.

Undergraduate achievement: 70% of fall 1993 freshmen returned for fall 1994 term. 38% of entering class graduates. 25% of students who complete a degree program immediately go on to graduate study.

PROGRAMS OF STUDY. Degrees: B.A., B.Mus.Ed., B.S., B.Soc.Work.

Majors: Art, Biology, Biology Education, Business Administration, Chemistry, Communications, Computer Science, Criminal Justice, Elementary Education, English, English Education, Environmental Health, Health/Physical Education, Industrial Technology, Mathematics, Mathematics Education, Music Education, Office Administration, Political Science, Secondary Education, Social Science Education, Social Work, Sociology, Speech.

Distribution of degrees: The majors with the highest enrollments are criminal justice, business administration, and education; music education, communications, and environmental health have the lowest.

Requirements: General education requirement.

Academic regulations: Freshmen must maintain minimum 1.5 GPA; sophomores, 1.7 GPA; juniors, 1.9 GPA; seniors, 2.0 GPA.

Special: Minors offered in accounting, biology, business administration, computer science, English, mathematics, physical education, recreation, and speech. Music major includes instrument maintenance/repair and jazz (commercial, performance, theory, and composition) options. Industrial/vocational education includes architectural, automotive, building construction, graphic, or machine tool technology concentrations. Special education courses offered. Freshmen may enroll in basic philosophy/humanities program before declaring major. Junior-year proficiency test in English required for directed teaching and graduation. Senior recital, exhibit, project, or comprehensive exam required for graduation. Double majors. Internships. Cooperative education programs. Graduate school at which qualified undergraduates may take graduate-level courses. Preprofessional programs in law, medicine, and dentistry. Member of Consortium/Alliance for Minority Participation and Writing/Thinking Consortium. Teacher certification in early childhood, elementary, secondary, and special education. Certification in specific subject areas. ROTC and AFROTC.

Honors: Honors program. Honor societies.

Academic Assistance: Remedial reading, writing, math, and study skills. Nonremedial tutoring.

STUDENT LIFE. Housing: Students may live on or off campus. Women's and men's dorms. Both on-campus and off-campus married-student housing. 63% of students live in college housing.

Services and counseling/handicapped student services: Placement services. Health service. Counseling services for older students. Birth control and personal counseling. Career and academic guidance services. Religious counseling. Physically disabled student services. Tutors.

Campus organizations: Undergraduate student government. Student newspaper (Delta Devils Gazette, published once/quarter). Yearbook. Radio station. Band, choirs, jazz ensembles, drama group, Trade and Industries Club, community and volunteer service, 34 organizations in all. Four fraternities, no chapter houses; four sororities, no chapter houses. 5% of men join a fraternity. 4% of women join a sorority.

Religious organizations: Baptist Student Union, Chapel Committee, Methodist group, Newman Club, Seventh-day Adventist group.

ATHLETICS. Physical education requirements: Two semesters of physical education required.

Intercollegiate competition: Football (M), track (indoor) (M,W), track (outdoor) (M,W). Member of NCAA Division I, NCAA Division I-AA for football.

Intramural and club sports: Intramural basketball, gymnastics, handball, paddleball, skating, squash, swimming, volleyball, weight training.

ADMISSIONS. Academic basis for candidate selection (in order of priority): Standardized test scores, secondary school record, class rank, school's recommendation, essay.

Nonacademic basis for candidate selection: Character and personality and geographical distribution are emphasized. Extracurricular participation is important. Particular talent or ability and alumni/ae relationship are considered.

Requirements: Graduation from secondary school is recommended; GED is accepted. The following program of study is required: 4 units of English, 3 units of math, 3 units of science including 1 unit of lab, 2.5 units of social studies, 1 unit of academic elective. Minimum composite ACT score of 13 and minimum 1.8 GPA required of in-state applicants; minimum composite ACT score of 16 and minimum 1.8 GPA required of out-of-state applicants. Conditional admission possible for applicants not meeting standard requirements. ACT is required; SAT I may be substituted. Campus visit and interview recommended. Off-campus interviews available with admissions and alumni representatives.

Procedure: Take SAT I or ACT by April 30 of 12th year. Visit college for interview by April 30 of 12th year. Suggest filing application by April 30. Application deadline is August 1. Notification of admission on rolling basis. $25 refundable room deposit. Freshmen accepted for all terms.

Special programs: Admission may be deferred one year. Credit may be granted through CLEP general and subject exams. Early entrance/early admission program.

Transfer students: Transfer students accepted for all terms. In fall 1994, 5% of all new students were transfers into all classes. 260 transfer applications were received, 235 were accepted. Application deadline is August 1 for fall; December 1 for spring. Minimum 2.0 GPA required. Lowest course grade accepted is "C."

Admissions contact: Maxcine Rush, M.B.A., Director of Admissions. 601 254-3347.

FINANCIAL AID. Available aid: Pell grants, SEOG, state grants, private scholarships, ROTC scholarships, and athletic scholarships. Perkins Loans (NDSL), PLUS, and Stafford Loans (GSL). Deferred payment plan.

Financial aid statistics: 7% of aid is not need-based. In 1994-95, 96% of all undergraduate aid applicants received aid; 95% of freshman aid applicants. Average amounts of aid awarded freshmen: Scholarships and grants, $2,103; loans, $1,300.

Supporting data/closing dates: FAFSA. FAF: Priority filing date is April 1. School's own aid application: Priority filing date is April 1. Income tax forms: Priority filing date is April 1. Notification of awards on rolling basis.

Financial aid contact: Darrell Boyd, M.B.A., Director of Financial Aid. 601 254-3335.

STUDENT EMPLOYMENT. Federal Work-Study Program. Institutional employment. 8% of full-time undergraduates work on campus during school year. Students may expect to earn an average of $1,200 during school year. Off-campus part-time employment opportunities rated "poor."

COMPUTER FACILITIES. 140 IBM/IBM-compatible and Apple/Macintosh microcomputers. Students may access IBM minicomputer/mainframe systems. Computer facilities are available to all students.

Fees: None.

Hours: 8 AM-10 PM (M-Th); 8 AM-4 PM (F); 6-10 PM (Su).

GRADUATE CAREER DATA. Graduate school percentages: 2% enter law school. 3% enter medical school. 3% enter dental school. 5% enter graduate business programs. 40% enter graduate arts and sciences programs. 1% enter theological school/seminary. Highest graduate school enrollments: Delta State U, Indiana U, Jackson State U, U of Southern Illinois. 12% of graduates choose careers in business and industry. Companies and businesses that hire graduates: AT&T, IBM, Standard Oil, State Corrections Department.

PROMINENT ALUMNI/AE. Dr. Samuel McGee and Dr. Carolyn Smith, educators; Jerry Rice, professional football player.

Morehouse College

Atlanta, GA 30314

404 681-2800

Undergraduate profile. 98% Black, 2% Other. 20% are state residents; 4% are transfers. Average age of undergraduates is 20.

Enrollment. 2,852 men (full-time). Freshman class: 3,708 applicants, 1,678 accepted, 722 enrolled. Graduate enrollment: 3,005 men.

Faculty. 153 full-time; 27 part-time. 75% of faculty holds doctoral degree. Student/faculty ratio: 17 to 1.

Test score averages/ranges. N/A.

1995-96 Costs. Tuition: $7,430. Room: $3,300. Board: $2,470. Fees, books, misc. academic expenses (school's estimate): $1,950.

PROFILE. Morehouse, founded in 1867, is a private, liberal arts college. Its 47-acre campus is located in downtown Atlanta.

Accreditation: SACS.

Religious orientation: Morehouse College is nonsectarian; one semester of religion required.

Library: Collections totaling over 500,000 volumes, 3,000 periodical subscriptions, and 100,000 microform items.

Athletic facilities: Athletic field, track, swimming pool, gymnasium, bowling alley.

STUDENT BODY. Freshman profile: 1% of freshmen who took SAT I scored 700 or over on verbal, 5% scored 700 or over on math; 13% scored 600 or over on verbal, 23% scored 600 or over on math; 52% scored 500 or over on verbal, 67% scored 500 or over on math; 100% scored 400 or over on verbal, 100% scored 400 or over on math. 79% of accepted applicants took SAT I; 21% took ACT. 74% of freshmen come from public schools.

Undergraduate achievement: 52% of entering class graduates.

Foreign students: 64 students are from out of the country. Countries represented include the Bahamas, Bangladesh, Bermuda, India, Pakistan, and Sierra Leone; 15 in all.

PROGRAMS OF STUDY. Degrees: B.A., B.S.

Majors: Accounting, Architecture, Art, Banking/Finance, Biology, Business Administration, Chemistry, Computer Science, Drama, Economics, Education, Engineering, English, French, German, Health/Physical Education, History, International Studies, Management, Marketing, Mathematics, Music, Philosophy, Physics, Political Science, Psychology, Real Estate, Religion, Social Welfare, Sociology, Spanish, Urban Studies.

Distribution of degrees: The majors with the highest enrollments are engineering, business administration, and biology/premedical; education, art, and German have the lowest.

Requirements: General education requirement.
Academic regulations: Minimum 2.0 GPA must be maintained.
Special: Minors offered in African studies, Afro-American studies, Caribbean studies, and library science. Courses offered in non-Western studies, Russian, and Swahili. Interdepartmental B.S. degree. Double majors. Dual degrees. Independent study. Internships. Cooperative education programs. Preprofessional programs in law, medicine, veterinary science, and dentistry. 3-2 engineering programs with Auburn U, Boston U, Georgia Tech, and Rochester Inst of Tech. Combined degree architecture program with U of Michigan. Member of Atlanta University Center Consortium, Associated Colleges of the South, and University Center of Georgia. Sea Semester. Exchange programs with Dartmouth Coll, U of California at San Diego, and Vassar Coll. Teacher certification in early childhood, elementary, and secondary education. Study abroad in England, Germany, Italy, Spain, and Zimbabwe. ROTC and NROTC. AFROTC at Georgia Tech.
Honors: Phi Beta Kappa. Honors program. Honor societies.
Academic Assistance: Remedial reading, math, and study skills. Nonremedial tutoring.

STUDENT LIFE. Housing: Freshmen encouraged to live on campus, but all students may live on or off campus. Men's dorms. School-owned/operated apartments. 55% of students live in college housing.
Services and counseling/handicapped student services: Placement services. Health service. Counseling services for military, veteran, and older students. Birth control, personal, and psychological counseling. Career and academic guidance services. Religious counseling. Learning disabled services.
Campus organizations: Undergraduate student government. Student newspaper (Maroon Tiger, published twice/month). Literary magazine. Yearbook. Glee club, marching band, jazz ensemble, King Players, forensics, Mathletes, 55 organizations in all. Six fraternities, no chapter houses. 3% of men join a fraternity.
Foreign student organizations: International Student Association.

ATHLETICS. Physical education requirements: Two semesters of physical education required.
Intercollegiate competition: 5% of students participate. Basketball (M), football (M), tennis (M), track (indoor) (M), track (outdoor) (M). Member of NCAA Division II, Southern Intercollegiate Athletic Conference.
Intramural and club sports: 1% of students participate. Intramural basketball, bowling, flag football, softball, swimming, track, volleyball.

ADMISSIONS. Academic basis for candidate selection (in order of priority): Secondary school record, standardized test scores, class rank, school's recommendation, essay.
Nonacademic basis for candidate selection: Character and personality and extracurricular participation are emphasized. Particular talent or ability and alumni/ae relationship are considered.
Requirements: Graduation from secondary school is required; GED is accepted. 16 units and the following program of study are required: 4 units of English, 3 units of math, 2 units of lab science, 2 units of social studies, 5 units of academic electives. Minimum combined SAT I score of 980 (composite ACT score of 21), rank in top half of secondary school class, and minimum 2.5 GPA required. Pre-college Summer Program for applicants not meeting standard requirements. SAT I is required; ACT may be substituted. Campus visit recommended. Off-campus interviews available with admissions and alumni representatives.
Procedure: Take SAT I or ACT by January of 12th year. Visit college for interview by November of 12th year. Suggest filing application by November 1. Application deadline is February 15. Notification of admission by April 1. Reply is required by May 1. $300 nonrefundable tuition deposit. Freshmen accepted for all terms.
Special programs: Admission may be deferred one year. Credit and/or placement may be granted through CEEB Advanced Placement exams for scores of 3 or higher. Credit and/or placement may be granted through CLEP general and subject exams. Placement may be granted through challenge exams and for military experience. Credit and placement may be granted through DANTES exams. Early decision program. Deadline for applying for early decision is December 15. Early entrance/early admission program. Concurrent enrollment program.

Transfer students: Transfer students accepted for all terms. In fall 1993, 4% of all new students were transfers into all classes. 497 transfer applications were received, 193 were accepted. Application deadline is February 15 for fall; October 1 for spring. Minimum 2.5 GPA required. Lowest course grade accepted is "C." At least 64 semester hours must be completed at the college to receive degree.

Admissions contact: Milford Green, Ph.D., Director of Admissions. 800 851-1254.

FINANCIAL AID. Available aid: Pell grants, SEOG, state scholarships and grants, school scholarships and grants, private scholarships and grants, ROTC scholarships, academic merit scholarships, athletic scholarships, and United Negro College Fund. Perkins Loans (NDSL), PLUS, Stafford Loans (GSL), and private loans. Tuition Plan Inc. and AMS.

Financial aid statistics: 35% of aid is not need-based. In 1993-94, 77% of all undergraduate aid applicants received aid; 62% of freshman aid applicants. Average amounts of aid awarded freshmen: Scholarships and grants, $3,000; loans, $2,500.

Supporting data/closing dates: FAFSA. FAF: Priority filing date is February 15; deadline is April 1. State aid form: Priority filing date is February 15. Income tax forms: Deadline is April 1. Notification of awards begins April 15.

Financial aid contact: Johnny Nimes, M.A., Director of Financial Aid. 404 215-2638.

STUDENT EMPLOYMENT. Federal Work-Study Program. Institutional employment. 18% of full-time undergraduates work on campus during school year. Students may expect to earn an average of $1,300 during school year. Off-campus part-time employment opportunities rated "fair."

COMPUTER FACILITIES. 250 IBM/IBM-compatible and Apple/Macintosh microcomputers. Students may access Digital, Prime, SUN minicomputer/mainframe systems. Residence halls may be equipped with stand-alone microcomputers, modems. Computer facilities are available to all students.

Fees: Computer fee is included in tuition/fees.

Hours: 9 AM-11 PM.

GRADUATE CAREER DATA. 31% of graduates choose careers in business and industry. Companies and businesses that hire graduates: Coca-Cola, Monsanto.

PROMINENT ALUMNI/AE. Martin Luther King, Jr., civil rights leader and Nobel Prize winner; Lerone Bennett, editor and historian; Maynard Jackson, mayor of Atlanta; Louis Sullivan, M.D., former secretary, U.S. Department of Health and Human Services; Edwin Moses, Olympic athlete; Spike Lee, filmmaker.

Morgan State University

Baltimore, MD 21239　　　　　　　　　　　　　　　　　**410 319-3333**

Undergraduate profile. 92% Black, 1% Asian-American, 1% Hispanic, 3% White, 3% Other. 58% are state residents; 18% are transfers. Average age of undergraduates is 19.

Enrollment. Undergraduates: 4,609 (full-time). Freshman class: 4,823 applicants, 2,223 accepted, 1,005 enrolled. Graduate enrollment: 410.

Test score averages/ranges. Average SAT I scores: 405 verbal, 441 math.

Faculty. 240 full-time, 100 part-time; 238 Black, 85 White, 17 Other. 80% of faculty holds doctoral degree. Student/faculty ratio: 18 to 1.

1995-96 Costs. Tuition: $2,832 (state residents), $6,462 (out-of-state). Room: $2,960. Board: $1,420-$1,880.

PROFILE. Morgan State, founded in 1867, is a public, comprehensive university. Programs are offered through the College of Arts and Sciences and the Schools of Business and Management, Education and Urban Studies, Engineering, and Graduate Studies. Its 122-acre campus is located in Baltimore, 37 miles north of Washington, D.C.

Accreditation: MSACS. Professionally accredited by the Accreditation Board for Engineering and Technology, Inc., the American Dietetic Association, the American Medical Association (CA-HEA), the Council on Social Work Education, the National Association of Schools of Art and Design, the National Association of Schools of Music, the National Council for Accreditation of Teacher Education.

Religious orientation: Morgan State University is nonsectarian; no religious requirements.

Library: Collections totaling 400,000 volumes, 2,003 periodical subscriptions, and 297,913 microform items.

Special facilities/museums: African-American collection, new science complex and school of engineering.

Athletic facilities: Field house, athletic center, gymnasium, stadium.

STUDENT BODY. Freshman profile: 99% of accepted applicants took SAT I; 1% took ACT.

Undergraduate achievement: 75% of fall 1993 freshmen returned for fall 1994 term.

Foreign students: 61 students are from out of the country. Countries represented include China, Korea, Nigeria, Trinidad, and the Virgin Islands; 48 in all.

PROGRAMS OF STUDY. Degrees: B.A., B.S.

Majors: Accounting, African-American Studies, Biology, Business Administration, Business Education, Chemistry, Civil Engineering, Computer Science, Economics, Electrical Engineering, Elementary Education, Engineering Physics, English, Finance, Fine Arts, French, Health Education, History, Human Ecology/Home Economics, Industrial Engineering, Information Sciences/Systems, Management, Marketing, Medical Technology, Mental Health, Music, Philosophy, Physical Education, Physics, Political Science, Psychology, Religious Studies, Social Work, Sociology, Spanish, Speech Communication, Telecommunication, Theatre Arts.

Distribution of degrees: The majors with the highest enrollments are business administration, accounting, and telecommunication; mental health has the lowest.

Requirements: General education requirement.

Academic regulations: Minimum 2.0 GPA must be maintained.

Special: Minors offered in food and nutrition. Dual degrees. Internships. Graduate school at which qualified undergraduates may take graduate-level courses. Preprofessional programs in law, medicine, pharmacy, dentistry, and physical therapy. 3-3 pharmacy honors program with U of Maryland. 3-4 predental and premedical programs with U of Maryland. Member of Historically Black Colleges and Universities. Cross-registration with Bowie State U, Coppin State Coll, Frostburg State Coll, Salisbury State Coll, U of Baltimore, and U of Maryland. Other cooperative programs with Goucher Coll, Johns Hopkins U, Loyola Coll, Coll of Notre Dame of Maryland, and Towson State U. Teacher certification in elementary and secondary education. Certification in specific subject areas. ROTC.

Honors: Honors program.

Academic Assistance: Remedial reading, writing, math, and study skills. Nonremedial tutoring.

STUDENT LIFE. Housing: Students may live on or off campus. Coed, women's, and men's dorms. School-owned/operated apartments. 30% of students live in college housing.

Services and counseling/handicapped student services: Health service. Counseling services for veteran students. Personal counseling. Career and academic guidance services. Physically disabled student services. Learning disabled services. Tutors.

Campus organizations: Undergraduate student government. Student newspaper (Spokesman, published twice/week). Yearbook. Radio station. Choir, Morgan Singers, marching band, symphonic band, symphony orchestra, drama group, dance club, Social Work Student Organization, American Marketing Association, Art Association, Commerce Club, departmental and special-interest groups, 25 organizations in all. Four fraternities, no chapter houses; four sororities, no chapter houses.

Religious organizations: Abundant Life Prayer Group, Apostolic Club, Baptist Club, Canterbury Club, Christian Center.

Foreign student organizations: International Student Association.

ATHLETICS. Physical education requirements: Two semesters of physical education required.

Intercollegiate competition: 3% of students participate. Basketball (M,W), cheerleading (M,W), cross-country (M,W), football (M), softball (W), tennis (M,W), track (indoor) (W), track and field (indoor) (M,W), track and field (outdoor) (M,W), volleyball (W), wrestling (M). Member of ECAC, Mid-Eastern Athletic Conference, NCAA Division I, NCAA Division I-AA for football.

Intramural and club sports: 5% of students participate. Intramural aerobics, basketball, football, weight lifting.

ADMISSIONS. Academic basis for candidate selection (in order of priority): Standardized test scores, secondary school record.

Nonacademic basis for candidate selection: Character and personality, extracurricular participation, and particular talent or ability are important. Alumni/ae relationship is considered.

Requirements: Graduation from secondary school is required; GED is accepted. The following program of study is recommended: 4 units of English, 3 units of math, 2 units of science, 1 unit of foreign language, 2 units of social studies, 2 units of history. Minimum combined SAT I score of 750 (composite ACT score of 18) and minimum 2.5 GPA required. Audition required of music program applicants. Connect Program with selected community colleges. SAT I or ACT is required. Campus visit and interview recommended. No off-campus interviews.

Procedure: Take SAT I or ACT by December of 12th year. Visit college for interview by February of 12th year. Suggest filing application by April 15. Application deadline is July 15. Notification of admission on rolling basis. $50 refundable tution deposit. $100 refundable room deposit. Freshmen accepted for all terms.

Special programs: Admission may be deferred one year. Credit may be granted through CEEB Advanced Placement for scores of 3 or higher. Credit may be granted through CLEP general and subject exams. Early decision program. Early entrance/early admission program. Concurrent enrollment program.

Transfer students: Transfer students accepted for all terms. In fall 1994, 18% of all new students were transfers into all classes. 1,104 transfer applications were received, 548 were accepted. Application deadline is April 15 for fall; December 1 for spring. Minimum 2.0 GPA required. Lowest course grade accepted is "C." Maximum number of transferable credits is 70 semester hours. At least 30 semester hours must be completed at the university to receive degree.

Admissions contact: Chelseia Harold Miller, M.P.A., Director of Admission and Recruitment. 410 319-3000.

FINANCIAL AID. Available aid: Pell grants, SEOG, state scholarships and grants, school scholarships and grants, private scholarships, ROTC scholarships, academic merit scholarships, athletic scholarships, and United Negro College Fund. Other race-based grants. Perkins Loans (NDSL), PLUS, Stafford Loans (GSL), state loars, and school loans. AMS and deferred payment plan.

Financial aid statistics: In 1993-94, 82% of all undergraduate aid applicants received aid; 80% of freshman aid applicants.

Supporting data/closing dates: FAFSA/FAF: Priority filing date is April 1. School's own aid application: Priority filing date is April 1. State aid form: Priority filing date is April 1. Income tax forms: Priority filing date is April 1. Notification of awards on rolling basis.

Financial aid contact: Reginald Cureton, M.S., Director of Financial Aid. 410 319-3170.

STUDENT EMPLOYMENT. Federal Work-Study Program. Institutional employment. Students may expect to earn an average of $2,000 during school year. Off-campus part-time employment opportunities rated "good."

COMPUTER FACILITIES. IBM/IBM-compatible and Apple/Macintosh microcomputers. Students may access Digital minicomputer/mainframe systems, Internet. Residence halls may be equipped with networked microcomputers. Client/LAN operating systems include DOS, Windows NT. Some microcomputers are restricted to departmental use.

Fees: None.

Hours: 9 AM-10 PM (M-F); 9 AM-4 PM (Sa).

GRADUATE CAREER DATA. Highest graduate school enrollments: Howard U, Morgan State U, and U of Maryland. 60% of graduates choose careers in business and industry. Companies and businesses that hire graduates: Allstate, Citicorp, Ford, Maryland National Bank, Social Security Administration, Westinghouse.

PROMINENT ALUMNI/AE. Darren J. Mitchell, former U.S. congressman; Kweisi Mfume, U.S. congressman; Joe Black, vice president, Greyhound; Yvonne Kennedy, president, S.D. Bishop Junior College; Wilson Goode, mayor, Philadelphia; Earl Graves, publisher, *Black Enterprise* magazine.

Morris Brown College
Atlanta, GA 30314   **404 220-0270**

Undergraduate profile. 98% Black, .7% Asian-American, .6% Native American, .7% White. 56% are state residents; 18% are transfers. Average age of undergraduates is 19.

Enrollment. Undergraduates: 791 men, 1,040 women (full-time). Freshman class: 3,307 applicants, 1,877 accepted, 720 enrolled.

Faculty. 94 full-time; 31 part-time. 70% of faculty holds doctoral degree. Student/faculty ratio: 14 to 1.

Test score averages/ranges. Average SAT I scores: 313 verbal, 345 math.

1995-96 Costs. Tuition: $7,244. Room & board: $4,750. Fees, books, misc. academic expenses (school's estimate): $1,544.

PROFILE. Morris Brown, founded in 1881, is a private, church-affiliated, historically Black college. Programs are offered through the Divisions of Education and Psychology, Humanities, Natural Science and Mathematics, and Social Science. Its 18-acre campus is located in Atlanta.

Accreditation: SACS.

Religious orientation: Morris Brown College is affiliated with the African Methodist Episcopal Church; no religious requirements.

Library: Collections totaling 366,407 volumes, 45,659 periodical subscriptions, and 233,796 microform items.

Special facilities/museums: Art gallery, language lab, electron microscope.

STUDENT BODY. Freshman profile: Majority of accepted applicants took SAT I. 90% of freshmen come from public schools.

Undergraduate achievement: 20% of students who complete a degree program immediately go on to graduate study.

Foreign students: 120 students are from out of the country. Countries represented include the Bahamas, Bermuda, Canada, Jamaica, Japan, and Nigeria; 26 in all.

PROGRAMS OF STUDY. Degrees: B.A., B.S.

Majors: Accounting, Allied Health, Art, Biology, Business Administration, Business Management, Chemistry, Computer Science, Criminal Justice, Early Childhood Education, Economics, Engineering, History, Hospitality Administration, Information Processing, Marketing, Mass Communications, Mathematics, Music, Nursing, Paralegal Studies, Political Science, Psychology, Religion, Sociology, Spanish, Therapeutic Recreation.

Distribution of degrees: The majors with the highest enrollments are business administration, mass communications, and education; chemistry, mathematics, and economics have the lowest.

Requirements: General education requirement.

Academic regulations: Minimum 2.0 GPA must be maintained.

Special: Minors offered in some majors and in analysis, computer/information science, English language and literature, information processing management, and recreation. All students in first two years follow prescribed distribution of courses in lower division; upper division is designed for specialization. Dual degrees. Preprofessional programs in medicine, pharmacy, and dentistry. Combined degree programs in architecture, building construction, industrial design, and engineering with Georgia Tech. 3-3 program in law with St. John U; 3-3 program in medicine with Boston U. Member of Atlanta University Center Consortium. Teacher certification in early childhood, elementary, and special education. ROTC, NROTC, and AFROTC.

Academic Assistance: Remedial reading, writing, math, and study skills.

STUDENT LIFE. Housing: Freshmen must live on campus. Women's and men's dorms. 37% of students live in college housing.

Services and counseling/handicapped student services: Placement services. Health service. Counseling services for veteran students. Birth control, personal, and psychological counseling. Career and academic guidance services. Religious counseling. Physically disabled student services. Learning disabled services. Notetaking services.

Campus organizations: Undergraduate student government. Student newspaper (Wolverine Observer, published once/month). Yearbook. Choir, glee clubs, orchestra, band, drama league, Sinfonette Society, debating club, academic groups, Association for Computer Machinery, Florida Club, Hospitality Management Association, Panhellenic Council, Pre-Alumni Council, 102 organizations in all. Four fraternities, no chapter houses; four sororities, no chapter houses. 50% of men join a fraternity. 50% of women join a sorority.

Religious organizations: Several religious associations.

Foreign student organizations: International Student Organization.

ATHLETICS. Physical education requirements: Two semesters of physical education required.

Intercollegiate competition: Basketball (M,W), cross-country (M,W), football (M), tennis (M,W), track (indoor) (M,W), track (outdoor) (M,W), volleyball (W). Member of NCAA Division II.

Intramural and club sports: Intramural basketball, bowling, chess, pool, table tennis, tag football, volleyball.

ADMISSIONS. Academic basis for candidate selection (in order of priority): Secondary school record, standardized test scores, class rank, school's recommendation, essay.

Nonacademic basis for candidate selection: Character and personality, extracurricular participation, particular talent or ability, and alumni/ae relationship are considered.

Requirements: Graduation from secondary school is required; GED is accepted. 12 units and the following program of study are required: 4 units of English, 3 units of math, 3 units of science, 2 units of social studies. Minimum 2.0 GPA required. Conditional admission possible for applicants not meeting standard requirements. SAT I or ACT is required. Campus visit recommended. No off-campus interviews.

Procedure: Take SAT I or ACT by November 15 of 12th year. Suggest filing application by June 30, for fall; Dec. 1 for spring. Notification of admission on rolling basis. $300 partially refundable room deposit for freshmen; $250 partially refundable room deposit for upperclass students. Freshmen accepted for all terms.

Special programs: Admission may be deferred one year. Credit and/or placement may be granted through CLEP general and subject exams. Early entrance/early admission program. Concurrent enrollment program.

Transfer students: Transfer students accepted for all terms. In fall 1994, 18% of all new students were transfers into all classes. Application deadline is June 30 for fall; December 1 for spring. Minimum 2.0 GPA required. Lowest course grade accepted is "C." Maximum number of transferable credits is 92 semester hours. At least 32 semester hours must be completed at the college to receive degree.

Admissions contact: Rev. Debra Grant, M.Div., Director of Enrollment Management. 404 220-0152.

FINANCIAL AID. Available aid: Pell grants, SEOG, state scholarships and grants, school scholarships, private scholarships and grants, ROTC scholarships, academic merit scholarships, athletic scholarships, and United Negro College Fund. Perkins Loans (NDSL), PLUS, Stafford Loans (GSL), unsubsidized Stafford Loans, and state loans. AMS and Tuition Management Systems.

Financial aid statistics: 13% of aid is not need-based. In 1994-95, 86% of all undergraduate aid applicants received aid; 81% of freshman aid applicants. Average amounts of aid awarded freshmen: Scholarships and grants, $3,044; loans, $3,000.

Supporting data/closing dates: FAFSA/FAF: Priority filing date is March 15; accepted on rolling basis; deadline is June 30. School's own aid application: Priority filing date is March 15; accepted on rolling basis. State aid form: Priority filing date is March 15; accepted on rolling basis; deadline is August 15. Income tax forms: Priority filing date is March 15; accepted on rolling basis; deadline is August 30. Notification of awards begins April 15.

Financial aid contact: Willie Williams, M.S., Director of Financial Aid. 404 220-0133.

STUDENT EMPLOYMENT. Federal Work-Study Program. Institutional employment. 8% of full-time undergraduates work on campus during school year. Students may expect to earn an average of $1,500 during school year. Off-campus part-time employment opportunities rated "excellent."

COMPUTER FACILITIES. 100 IBM/IBM-compatible and Apple/Macintosh microcomputers; all are networked. Students may access IBM minicomputer/mainframe systems. Residence halls may be equipped with stand-alone microcomputers. Client/LAN operating systems include Apple/Macintosh, DOS, Windows NT, Novell. Computer facilities are available to all students. **Fees:** None.

GRADUATE CAREER DATA. Graduate school percentages: 4% enter medical school. 4% enter dental school. 10% enter graduate business programs. 5% enter graduate arts and sciences programs. Highest graduate school enrollments: Clark Atlanta U, U of Georgia. Companies and businesses that hire graduates: AT&T, Atlanta Gas Light Company, Atlanta Board of Education, Bell South, Delta Airlines, Georgia Power, IBM, Mobil Oil, Northfolk Southern Railway, United Parcel Service, Xerox.

PROMINENT ALUMNI/AE. James McPherson, Pulitzer Prize-winning author; Rachelle and James G. Reddick, prominent in nuclear energy field; Beverly J. Harvard, chief of police, Atlanta; Calvin Mapp, judge, Dade County, Florida; Robert James, bank president; Mary Taylor Williams, M.D., neurosurgeon.

Morris College
Sumter, SC 29150-3599   803 775-9371

Undergraduate profile. 100% Black. 93% are state residents; 5% are transfers. Average age of undergraduates is 21.

Enrollment. Undergraduates: 309 men, 567 women (full-time). Freshman class: 874 applicants, 522 accepted, 249 enrolled.

Faculty. 46 full-time, 17 part-time; 40 Black, 20 White, 3 Other. 51% of faculty holds doctoral degree. Student/faculty ratio: 16 to 1.

Test score averages/ranges. N/A.

1995-96 Costs. Tuition: $4,752. Room & board: $2,601. Fees, books, misc. academic expenses (school's estimate): $1,065.

PROFILE. Morris, founded in 1908, is a private, church-affiliated, historically Black college. Programs are offered through the Divisions of Business Administration, Education, General Studies, Humanities, Natural Sciences and Mathematics, and Social Sciences, History, and Pre-Law Studies. Its 34-acre campus is located in Sumter, east of Columbia.

Accreditation: SACS.

Religious orientation: Morris College is affiliated with the Baptist Church; two semesters of religion required.

Library: Collections totaling 111,630 volumes, 765 periodical subscriptions, 152,243 microform items, one CD-ROM, and 3,022 audiovisual items.

Special facilities/museums: Satellite, commercial radio station.

Athletic facilities: Gymnasium, athletic field.

STUDENT BODY.

Freshman profile: 97% of freshmen come from public schools.

Undergraduate achievement: 56% of fall 1993 freshmen returned for fall 1994 term. 18% of entering class graduates. 10% of students who complete a degree program immediately go on to graduate study.

PROGRAMS OF STUDY. Degrees: B.A., B.F.A., B.S., B.S.Ed.

Majors: Biology, Biology Teaching, Broadcast Media, Business Administration, Community Health, Criminal Justice, Early Childhood Education, Elementary Education, English, English Education, History, History Education, Journalism, Liberal Studies, Liberal/Technical Studies, Mathematics, Mathematics Education, Political Science/History, Recreation Administration, Social Studies, Social Studies Education, Sociology.

Distribution of degrees: The majors with the highest enrollments are business administration, sociology, and political science/history; social studies, criminal justice, and early childhood education have the lowest.

Requirements: General education requirement.

Academic regulations: Freshmen must maintain minimum 1.2 GPA; sophomores, 1.5 GPA; juniors, 1.7 GPA; seniors, 2.0 GPA.

Special: Minors offered in some majors and in accounting, computer information science, gerontology, international relations, management, marketing, media arts, minority studies, music, office administration, pre-law, and religious education. Double majors. Internships. Cooperative education programs. Preprofessional programs in law, medicine, veterinary science, pharmacy, dentistry, and nursing. Teacher certification in early childhood, elementary, and secondary education. Certification in specific subject areas. ROTC.

Honors: Honors program. Honor societies.

Academic Assistance: Remedial reading, writing, math, and study skills. Nonremedial tutoring.

STUDENT LIFE. Housing: Students may live on or off campus. Women's and men's dorms. 74% of students live in college housing.

Services and counseling/handicapped student services: Placement services. Health service. Counseling services for military, veteran, and older students. Birth control and personal counseling. Career and academic guidance services.

Campus organizations: Undergraduate student government. Student newspaper (Heritage, published six times/year). Literary magazine. Yearbook. Radio station. NAACP. Chorale, gospel choir, College Players, Literary Society, Library Club, Block "M" Club, academic clubs, National Student Business League, chess club, cheerleaders, veterans, pre-alumni clubs, co-op club, Men's Senate, Women's Senate, health science club, 33 organizations in all. Four fraternities, no chapter houses; four sororities, no chapter houses. 5% of men join a fraternity. 5% of women join a sorority.

Religious organizations: Baptist Student Union, Durham Ministerial Union.

ATHLETICS. Physical education requirements: None.

Intercollegiate competition: 1% of students participate. Baseball (M), basketball (M,W), softball (W), track (outdoor) (M,W). Member of EIAC, NAIA.

Intramural and club sports: Intramural baseball, basketball, flag football, softball, tennis.

ADMISSIONS. Academic basis for candidate selection (in order of priority): Secondary school record, class rank, standardized test scores.

Nonacademic basis for candidate selection: Character and personality are emphasized. Extracurricular participation, particular talent or ability, geographical distribution, and alumni/ae relationship are considered.

Requirements: Graduation from secondary school is required; GED is accepted. 20 units and the following program of study are required: 4 units of English, 3 units of math, 2 units of science, 2 units of social studies, 1 unit of history, 8 units of electives including 7 units of academic electives. Completion of 60 credit hours (with minimum 2.5 GPA) and EEE required for admission to teacher education program. SAT I or ACT is recommended. Campus visit and interview recommended. Off-campus interviews available with an admissions representative.

Procedure: Take SAT I or ACT by January of 12th year. Notification of admission on rolling basis. $25 room deposit. Freshmen accepted for all terms.

Special programs: Admission may be deferred one semester. Credit may be granted through CLEP general and subject exams. Credit may be granted for military experience.

Transfer students: Transfer students accepted for all terms. In fall 1994, 5% of all new students were transfers into all classes. 90 transfer applications were received, 41 were accepted. Application deadline is rolling for fall; rolling for spring. Minimum 2.0 GPA required. Lowest course grade accepted is "C." Maximum number of transferable credits is 94 semester hours. At least 30 semester hours must be completed at the college to receive degree.

Admissions contact: Queen W. Spann, M.Ed., Admissions and Records Officer. 803 775-9371, extension 225.

FINANCIAL AID. Available aid: Pell grants, SEOG, state scholarships and grants, school scholarships and grants, private scholarships and grants, ROTC scholarships, academic merit scholarships, athletic scholarships, and United Negro College Fund. Perkins Loans (NDSL), PLUS, Stafford Loans (GSL), state loans, and private loans. Federal Direct Student Loans.

Financial aid statistics: 10% of aid is not need-based. In 1994-95, 100% of all undergraduate aid applicants received aid; 100% of freshman aid applicants. Average amounts of aid awarded freshmen: Scholarships and grants, $3,810; loans, $2,625.

Supporting data/closing dates: FAFSA: Priority filing date is March 30. School's own aid application: Priority filing date is April 30. State aid form: Priority filing date is April 30. Income tax forms: Priority filing date is April 30. Notification of awards on rolling basis.

Financial aid contact: Sandra S. Gibson, M.Ed., Director of Financial Aid. 803 775-9371, extension 238.

STUDENT EMPLOYMENT. Federal Work-Study Program. Institutional employment. 50% of full-time undergraduates work on campus during school year. Students may expect to earn an average of $1,800 during school year. Off-campus part-time employment opportunities rated "good."

COMPUTER FACILITIES. 121 IBM/IBM-compatible and Apple/Macintosh microcomputers; 56 are networked. Students may access Digital minicomputer/mainframe systems. Client/LAN operating systems include DOS, Novell. Computer facilities are available to all students.

Fees: $50 computer fee per semester; included in tuition/fees.

Hours: 8 AM-10 PM (M-Th); 8 AM-5 PM (F); 9 AM-4 PM (Sa); 3-9 PM (Su).

GRADUATE CAREER DATA. Graduate school percentages: 10% enter graduate arts and sciences programs. Highest graduate school enrollments: Bowling Green State U, Ohio State U, South Carolina State U, and U of South Carolina. 20% of graduates choose careers in business and industry.

PROMINENT ALUMNI/AE. Margaret W. Davis, chair, Sumter School Board of Trustees; Ralph W. Lanty, director, Job's Mortuary, legislator/minister.

Norfolk State University

Norfolk, VA 23504   **804 683-8600**

Undergraduate profile. 80% Black, 17% White, 3% Other. 70% are state residents; 23% are transfers. Average age of undergraduates is 26.

Enrollment. Undergraduates: 2,425 men, 3,821 women (full-time). Freshman class: 2,950 applicants, 2,901 accepted, 1,154 enrolled. Graduate enrollment: 318 men, 1,097 women.

Faculty. 411 full-time, 193 part-time; 400 Black, 130 White, 74 Other. 57% of faculty holds doctoral degree. Student/faculty ratio: 22 to 1.

Test score averages/ranges. N/A.

1995-96 Costs. Tuition: $2,865 (state residents), $6,392 (out-of-state). Room: $3,720-$4,720. Board: $1,620. Fees, books, misc. academic expenses (school's estimate): $400.

PROFILE. Norfolk State, founded in 1935, is a public, historically Black university. Programs are offered through the Schools of Arts and Letters, Business, Education, General and Continuing Education, Health-Related Professions and Sciences, Social Sciences, Social Work, and Technology. Its 110-acre campus is located in Norfolk, the center of the state's Tidewater region.

Accreditation: SACS. Professionally accredited by the American Assembly of Collegiate Schools of Business, the American Psychological Association, the Committee on Allied Health Education and Accreditation, the Computing Sciences Accreditation Board, the Council on Social Work Education, the National Association of Schools of Music, the National Council for Accreditation of Teacher Education, the National League for Nursing.

Religious orientation: Norfolk State University is nonsectarian; no religious requirements.

Library: Collections totaling 318,829 volumes, 1,289 periodical subscriptions, and 71,786 microform items.

Athletic facilities: Basketball, racquetball, and tennis courts, baseball, football, and softball fields, gymnasiums, swimming pool.

STUDENT BODY. Undergraduate achievement: 60% of fall 1993 freshmen returned for fall 1994 term.

Foreign students: 100 students are from out of the country.

PROGRAMS OF STUDY. Degrees: B.A., B.Mus., B.S., B.Soc.Work.

Majors: Accounting, Administrative Systems Management, Biology, Building Construction Technology, Business, Business Education, Chemistry, Computer Science, Computer Technology, Consumer Service, Design Technology, Early Childhood Education, Economics, Electronic Technology, Electronics Engineering, English, Fine Arts, Foreign Languages, Health Education, Health Information Management, Health Services Management, History, Home Economics, Hotel/Restaurant/Institutional Management, Industrial Electronics Technology, Interdisciplinary Studies, Journalism, Mass Communications, Mathematics, Medical Technology, Mental Retardation, Music Media, Nursing, Personnel/Industrial Relations, Physical Education/Exercise Science, Physics, Political Science, Psychology, Public School Music, Recreation, Social Work, Sociology, Speech Pathology/Audiology, Vocational Industrial Education.

Distribution of degrees: The majors with the highest enrollments are business, mass communications, and nursing.

Requirements: General education requirement.

Special: Associate degrees offered. Accelerated study. Internships. Cooperative education programs. Graduate school at which qualified undergraduates may take graduate-level courses. Preprofessional programs in law and medicine. 2-2 programs with Southside Virginia Comm Coll, Northern Virginia Comm Coll, Tidewater Comm Coll, and Thomas Nelson Comm Coll. Member of Tidewater Consortium. Teacher certification in early childhood, elementary, secondary, and special education. ROTC and NROTC.

Honors: Honors program. Honor societies.

Academic Assistance: Remedial reading, writing, and math. Nonremedial tutoring.

STUDENT LIFE. Housing: Students may live on or off campus. Women's and men's dorms. 21% of students live in college housing.

Services and counseling/handicapped student services: Placement services. Health service. Personal counseling. Academic guidance services.

Campus organizations: Undergraduate student government. Student newspaper (Spartan Echo, published once/week). Yearbook. Radio station. NAACP. Choir, gospel choir, sextet, bands, brass and saxophone ensembles, opera workshops, Norfolk State Players, debating, athletic, departmental, and special-interest groups. Eight fraternities, no chapter houses; seven sororities, no chapter houses.

Religious organizations: Christian Fellowship.

Foreign student organizations: International Students Union.

ATHLETICS. Physical education requirements: One semester of physical education required.

Intercollegiate competition: 10% of students participate. Baseball (M), basketball (M,W), cheerleading (M,W), cross-country (M,W), football (M), softball (W), tennis (M), track (indoor) (M,W), track (outdoor) (M,W), track and field (indoor) (M,W), track and field (outdoor) (M,W), volleyball (W), wrestling (M). Member of Central Intercollegiate Athletic Association, NCAA Division II.

Intramural and club sports: 70% of students participate. Intramural basketball, football, softball, track and field, volleyball.

ADMISSIONS. Academic basis for candidate selection (in order of priority): Secondary school record, standardized test scores, school's recommendation, class rank.

Nonacademic basis for candidate selection: Character and personality, extracurricular participation, particular talent or ability, and alumni/ae relationship are considered.

Requirements: Graduation from secondary school is required; GED is accepted. 23 units and the following program of study are recommended: 4 units of English, 2 units of math, 2 units of science, 3 units of history, 9 units of electives, 3 units health/physical education. Minimum 2.0 GPA recommended. 2 units of science required of nursing program applicants. 2 units of math (including algebra) required of computer science program applicants. Special services program for applicants not normally admissible. SAT I or ACT is required. Campus visit and interview recommended. No off-campus interviews.

Procedure: Take SAT I or ACT by January of 12th year. Notification of admission on rolling basis. $50 room deposit. Freshmen accepted for all terms.

Special programs: Credit may be granted through CEEB Advanced Placement for scores of 3 or higher. Credit may be granted through CLEP general and subject exams. Credit may be granted through DANTES exams and for military experience. Placement may be granted through challenge exams.

Transfer students: Transfer students accepted for all terms. In fall 1994, 23% of all new students were transfers into all classes. 871 transfer applications were received, 827 were accepted. Minimum 2.0 GPA required. Lowest course grade accepted is "C."

Admissions contact: Frank Cool, Director of Admissions. 804 683-8396.

FINANCIAL AID. Available aid: Pell grants, SEOG, state scholarships and grants, school scholarships, private scholarships and grants, ROTC scholarships, and athletic scholarships. Perkins Loans (NDSL), Stafford Loans (GSL), and state loans. Tuition Plan Inc. and deferred payment plan.

Financial aid statistics: In 1994-95, 75% of all undergraduate aid applicants received aid; 85% of freshman aid applicants. Average amounts of aid awarded freshmen: Scholarships and grants, $5,850.

Supporting data/closing dates: FAFSA: Deadline is April 1. School's own aid application: Deadline is April 1. Income tax forms.

Financial aid contact: Estherine Harding, Director of Financial Aid. 804 683-8381.

STUDENT EMPLOYMENT. Federal Work-Study Program. Institutional employment. Off-campus part-time employment opportunities rated "good."

COMPUTER FACILITIES. 1,519 IBM/IBM-compatible and Apple/Macintosh microcomputers; 500 are networked. Students may access AT&T, Cray, Digital minicomputer/mainframe systems, Internet. Residence halls may be equipped with modems. Client/LAN operating systems include Apple/Macintosh, DOS, OS/2, UNIX/XENIX/AIX, Windows NT, X-windows, DEC, LocalTalk/AppleTalk, Novell. Computer facilities are available to all students.

Fees: None.

North Carolina Agricultural and Technical State University

Greensboro, NC 27411　　　　　910 334-7500

Undergraduate profile. 91% Black, .8% Asian-American, .2% Hispanic, .2% Native American, 7.3% White, .5% Other. 83% are state residents; 22% are transfers. Average age of undergraduates is 21.

Enrollment. Undergraduates: 3,106 men, 3,138 women (full-time). Freshman class: 4,507 applicants, 2,817 accepted, 1,356 enrolled. Graduate enrollment: 492 men, 504 women.

Faculty. 430 full-time, 77 part-time; 291 Black, 149 White, 67 Other. 62% of faculty holds doctoral degree. Student/faculty ratio: 16 to 1.

Test score averages/ranges. Average SAT I scores: 387 verbal, 447 math. Range of SAT I scores of middle 50%: 350-399 verbal, 400-449 math. Average ACT scores: 18 composite.

1994-95 Costs. Tuition: $1,430 (state residents), $7,914 (out-of-state). Room & board: $3,130. Fees, books, misc. academic expenses (school's estimate): $600.

PROFILE. North Carolina A&T State, founded in 1891, is a public, historically Black university. Programs are offered through the Schools of Agriculture, Arts and Sciences, Business, Education, Engineering, Nursing, and Technology. Its 187-acre campus is located in Greensboro, 90 miles north of Charlotte.

Accreditation: SACS. Professionally accredited by the Accreditation Board for Engineering and Technology, Inc., the American Assembly of Collegiate Schools of Business, the American Home Economics Association, the Council on Social Work Education, the National Association of Schools of Music, the National Council for Accreditation of Teacher Education, the National League for Nursing.

Religious orientation: North Carolina Agricultural and Technical State University is nonsectarian; no religious requirements.

Special facilities/museums: Art gallery, African heritage center, child development laboratory, microelectronics center of North Carolina, planetarium, herbarium.

Athletic facilities: Swimming pool, gymnasium, basketball, racquetball, and volleyball courts, weight lifting facility, track, football stadium.

STUDENT BODY. Freshman profile: 1% of freshmen who took SAT I scored 700 or over on math; 1% scored 600 or over on verbal, 4% scored 600 or over on math; 7% scored 500 or over on verbal, 24% scored 500 or over on math; 36% scored 400 or over on verbal, 58% scored 400 or over on math; 75% scored 300 or over on verbal, 82% scored 300 or over on math. 81% of accepted applicants took SAT I; 18% took ACT.

Undergraduate achievement: 74% of fall 1993 freshmen returned for fall 1994 term.

Foreign students: Countries represented include the Bahamas, China, India, Nigeria, Pakistan, and South Africa; 39 in all.

PROGRAMS OF STUDY. Degrees: B.A., B.F.A., B.S., B.S.Nurs., B.Soc.Work.

Majors: Accounting, Administrative Services, Agricultural Education, Agricultural Engineering, Agricultural Science, Agricultural Technology, Architectural Engineering, Biology, Business Education, Business Finance, Business Management, Business Marketing, Chemical Engineering, Chemistry, Child Development, Clothing/Textiles, Computer Science, Driver/Safety Education, Early Childhood Education, Economics, Education, Electrical Engineering, Electronics, Engineering Mathematics, Engineering Physics, English, Food Administration, Food/Nutrition, French, Graphics Communications, Health/Physical Education, History, Home Economics Education, Industrial Arts Education, Industrial Education, Industrial Engineering, Industrial Technology, Laboratory Animal Technology, Landscape Architecture, Manufacturing, Mathematics, Mechanical Engineering, Music, Nursing, Occupational Safety/Health, Physics, Political Science, Professional Theatre, Psychology, Recreation Administration, Social Sciences, Social Services, Sociology, Speech, Transportation, Vocational Education, Vocational Industrial Education.

Distribution of degrees: The majors with the highest enrollments are accounting, electrical engineering, and industrial technology; French, physics, and agricultural technology have the lowest.

Requirements: General education requirement.

Academic regulations: Minimum 2.0 GPA must be maintained.

Special: Double majors. Internships. Cooperative education programs. Graduate school at which qualified undergraduates may take graduate-level courses. Member of Piedmont Independent College Association of North Carolina. Teacher certification in early childhood, elementary, secondary, special education, and vo-tech education. Certification in specific subject areas. Study abroad in England, France, and Mexico. ROTC and AFROTC.

Honors: Honors program. Honor societies.

Academic Assistance: Remedial reading, writing, and math. Nonremedial tutoring.

STUDENT LIFE. Housing: Students may live on or off campus. Women's and men's dorms. Honor student housing. 36% of students live in college housing.

Services and counseling/handicapped student services: Placement services. Health service. Personal and psychological counseling. Academic guidance services. Religious counseling. Physically disabled student services. Learning disabled services. Notetaking services. Tape recorders. Tutors. Reader services for the blind.

Campus organizations: Minority Student Association. Undergraduate student government. Student newspaper (A&T Register, published once/week). Yearbook. Radio station. Richard B. Harrison Players, senior band, symphony concert band, choirs, Fellowship Gospel Choir, departmental groups, 150 organizations in all. Four fraternities, no chapter houses; four sororities, no chapter houses. 1% of men join a fraternity. 1% of women join a sorority.

Religious organizations: Brothers in Christ, Sisters of Brothers in Christ, Newman Club, Wesley Foundation, University Usher Board.

Foreign student organizations: International Student Association.

ATHLETICS. Physical education requirements: Two semesters of physical education required.

Intercollegiate competition: 3% of students participate. Baseball (M), basketball (M,W), cheerleading (M,W), cross-country (M,W), football (M), softball (W), tennis (M,W), track (indoor) (M,W), track (outdoor) (M,W), track and field (indoor) (M,W), track and field (outdoor) (M,W), volleyball (W). Member of Mid Eastern Athletic Conference, NCAA Division I, NCAA Division I-AA for football.

Intramural and club sports: 8% of students participate. Intramural aerobics, basketball, billiards, bowling, dance, football, softball, swimming, tennis, track, volleyball.

ADMISSIONS. Academic basis for candidate selection (in order of priority): Secondary school record, standardized test scores, class rank, school's recommendation.

Requirements: Graduation from secondary school is required; GED is not accepted. 16 units and the following program of study are required: 4 units of English, 3 units of math, 3 units of science including 1 unit of lab, 2 units of social studies, 4 units of academic electives. Secondary school units must include biology and history. Minimum 2.0 GPA recommended of in-state applicants; minimum combined SAT I score of 800 (composite ACT score of 21) and minimum 2.5 GPA recommended of out-of-state applicants. 2 units of algebra, 1/2 unit of plane geometry, and 1/2 unit of trigonometry required of business, economics, and science program applicants. Audition required of fine arts program applicants. SAT I or ACT is required.

Procedure: Take SAT I or ACT by December of 12th year. Notification of admission on rolling basis. Reply is required by May 1. $75 refundable room deposit. Freshmen accepted for all terms.

Special programs: Credit may be granted through CEEB Advanced Placement for scores of 3 or higher. Credit may be granted through CLEP general and subject exams. Credit may be granted through DANTES exams and for military experience. Credit and placement may be granted through challenge exams.

Transfer students: Transfer students accepted for all terms. In fall 1994, 22% of all new students were transfers into all classes. 824 transfer applications were received, 656 were accepted. Application deadline is June 1 for fall; December 1 for spring. Minimum 2.0 GPA required. Lowest course grade accepted is "C." Maximum number of transferable credits is 62 semester hours. At least 36 semester hours must be completed at the university to receive degree.

Admissions contact: John F. Smith, M.S., Director of Admissions. 910 334-7946.

FINANCIAL AID. Available aid: Pell grants, SEOG, Federal Nursing Student Scholarships, state scholarships and grants, school scholarships and grants, private scholarships and grants, ROTC scholarships, academic merit scholarships, and athletic scholarships. Perkins Loans (NDSL), PLUS, Stafford Loans (GSL), Health Professions Loans, state loans, and private loans. Deferred payment plan.

Financial aid statistics: 24% of aid is not need-based. In 1994-95, 74% of all undergraduate aid applicants received aid. Average amounts of aid awarded freshmen: Loans, $1,800.

Supporting data/closing dates: FAFSA: Priority filing date is March 15. Notification of awards on rolling basis.

Financial aid contact: Renee H. Martin, M.B.A., Acting Director of Financial Aid. 910 334-7973.

STUDENT EMPLOYMENT. Federal Work-Study Program. Institutional employment. 14% of full-time undergraduates work on campus during school year. Students may expect to earn an average of $1,863 during school year. Off-campus part-time employment opportunities rated "good."

COMPUTER FACILITIES. 325 IBM/IBM-compatible and Apple/Macintosh microcomputers; 75 are networked. Students may access Digital minicomputer/mainframe systems, Internet. Client/ LAN operating systems include UNIX/XENIX/AIX, Windows NT, DEC, Novell. Computer facilities are available to all students.

Fees: None.

Hours: 8 AM-midn. (M-F); 8 AM-5 PM (Sa).

PROMINENT ALUMNI/AE. Dr. Ronald McNair, astronaut; Col. Clara Adams-Ender, chief Army nurse; Lou Donaldson, jazz musician and composer; Henry E. Frye, associate justice, North Carolina supreme court; Dr. Dwight Davis, coronary medicine; Hon. Adolphus Towns, congressman, New York State; Rev. Jesse Jackson.

North Carolina Central University

Durham, NC 27707

919 560-6100

Undergraduate profile. 93% Black, 6% White, 1% Other. 86% are state residents; 3% are transfers. Average age of undergraduates is 22.

Enrollment. Undergraduates: 1,355 men, 2,224 women (full-time). Freshman class: 2,707 applicants, 2,015 accepted, 855 enrolled. Graduate enrollment: 450 men, 867 women.

Faculty. 275 full-time, 103 part-time; 175 Black, 86 White, 14 Other. 63% of faculty holds doctoral degree. Student/faculty ratio: 15 to 1.

Test score averages/ranges. Average SAT I scores: 371 verbal, 410 math. Range of SAT I scores of middle 50%: 320-410 verbal, 360-450 math. Average ACT scores: 16 composite. Range of ACT scores of middle 50%: 14-17 composite.

1995-96 Costs. Tuition: $1,650 (state residents), $8,800 (out-of-state). Room & board: $3,355.

PROFILE. North Carolina Central is a public, comprehensive university. Founded in 1909 as a private institution, it joined the state system in 1923. Its 72-acre campus is located in Durham, 25 miles northwest of Raleigh.

Accreditation: SACS.

Religious orientation: North Carolina Central University is nonsectarian; no religious requirements.

Library: Collections totaling 600,422 volumes, 4,182 periodical subscriptions, and 67,867 microform items.

Special facilities/museums: Treasury Room collection of primary resources on Black life and culture, art museum with works of Afro-American culture.

Athletic facilities: Gymnasium, recreation complex, swimming pool, track, racquetball and tennis courts, stadium.

STUDENT BODY. Freshman profile: 3% of freshmen who took ACT scored 30 or over on composite; 4% scored 24 or over on composite; 19% scored 18 or over on composite; 100% scored 12 or over on composite. 18% of accepted applicants took SAT I; 11% took ACT.

Undergraduate achievement: 15% of entering class graduates.

PROGRAMS OF STUDY. Degrees: B.A., B.Arch., B.S., B.S.Chem., B.S.Home Econ., B.S.Nurs. **Majors:** Accounting, Art Education, Biology, Business Administration, Business Economics, Chemistry, Clothing/Textiles, Computer Information Systems, Computer Science, Dramatic Arts, Early Childhood Education, Elementary Education, English, English Education, Finance, Fine Arts, Food Sciences/Human Nutrition, Foreign Language Education, French, Geography, Graphic Design, Health Education, History, Home Economics, Home Economics Education, Junior High Education, Law Enforcement/Corrections, Marketing/Distribution, Mathematics, Mathematics Education, Music, Music Education, Nursing, Parks/Recreation Management, Philosophy, Physical Education, Physics, Physics Education, Political Science, Psychology, Sacred Music, Science Education, Secondary Education, Social Sciences, Social Studies Education, Sociology, Spanish, Speech/Communication/Theatre, Theatre Arts Education, Visual Communications.

Requirements: General education requirement.

Special: Double majors. Dual degrees. Independent study. Internships. Cooperative education programs. Graduate school at which qualified undergraduates may take graduate-level courses. 3-2 dual-degree engineering program with Georgia Tech. Exchange program with U of Wisconsin. Teacher certification in elementary, secondary, and special education. ROTC and AFROTC.

Honors: Honors program.

Academic Assistance: Remedial reading and math. Nonremedial tutoring.

STUDENT LIFE. Housing: Students may live on or off campus. Coed, women's, and men's dorms. School-owned/operated apartments. 35% of students live in college housing.

Services and counseling/handicapped student services: Placement services. Health service. Chaplain. Counseling services for military and veteran students. Birth control and personal counseling. Academic guidance services. Physically disabled student services.

Campus organizations: Undergraduate student government. Student newspaper (Campus Echo, published once/month). Literary magazine. Yearbook. Theatre, marching, concert, and jazz bands, performing musical ensembles. 11 fraternities, no chapter houses; 11 sororities, no chapter houses.

ATHLETICS. Physical education requirements: Two semesters of health or two semesters of physical education and one semester of health required.

Intercollegiate competition: 5% of students participate. Basketball (M,W), cheerleading (M,W), cross-country (M,W), football (M), softball (W), tennis (M), volleyball (W). Member of Central Intercollegiate Athletic Association, NCAA Division II.

Intramural and club sports: 25% of students participate. Intramural archery, badminton, racquet-ball, softball, swimming, tennis, touch football, volleyball. Men's club bowling. Women's club bowling.

ADMISSIONS. Academic basis for candidate selection (in order of priority): Secondary school record, class rank, standardized test scores, school's recommendation.

Nonacademic basis for candidate selection: Character and personality and particular talent or ability are important. Extracurricular participation is considered.

Requirements: Graduation from secondary school is required; GED is accepted. 11 units and the following program of study are required: 3 units of English, 3 units of math, 2 units of science including 1 unit of lab, 2 units of social studies. 2 units of foreign language recommended. Rank in top half of secondary school class required. Minimum 2.0 GPA required of business program applicants. Minimum 2.0 GPA in general science courses required of nursing program applicants. SAT I or ACT is required.

Procedure: Take SAT I or ACT by March of 12th year. Suggest filing application by July 1. Application deadline is August 1. Notification of admission on rolling basis. $50 refundable room deposit. Freshmen accepted for all terms.

Special programs: Admission may be deferred. Credit may be granted through CEEB Advanced Placement for scores of 4 or higher. Credit may be granted through CLEP general and subject exams. Credit may be granted through challenge exams.

Transfer students: Transfer students accepted for all terms. In fall 1994, 3% of all new students were transfers into all classes. 381 transfer applications were received, 378 were accepted. Lowest course grade accepted is "C." Maximum number of transferable credits is 60 semester hours. At least 30 semester hours must be completed at the university to receive degree.

Admissions contact: Nancy R. Rowland, Director of Admissions. 919 560-6298.

FINANCIAL AID. Available aid: Pell grants, SEOG, state grants, school scholarships, private scholarships and grants, academic merit scholarships, and athletic scholarships. SSIG. Perkins Loans (NDSL), PLUS, and Stafford Loans (GSL). Tuition Management Systems and deferred payment plan.

Financial aid statistics: 5% of aid is not need-based. In 1994-95, 85% of all undergraduate aid applicants received aid; 75% of freshman aid applicants. Average amounts of aid awarded freshmen: Scholarships and grants, $2,216; loans, $1,800.

Supporting data/closing dates: FAFSA/FAF: Priority filing date is April 15; deadline is in May. Notification of awards on rolling basis.

Financial aid contact: Carmella Conner, M.S.Ed., Director of Financial Aid. 502 227-5960.

STUDENT EMPLOYMENT. Federal Work-Study Program. Institutional employment. 32% of full-time undergraduates work on campus during school year. Students may expect to earn an average of $1,000 during school year. Off-campus part-time employment opportunities rated "good."

COMPUTER FACILITIES. 600 IBM/IBM-compatible and Apple/Macintosh microcomputers; 200 are networked. Students may access IBM minicomputer/mainframe systems. Residence halls may be equipped with networked terminals, modems. Client/LAN operating systems include DOS, Novell. Computer facilities are available to all students.

Fees: $10 computer fee per semester.

Hours: 8 AM-9 PM (M-F); 10 AM-4 PM (Sa).

GRADUATE CAREER DATA. Highest graduate school enrollments: Jackson State U, U of Kentucky, U of Louisville. 47% of graduates choose careers in business and industry. Companies and businesses that hire graduates: Ashland Oil, AT&T, Darcom, Department of Defense, Humana, Internal Revenue Service, Kroger, McDonnell Douglas.

PROMINENT ALUMNI/AE. Patricia Russel McCloud, attorney; Moneta Sleet, Pulitzer prize-winning photographer; Dr. Bailus Walker, Jr., Commissioner of Public Health, Massachusetts; Harrison B. Wilson, president, Norfolk State U; George Wilson, secretary, Corrections Cabinet, Kentucky.

Oakwood College

Huntsville, AL 35896   205 726-7000

Undergraduate profile. 87% Black, 1% Hispanic, 12% Other. 29% are state residents; 22% are transfers. Average age of undergraduates is 22.

Enrollment. Undergraduates: 558 men, 834 women (full-time). Freshman class: 863 applicants, 569 accepted, 342 enrolled.

Faculty. 80 full-time, 51 part-time; 70 Black, 6 White, 4 Other. 53% of faculty holds doctoral degree. Student/faculty ratio: 17 to 1.

Test score averages/ranges. Average SAT I scores: 387 verbal, 398 math. Average ACT scores: 17 English, 16 math, 17 composite.

1995-96 Costs. Tuition: $6,904. Room & board: $4,160. Fees, books, misc. academic expenses (school's estimate): $994.

PROFILE. Oakwood, founded in 1896, is a private, church-affilitated, liberal arts college. Its 1,185-acre campus is located five miles from downtown Huntsville.

Accreditation: SACS. Professionally accredited by the American Dietetic Association, the Council on Social Work Education, the National Council for Accreditation of Teacher Education.

Religious orientation: Oakwood College is affiliated with the General Conference of Seventh-day Adventists; 16 quarter hours of religion/theology required.

Library: Collections totaling 98,364 volumes, 590 periodical subscriptions, 1,550 microform items, eight CD-ROMs, and 3,676 audiovisual items.

Special facilities/museums: On-campus elementary and secondary school, child development lab.

Athletic facilities: Tennis and racquetball courts, ball fields, gymnasium.

STUDENT BODY. Freshman profile: 5% of freshmen who took SAT I scored 600 or over on verbal, 5% scored 600 or over on math; 13% scored 500 or over on verbal, 17% scored 500 or over on math; 40% scored 400 or over on verbal, 49% scored 400 or over on math; 83% scored 300 or over on verbal, 87% scored 300 or over on math. 11% of freshmen who took ACT scored 24 or over on English, 3% scored 24 or over on math, 7% scored 24 or over on composite; 46% scored 18 or over on English, 32% scored 18 or over on math, 46% scored 18 or over on composite; 87% scored 12 or over on English, 96% scored 12 or over on math, 97% scored 12 or over on composite; 100% scored 6 or over on English, 99% scored 6 or over on math, 99% scored 6 or over on composite. 50% of accepted applicants took SAT I; 60% took ACT. 46% of freshmen come from public schools.

Undergraduate achievement: 68% of fall 1993 freshmen returned for fall 1994 term.

Foreign students: 177 students are from out of the country. Countries represented include the Bahamas, Barbados, Bermuda, Canada, Jamaica, and Trinidad and Tobago; 28 in all.

PROGRAMS OF STUDY. Degrees: B.A., B.Mus.Perf., B.S., B.Soc.Work.

Majors: Accounting, Biochemistry, Biology, Biology Education, Business Education, Chemical Engineering, Chemistry, Chemistry Education, Communications, Computer Science, Dietetics, Economics, Elementary Education, English, English Education, History, Home Economics, Home Economics Education, Human Development/Family Studies, Interdisciplinary Studies, Language Arts Education, Management, Mathematics, Mathematics/Computer Science, Mathematics Education, Ministerial Theology, Music, Music Education, Natural Science, Office Systems Management, Physical Education, Psychology, Religion, Religious Education, Social Science Education, Social Work.

Distribution of degrees: The majors with the highest enrollments are social work, accounting, and psychology; chemistry, office management, and mathematics have the lowest.

Requirements: General education requirement.

Academic regulations: Minimum 2.0 GPA must be maintained.

Special: Minors offered in some majors and in art, child development, correctional science, gerontology, office administration, physics, political science, sociology, and theology. Student missionary program. Associate degrees offered. Double majors. Dual degrees. Pass/fail grading option. Internships. Preprofessional programs in law, medicine, veterinary science, pharmacy, dentistry, allied health sciences, and engineering. 2-2 occupational therapy program with U of Alabama at Birmingham. 2-2 natural science program. Two-year transfer programs in anesthesia, dental hygiene, occupational therapy, physical therapy, and public health with Loma Linda U. Two-year transfer program in engineering with Walla Walla Coll. Two-year transfer programs in medical technology, occupational therapy, and physical therapy with Andrews U, Florida Hospital, Howard U, Meharry Medical Coll, Tennessee State U, and U of Alabama at Birmingham. 3-1 medical technology program. 3-2 engineering program with Alabama A&M U. B.S. in natural science awarded for successful completion of three years of undergraduate work and one year of professional study in dentistry, medicine, or allied health sciences. Member of Alabama Center for Higher Education. Cross-registration with Alabama A&M U, Athens State Coll, John C. Calhoun State Comm Coll, and U of Alabama at Huntsville. Teacher certification in early childhood, elementary, secondary, and special education. Study abroad in France.

Academic Assistance: Remedial reading, writing, math, and study skills. Nonremedial tutoring.

STUDENT LIFE. Housing: All unmarried students under age 21 must live on campus unless living near campus with relatives. Women's and men's dorms. On-campus married-student housing. 71% of students live in college housing.

Social atmosphere: Oakwood students frequent the cafeteria, the skating rink, Moran Hall, the gym, and the college church. The Adventist Youth Society, the United Student Movement, Dynamic Praise, Aeolians, and Men of Distinction are strong influences on student social life. Highlights of the school year include the Spirit Week of Emphasis, the College Bowl, the International Food Festival, the Student Week of Prayer, the United Student Movement Banquet, Black History Month, and Alumni Weekend. "Oakwood provides many activities which stimulate the physical, social, mental, and spiritual being," writes the editor of the student newspaper. "We seek to do everything in moderation and with the sense that God is the center of it all. Oakwood (a predominantly Black school) also seeks to uplift the race to which the majority of its students belong."

Services and counseling/handicapped student services: Placement services. Health service. Counseling services for veteran and older students. Personal and psychological counseling. Career and academic guidance services. Religious counseling.

Campus organizations: Undergraduate student government. Student newspaper (Spreading Oak, published once/month). Yearbook. Radio station. Choir, band, other music groups, dormitory clubs, United Student Movement.

Religious organizations: Adventist Youth Society, Religion and Theology Forum, Outreach.

Foreign student organizations: International Student Club.

ATHLETICS. Physical education requirements: Six quarter hours of physical education required.

Intramural and club sports: 65% of students participate. Intramural basketball, flagball, soccer, volleyball.

ADMISSIONS. Academic basis for candidate selection (in order of priority): Secondary school record, standardized test scores, school's recommendation, class rank.

Nonacademic basis for candidate selection: Character and personality are important. Extracurricular participation is considered.

Requirements: Graduation from secondary school is required; GED is accepted. 16 units and the following program of study are required: 4 units of English, 2 units of math, 2 units of science, 2 units of social studies, 6 units of electives. 2 units of foreign language recommended. Minimum 2.0 GPA required. Minimum composite ACT score of 16 (combined SAT I score of 745), minimum 2.5 GPA, and satisfactory performance on Alabama English Proficiency Test required of teacher education program applicants (entered after sophomore year). Minimum ACT scores of 21 in English and 17 in both math and social science, minimum 2.5 GPA, and minimum grade of "C" in secondary school chemistry and U.S. history required of nursing program applicants. SAT I or ACT is required. Campus visit recommended. Off-campus interviews available with an alumni representative.

Procedure: Take SAT I or ACT by spring of 12th year. Notification of admission on rolling basis. $150 refundable room deposit. Freshmen accepted for all terms.

Special programs: Admission may be deferred one year. Credit may be granted through CLEP subject exams. Credit may be granted for life experience.

Transfer students: Transfer students accepted for all terms. In fall 1994, 22% of all new students were transfers into all classes. 141 transfer applications were received, 127 were accepted. Minimum 2.0 GPA recommended. Lowest course grade accepted is "C." Maximum number of transferable credits is 96 quarter hours. At least 36 quarter hours must be completed at the college to receive degree.

Admissions contact: Robert Edwards, M.Div., Enrollment Management. 205 726-7030.

FINANCIAL AID. Available aid: Pell grants, SEOG, Federal Nursing Student Scholarships, state grants, school scholarships, private scholarships, academic merit scholarships, aid for undergraduate foreign students, and United Negro College Fund. PLUS and Stafford Loans (GSL). AMS, deferred payment plan, and family tuition reduction.

Financial aid statistics: Average amounts of aid awarded freshmen: Scholarships and grants, $2,018; loans, $2,625.

Supporting data/closing dates: FAFSA/FAF: Priority filing date is April 15; accepted on rolling basis. Income tax forms: Priority filing date is April 15; accepted on rolling basis. Notification of awards on rolling basis.

Financial aid contact: Charlotte Smith, Acting Director of Financial Aid. 205 726-7208.

STUDENT EMPLOYMENT. Federal Work-Study Program. Institutional employment. 61% of full-time undergraduates work on campus during school year. Students may expect to earn an average of $1,836 during school year. Off-campus part-time employment opportunities rated "fair."

COMPUTER FACILITIES. 181 IBM/IBM-compatible and Apple/Macintosh microcomputers; 112 are networked. Students may access AT&T, IBM minicomputer/mainframe systems. Residence halls may be equipped with stand-alone microcomputers. Client/LAN operating systems include Apple/Macintosh, DOS, UNIX/XENIX/AIX, Novell. Computer facilities are available to all students.

Fees: $10 computer fee per class.

Hours: 8 AM-10 PM (M,T,Th); 8 AM-7 PM (W); 9 AM-10 PM (Su).

Paine College
Augusta, GA 30910

706 821-8200

Undergraduate profile. 98% Black, 1% White, 1% Other. 77% are state residents; 44% are transfers.

Enrollment. Undergraduates: 188 men, 401 women (full-time). Freshman class: 1,143 applicants, 636 accepted, 225 enrolled.

Faculty. 55 full-time, 8 part-time; 27 Black, 16 White, 12 Other. 44% of faculty holds doctoral degree. Student/faculty ratio: 11 to 1.

Test score averages/ranges. Average SAT I scores: 328 verbal, 371 math. Range of SAT I scores of middle 50%: 260-390 verbal, 300-430 math. Average ACT scores: 15 composite. Range of ACT scores of middle 50%: 14-18 composite.

1995-96 Costs. Tuition: $5,924. Room & board: $2,935. Fees, books, misc. academic expenses (school's estimate): $900.

PROFILE. Paine, founded in 1882, is a private, church-affiliated, historically Black college. Its 41-acre campus is situated in the center of Augusta, east of Atlanta.

Accreditation: SACS.

Religious orientation: Paine College is affiliated with the Christian Methodist Episcopal and United Methodist Churches; one semester of religion/theology required.

Library: Collections totaling 85,025 volumes, 437 periodical subscriptions, and 10,024 microform items.

Special facilities/museums: Early childhood development center.

STUDENT BODY. Freshman profile: 72% of accepted applicants took SAT I; 20% took ACT.

Undergraduate achievement: 11% of entering class graduates.

Foreign students: 13 students are from out of the country. Countries represented include African countries and the Bahamas.

PROGRAMS OF STUDY. Degrees: B.A., B.S.

Majors: Biology, Business Administration, Chemistry, Early Childhood Education, English, History, Mass Communications, Mathematics, Middle Grade Education, Music Education, Philosophy/Religion, Psychology, Sociology.

Distribution of degrees: The majors with the highest enrollments are business administration, sociology, education, and biology; philosophy/religion, English, and mathematics have the lowest.

Requirements: General education requirement.

Academic regulations: Freshmen must maintain minimum 1.7 GPA; sophomores, 1.8 GPA; juniors, 1.9 GPA; seniors, 2.0 GPA.

Special: Minors offered in all majors and in art, French, German, health/physical education, music, physics, and secondary education. Courses offered in economics, geography, and political science. Developmental courses. Dual degrees. Independent study. Internships. Cooperative education programs. 3-2 engineering programs with Florida A&M U and Georgia Tech. Combined biomedical science and chemistry programs with Meharry Medical Coll. Combined mass communications program with Clark Atlanta U. Cross-registration with Augusta Coll. Teacher certification in early childhood, elementary, and secondary education. ROTC.

Honors: Honors program. Honor societies.

Academic Assistance: Remedial reading, writing, math, and study skills. Nonremedial tutoring.

STUDENT LIFE. Housing: All students must live on campus unless living with family. Women's and men's dorms. 63% of students live in college housing.

Services and counseling/handicapped student services: Placement services. Health service. Testing service. Office of Freshman Studies. Counseling services for military and veteran students. Personal and psychological counseling. Career and academic guidance services. Religious counseling.

Campus organizations: Undergraduate student government. Student newspaper (Paineite). Yearbook. Concert choir, gospel choir, jazz ensemble, drama club, debating, academic and special-interest groups, 34 organizations in all. Four fraternities, no chapter houses; five sororities, no chapter houses. 10% of men join a fraternity. 10% of women join a sorority.

Religious organizations: Baptist and Methodist groups, other religious groups.

Foreign student organizations: International Student Organization.

ATHLETICS. Physical education requirements: Two semesters of physical education required.

Intercollegiate competition: 8% of students participate. Baseball (M), basketball (M). Member of NCAA Division II.

Intramural and club sports: Intramural basketball, softball, tennis, volleyball.

ADMISSIONS. Academic basis for candidate selection (in order of priority): Secondary school record, standardized test scores, school's recommendation, essay, class rank.

Nonacademic basis for candidate selection: Particular talent or ability is important. Character and personality, extracurricular participation, and alumni/ae relationship are considered.

Requirements: Graduation from secondary school is required; GED is accepted. 15 units and the following program of study are recommended: 4 units of English, 2 units of math, 1 unit of science, 2 units of foreign language, 1 unit of social studies, 1 unit of history, 4 units of electives. Electives may include commercial/vocational courses, fine arts, foreign language, health, and physical education. Minimum 2.0 GPA recommended. Conditional admission possible for applicants not meeting standard requirements. SAT I or ACT is required. Campus visit and interview recommended. Off-campus interviews available with admissions and alumni representatives.

Procedure: Take SAT I or ACT by December of 12th year. Suggest filing application by March. Application deadline is August 1. Notification of admission on rolling basis. $25 refundable room deposit. Freshmen accepted for all terms.

Special programs: Admission may be deferred. Credit may be granted through CEEB Advanced Placement for scores of 3 or higher. Credit may be granted through CLEP general and subject exams. Credit may be granted for military and life experience. Early entrance/early admission program. Concurrent enrollment program.

Transfer students: Transfer students accepted for all terms. Minimum 2.0 GPA required. Lowest course grade accepted is "C." At least 42 semester hours must be completed at the college to receive degree.

Admissions contact: Phillis Wyatt-Woodruff, M.S., Director of Enrollment Management. 706 821-8320.

FINANCIAL AID. Available aid: Pell grants, SEOG, state scholarships, school scholarships and grants, private scholarships and grants, ROTC scholarships, academic merit scholarships, athletic scholarships, and aid for undergraduate foreign students. Perkins Loans (NDSL), PLUS, and Stafford Loans (GSL). Deferred payment plan and family tuition reduction.

Supporting data/closing dates: FAFSA. FAF: Priority filing date is March 1. School's own aid application: Priority filing date is March 1. State aid form: Priority filing date is March 1. Income tax forms: Priority filing date is March 1. Notification of awards on rolling basis.

Financial aid contact: Ardrina Scott-Elliott, Director of Financial Aid. 706 821-8320.

STUDENT EMPLOYMENT. Federal Work-Study Program. 65% of full-time undergraduates work on campus during school year. Students may expect to earn an average of $1,800 during school year. Off-campus part-time employment opportunities rated "excellent."

COMPUTER FACILITIES. 125 IBM/IBM-compatible and Apple/Macintosh microcomputers; 75 are networked. Computer facilities are available to all students.

Fees: None.

Hours: 8 AM-8 PM (M-Th); 8 AM-5 PM (F).

GRADUATE CAREER DATA. Graduate school percentages: 2% enter law school. 6% enter medical school. 3% enter graduate business programs. 2% enter graduate arts and sciences programs. 2% enter theological school/seminary. Highest graduate school enrollments: Clark Atlanta U, Georgia State, Medical Coll of Georgia, Texas Southern U, Tuskegee U, U of South Carolina.

PROMINENT ALUMNI/AE. Dr. Mack Gibson, geologist; Frank Yerby, author; Dr. Shirley McBay, educator; Dr. Charles Gomillion, educator and civil rights activist; Dr. William Harris, former president, Texas Southern U.

Paul Quinn College

Dallas, TX 75241

214 376-1000

Undergraduate profile. 94% Black, 1% Hispanic, 4% White, 1% Other. 80% are state residents. Average age of undergraduates is 20.

Enrollment. Undergraduates: 229 men, 234 women (full-time).

Faculty. 37 full-time; 14 part-time. 39% of faculty holds doctoral degree. Student/faculty ratio: 12 to 1.

Test score averages/ranges. N/A.

1995-96 Costs. Tuition: $3,400. Room & board: $2,950. Fees, books, misc. academic expenses (school's estimate): $1,180.

PROFILE. Paul Quinn, founded in 1872, is a private, church-affiliated, liberal arts college. The campus is located in Lancaster, 14 miles from downtown Dallas.

Accreditation: SACS. Professionally accredited by the Council on Social Work Education.

Religious orientation: Paul Quinn College is affiliated with the African Methodist Episcopal church; one semester of religion required.

Athletic facilities: Gymnasium, football stadium.

STUDENT BODY. Undergraduate achievement: 35% of students who complete a degree program go on to graduate study within five years.

Foreign students: Four students are from out of the country. Countries represented include Liberia and Nigeria.

PROGRAMS OF STUDY. Degrees: B.A., B.S.

Majors: Accounting, Administrative Office Management, Biology, Business Administration, Computer Science, Criminal Justice, Education, English, History, Mathematics, Music, Physical Education, Recreation, Religion, Social Work, Sociology.

Requirements: General education requirement.

Special: Minors offered in most majors. Internships. Cooperative education programs. Teacher certification in elementary and secondary education.

Academic Assistance: Nonremedial tutoring.

STUDENT LIFE. Housing: Students may live on or off campus. Women's and men's dorms.

Services and counseling/handicapped student services: Placement services. Career and academic guidance services.

Campus organizations: Undergraduate student government. Student newspaper (Quinn Quill, published once/quarter). Choir, pep squad, science, history, business, Spanish, English, and social work clubs. Four fraternities, no chapter houses; four sororities, no chapter houses.

Religious organizations: Ministerial Alliance Club.

ATHLETICS. Physical education requirements: Two semesters of physical education required.

Intercollegiate competition: 10% of students participate. Baseball (M), basketball (M,W), volleyball (W). Member of Interregional Athletic Conference, NSCAA.

Intramural and club sports: 7% of students participate. Intramural basketball, flag football, volleyball. Men's club cheerleading. Women's club cheerleading.

ADMISSIONS. Academic basis for candidate selection (in order of priority): Class rank, secondary school record, school's recommendation, standardized test scores.

Nonacademic basis for candidate selection: Character and personality are important.

Requirements: Graduation from secondary school is required; GED is accepted. No specific distribution of secondary school units required. Developmental Studies Program for applicants not normally admissible. SAT I or ACT is required. Campus visit and interview recommended. No off-campus interviews.

Procedure: Notification of admission on rolling basis. $55 refundable room deposit. Freshmen accepted for all terms.

Special programs: Admission may be deferred. Credit and/or placement may be granted through CLEP subject exams. Placement may be granted through challenge exams.

Transfer students: Transfer students accepted for all terms. Lowest course grade accepted is "C."

Admissions contact: Marilyn O. Marshall, J.D., Vice President, Enrollment Management. 214 302-3520.

FINANCIAL AID. Available aid: Pell grants, SEOG, state scholarships and grants, private scholarships, and United Negro College Fund. PLUS, Stafford Loans (GSL), unsubsidized Stafford Loans, Health Professions Loans, state loans, school loans, and private loans. Deferred payment plan.

Supporting data/closing dates: FAFSA/FAF: Accepted on rolling basis. School's own aid application: Accepted on rolling basis.

Financial aid contact: Marilyn O. Marshall, J.D., Vice President, Enrollment Management. 214 302-3540.

STUDENT EMPLOYMENT. Federal Work-Study Program. Off-campus part-time employment opportunities rated "fair."

COMPUTER FACILITIES. IBM/IBM-compatible microcomputers. Two terminals are available for student use. Computer facilities are not available to all students.

Fees: None.

GRADUATE CAREER DATA. 60% of graduates choose careers in business and industry. Companies and businesses that hire graduates: K-Mart.

Philander Smith College

Little Rock, AR 72202

501 375-9845

Undergraduate profile. 90% Black, 10% White. Average age of undergraduates is 19.
Enrollment. Undergraduates: 280 men, 421 women (full-time). Freshman class: 434 enrolled.
Faculty. Student/faculty ratio: 16 to 1.
Test score averages/ranges. N/A.
1992-93 Costs. Tuition: $2,620. Room & board: $2,415. Fees, books, misc. academic expenses (school's estimate): $1,150.

PROFILE. Philander Smith, founded in 1877, is a private, church-affiliated, historically Black, liberal arts college. Its 25-acre campus is located in the Quapaw Quarter in the heart of downtown Little Rock.

Accreditation: SACS.

Religious orientation: Philander Smith College is affiliated with the United Methodist Church; no religious requirements.

PROGRAMS OF STUDY.

Degrees: B.A., B.S.

Majors: Biology, Business Administration/Management, Chemistry, Computer/Information Sciences, Elementary Education, English, Foreign Languages/Multiple Emphasis, Home Economics, Mathematics, Music, Philosophy, Psychology, Radio/Television, Secretarial/Related Programs, Social Work, Sociology, Special Education.

Requirements: General education requirement.

Academic regulations: Freshmen must maintain minimum 2.0 GPA.

Special: Cooperative education programs. ROTC.

STUDENT LIFE.

Housing: Women's and men's dorms.

Services and counseling/handicapped student services: Health service. Counseling services for veteran students. Career guidance services. Learning disabled services.

Campus organizations: Undergraduate student government. Student newspaper. Yearbook. Radio station. Choral groups, drama, jazz band, music ensembles, pep band, Alpha Phi Omega.

ATHLETICS.

Physical education requirements: None.

Intercollegiate competition: Baseball (M), basketball (M,W), softball (M,W), volleyball (M,W). Member of NAIA.

Intramural and club sports: Intramural badminton, basketball, swimming, table tennis, tennis. Men's club soccer.

ADMISSIONS.

Requirements: Graduation from secondary school is recommended. No specific distribution of secondary school units required. SAT I is required; ACT may be substituted.

Procedure: Notification of admission on rolling basis. Freshmen accepted for fall term only.

Special programs: Admission may be deferred.

FINANCIAL AID.

Supporting data/closing dates: FAFSA: Priority filing date is May 1; accepted on rolling basis. Notification of awards on rolling basis.

Prairie View A&M University
Prairie View, TX 77446 409 857-3311

Undergraduate profile. 85% Black, 1% Asian-American, 2% Hispanic, 8% White, 4% Other. 87% are state residents; 23% are transfers. Average age of undergraduates is 23.
Enrollment. Undergraduates: 2,790 men, 3,058 women (full-time). Freshman class: 1,107 enrolled. Graduate enrollment: 247 men, 493 women.
Faculty. 267 full-time; 36 part-time. 167 Black, 39 White, 37 Other. 38% of faculty holds doctoral degree. Student/faculty ratio: 25 to 1.
Test score averages/ranges. Average SAT I scores: 367 verbal, 393 math. Average ACT scores: 15 composite.
1995-96 Costs. Tuition: $900 (state residents), $6,660 (out-of-state). Room & board: $3,618. Fees, books, misc. academic expenses (school's estimate): $1,320.

PROFILE. Prairie View A&M, founded in 1876, is a public university. Programs are offered through the Colleges of Applied Sciences and Engineering Technology, Arts and Sciences, Business, Education, Engineering, and Nursing. Its 1,440-acre campus is located in Prairie View, 45 miles from Houston.
Accreditation: SACS. Professionally accredited by the Accreditation Board for Engineering and Technology, Inc., the American Home Economics Association, the National League for Nursing.
Religious orientation: Prairie View A&M University is nonsectarian; no religious requirements.
Library: Collections totaling 240,117 volumes, 1,557 periodical subscriptions, and 261,318 microform items.
Athletic facilities: Health, physical education, and recreation building, baseball, football, and softball fields, golf course, tennis courts, track/field, jogging trail.
STUDENT BODY. Freshman profile: 1% of freshmen who took SAT I scored 700 or over on verbal, 1% scored 700 or over on math; 3% scored 600 or over on verbal, 5% scored 600 or over on math; 13% scored 500 or over on verbal, 25% scored 500 or over on math; 46% scored 400 or over on verbal, 54% scored 400 or over on math; 84% scored 300 or over on verbal, 85% scored 300 or over on math. Majority of accepted applicants took SAT I.
Undergraduate achievement: 20% of students who complete a degree program immediately go on to graduate study.
Foreign students: 330 students are from out of the country. Countries represented include the Bahamas, Ghana, Iran, Jamaica, Liberia, and Nigeria; 46 in all.
PROGRAMS OF STUDY. Degrees: B.A., B.A.Soc.Work, B.Bus.Admin., B.F.A., B.S., B.S.Elec.Eng., B.S.Mech.Eng., B.S.Nurs.
Majors: Accounting, Administrative Information Systems, Advertising Art, Agri-Agronomy, Agricultural Economics, Agricultural Engineering, Agriculture, Agriculture/Human Resources, Animal Science, Applied Music, Applied Music/Percussion, Applied Music/Piano, Applied Music/Saxophone, Applied Music/Trombone, Applied Music/Trumpet, Applied Music/Voice, Architecture, Biology, Business, Chemical Engineering, Chemistry, Civil Engineering, Communication/Journalism, Communication/Radio/TV, Communications, Computer-Aided Drafting/Design, Computer Engineering Technology, Computer Science, Drama, Economics, Electrical Engineering, Electrical Engineering Technology, English, Family/Community Service, Finance, General Business Administration, Geography, History, Human Development/the Family, Human Nutrition/Food, Human Performance, Industrial Technology, Interdisciplinary, Law Enforcement, Management, Marketing, Mathematics, Mechanical Engineering, Mechanical Engineering Technology, Medical Technology, Merchandising/Design, Music, Nursing/Clinical, Nursing/Preclinical, Physics, Political Science, Psychology, Social Work, Sociology, Spanish, Speech.
Distribution of degrees: The majors with the highest enrollments are engineering, business, and nursing.
Requirements: General education requirement.
Academic regulations: Minimum 2.0 GPA must be maintained.

Special: Minors offered in most majors. Benjamin Banneker Honors College, a residential college, prepares selected students in the applied and natural sciences for future graduate and professional studies. Independent study. Internships. Cooperative education programs. Graduate school at which qualified undergraduates may take graduate-level courses. Teacher certification in early childhood, secondary, and special education. ROTC and NROTC.

Honors: Honors program.

Academic Assistance: Remedial reading, writing, math, and study skills. Nonremedial tutoring.

STUDENT LIFE. Housing: All students must live on campus unless living with family within a 60-mile radius of campus. Women's and men's dorms. 75% of students live in college housing.

Services and counseling/handicapped student services: Placement services. Health service. Counseling services for military and veteran students. Birth control and personal counseling. Career and academic guidance services. Religious counseling.

Campus organizations: Undergraduate student government. Student newspaper (Panther). Yearbook. Radio station. CHISPAS. Symphonic, jazz, and marching bands, choirs, drama group, forensic club, rodeo club, professional groups, 22 organizations in all. Four fraternities, no chapter houses; four sororities, no chapter houses. 8% of men join a fraternity. 8% of women join a sorority.

Religious organizations: Baptist Student Movement, Catholic and Moslem groups.

Foreign student organizations: Bahamian, Jamaican, and Nigerian student groups.

ATHLETICS. Physical education requirements: Four semesters of physical education required.

Intercollegiate competition: 4% of students participate. Baseball (M), basketball (M,W), cross-country (M,W), football (M), golf (M), tennis (M), track (indoor) (M,W), track (outdoor) (M,W), track and field (indoor) (M,W), track and field (outdoor) (M,W), volleyball (W). Member of NAIA, NCAA Division I, NCAA Division I-AA for football, Southwestern Athletic Conference.

Intramural and club sports: 30% of students participate. Intramural basketball, football, softball, tennis, volleyball.

ADMISSIONS. Academic basis for candidate selection (in order of priority): Secondary school record, standardized test scores, class rank, school's recommendation, essay.

Nonacademic basis for candidate selection: Character and personality are important. Extracurricular participation, particular talent or ability, and alumni/ae relationship are considered.

Requirements: Graduation from secondary school is required; GED is accepted. 16 units and the following program of study are required: 4 units of English, 3 units of math, 3 units of science, 2 units of social studies, 4 units of academic electives. Minimum combined SAT I score of 700 (composite ACT score of 18), rank in top half of secondary school class, and minimum 2.0 GPA required. Conditional admission possible for applicants not meeting standard requirements. SAT I or ACT is required. Campus visit recommended. Off-campus interviews available with admissions and alumni representatives.

Procedure: Notification of admission on rolling basis. $200 refundable room deposit. Freshmen accepted for all terms.

Special programs: Admission may be deferred one year. Credit and/or placement may be granted through CEEB Advanced Placement exams for scores of 3 or higher. Credit and/or placement may be granted through CLEP general exams. Placement may be granted through challenge exams. Early decision program. Early entrance/early admission program. Concurrent enrollment program.

Transfer students: Transfer students accepted for all terms. In fall 1993, 23% of all new students were transfers into all classes. 625 transfer applications were received, 489 were accepted. Application deadline is rolling for fall; rolling for spring. Minimum 2.0 GPA required. Lowest course grade accepted is "C." Maximum number of transferable credits is 90 semester hours.

Admissions contact: Mr. Sharon Marshall, Director of Admissions. 409 857-2618, 409 857-2626.

FINANCIAL AID. Available aid: Pell grants, SEOG, state scholarships and grants, school scholarships and grants, private scholarships, and academic merit scholarships. Perkins Loans (NDSL), PLUS, Stafford Loans (GSL), and state loans.

Financial aid statistics: 25% of aid is not need-based. In 1993-94, 80% of all undergraduate aid applicants received aid; 80% of freshman aid applicants. Average amounts of aid awarded freshmen: Scholarships and grants, $4,000; loans, $2,625.

Supporting data/closing dates: FAFSA. FAF: Priority filing date is May 1. School's own aid application: Accepted on rolling basis. Income tax forms: Priority filing date is May 1. Notification of awards on rolling basis.
Financial aid contact: A.D. James, Jr., M.S., Director of Financial Aid. 409 857-2424.
STUDENT EMPLOYMENT. Federal Work-Study Program. Institutional employment. 30% of full-time undergraduates work on campus during school year. Students may expect to earn an average of $3,000 during school year. Off-campus part-time employment opportunities rated "poor."
COMPUTER FACILITIES. IBM/IBM-compatible microcomputers. Computer facilities are available to all students.
Fees: None.
Hours: 9 AM-10 PM (M-F).
GRADUATE CAREER DATA. Graduate school percentages: 2% enter law school. 3% enter medical school. 1% enter dental school. 15% enter graduate business programs. 7% enter graduate arts and sciences programs. Highest graduate school enrollments: Prairie View A&M U, Texas A&M U, and U of Houston. 32% of graduates choose careers in business and industry.
PROMINENT ALUMNI/AE. Craig Washington, state senator; Gen. Julius W. Becton, Jr., U.S. Army (retired).

Rust College
Holly Springs, MS 38635
601 252-8000

Undergraduate profile. 94% Black, 2% White, 4% Other. 67% are state residents; 4% are transfers. Average age of undergraduates is 19.
Enrollment. Undergraduates: 335 men, 548 women (full-time). Freshman class: 1,113 applicants, 559 accepted, 288 enrolled.
Faculty. 62 full-time, 6 part-time; 28 Black, 6 White, 28 Other. 53% of faculty holds doctoral degree. Student/faculty ratio: 18 to 1.
Test score averages/ranges. Average ACT scores: 16 English, 15 math, 16 composite.
1995-96 Costs. Tuition: $4,625. Room & board: $2,175.

PROFILE. Rust, founded in 1866, is a private, church-affiliated college. Its 11-acre campus is located in Holly Springs, 35 miles from Memphis.
Accreditation: SACS.
Religious orientation: Rust College is affiliated with the United Methodist Church; one semester of religion required.
Library: Collections totaling 110,002 volumes, 339 periodical subscriptions, and 6,409 microform items.
Special facilities/museums: Art collection, child care center.
Athletic facilities: Tennis court, swimming pool, exercise room, gymnasium, track, baseball and softball fields.
STUDENT BODY. Freshman profile: 72% of accepted applicants took ACT. 80% of freshmen come from public schools.
Undergraduate achievement: 26% of entering class graduates. 25% of students who complete a degree program immediately go to graduate study.
Foreign students: 41 students are from out of the country. Countries represented include Ethiopia, Gambia, Kenya, Mexico, Nigeria, and Pakistan; six in all.
PROGRAMS OF STUDY. Degrees: B.A., B.S.
Majors: Biology, Business Administration, Business Education, Chemistry, Computer Science, Economics, Elementary Education, English, English Education, Health/Physical Education/Recreation, Mass Communication/Journalism/Broadcasting Journalism, Mathematics, Mathematics Education, Medical Technology, Music, Music Education, Nursing, Political Science, Pre-Engineering, Science Education, Social Work, Sociology.

Distribution of degrees: The majors with the highest enrollments are business administration, social work, and political science; music and mathematics have the lowest.

Requirements: General education requirement.

Academic regulations: Freshmen must maintain minimum 1.5 GPA; sophomores, 1.85 GPA; juniors, 2.0 GPA; seniors, 2.0 GPA.

Special: Minors offered in most majors. Business administration major has various concentrations. Associate degrees offered. Dual degrees. Independent study. Accelerated study. Internships. Cooperative education programs. Preprofessional programs in medicine, pharmacy, dentistry, and engineering. 3-2 chemistry/engineering programs, mathematics/engineering programs, interdisciplinary science/engineering programs, and nursing/biology programs with Alcorn State U, Auburn U, Georgia Tech, Mississippi State U, Tuskegee U, U of Memphis, and U of Mississippi. Teacher certification in elementary and secondary education. Certification in specific subject areas.

Honors: Honors program. Honor societies.

Academic Assistance: Remedial reading, writing, and math.

STUDENT LIFE. Housing: Unmarried students are strongly encouraged to live on campus unless living with family. Women's and men's dorms. On-campus married-student housing. 75% of students live in college housing.

Social atmosphere: Popular hangouts include the student recreation center, gymnasium, library, laundry room, Doxey Fine Arts Building, McDonald's, KFC, Club Octagon, Pizza Hut, Pizza Inn, and Victor's. Influential student groups include Omega Psi Phi, Zeta Phi Beta, the basketball team, the Baptist Student Union Choir, and the Student Government Association. Eagerly anticipated social/cultural/sporting events include Founder's Weekend, Health Fair, SIAC Basketball Tournament, Religious Emphasis Week, Theatre Productions, dances, movies, and commencement. "The students interact well with each other, enjoying intelligent conversations and physical recreation," reports the student newspaper. "They are culturally aware and very proud of their African-American heritage."

Services and counseling/handicapped student services: Health service. Day care. Counseling services for veteran students. Personal counseling. Academic guidance services. Religious counseling.

Campus organizations: Undergraduate student government. Student newspaper (Rustorian, published biweekly). Yearbook. Radio and TV stations. NAACP. Choir, band, cheerleaders, Theatre Guild, Student National Education group, academic groups. Four fraternities, no chapter houses; three sororities, no chapter houses. 30% of men join a fraternity. 31% of women join a sorority.

Religious organizations: Baptist Student Movement, Catholic Student Association, All Saints Movement, Methodist Student Movement, Sunday School.

Foreign student organizations: International Student Organization.

ATHLETICS. Physical education requirements: Two semesters of physical education required.

Intercollegiate competition: 15% of students participate. Baseball (M), basketball (M,W), cheerleading (W), cross-country (M,W), tennis (M,W), track (outdoor) (M,W), track and field (outdoor) (M,W). Member of NCAA Division III.

Intramural and club sports: 70% of students participate. Intramural archery, badminton, basketball, bowling, flag football, horseshoes, shuffleboard, softball, swimming, table tennis, tennis, track/field, volleyball.

ADMISSIONS. Academic basis for candidate selection (in order of priority): Secondary school record, class rank, school's recommendation, standardized test scores, essay.

Nonacademic basis for candidate selection: Character and personality, particular talent or ability, geographical distribution, and alumni/ae relationship are important. Extracurricular participation is considered.

Requirements: Graduation from secondary school is required; GED is accepted. 19 units and the following program of study are required: 4 units of English, 3 units of math, 3 units of science, 3 units of social studies, 6 units of electives. Minimum 2.0 GPA required. Audition required of music program applicants. Special Services Program for students not normally admissible. ACT is required; SAT I may be substituted. Campus visit and interview recommended. Off-campus interviews available with admissions and alumni representatives.

Procedure: Take SAT I or ACT by January of 12th year. Suggest filing application by May 1. Application deadline is July 15. Notification of admission on rolling basis. $25 refundable room deposit. Freshmen accepted for all terms.

Special programs: Admission may be deferred for varying periods. Credit may be granted through CLEP general and subject exams. Placement may be granted through challenge exams. Early decision program. Deadline for applying for early decision is July 15. Early entrance/early admission program.

Transfer students: Transfer students accepted for all terms. In fall 1993, 4% of all new students were transfers into all classes. 86 transfer applications were received, 58 were accepted. Application deadline is July 15 for fall; December 15 for spring. Minimum 2.0 GPA required. Lowest course grade accepted is "C."

Admissions contact: Jo Ann Scott, Director of Admissions. 601 252-8000, extension 4068.

FINANCIAL AID. Available aid: Pell grants, SEOG, state grants, school scholarships and grants, private scholarships, academic merit scholarships, aid for undergraduate foreign students, and United Negro College Fund. Perkins Loans (NDSL), PLUS, Stafford Loans (GSL), unsubsidized Stafford Loans, and school loans. United Methodist Loan. AMS and family tuition reduction. Institutional payment plan.

Financial aid statistics: 18% of aid is not need-based. In 1994-95, 99% of all undergraduate aid applicants received aid; 97% of freshman aid applicants. Average amounts of aid awarded freshmen: Scholarships and grants, $3,000; loans, $1,500.

Supporting data/closing dates: FAFSA: Priority filing date is May 1; deadline is June 15. School's own aid application: Priority filing date is May 1; deadline is June 15. State aid form: Priority filing date is June 15; deadline is July 1. Income tax forms: Priority filing date is May 1; deadline is June 15. Notification of awards begins June 1.

Financial aid contact: Helen Street, Director of Financial Aid. 601 252-8000, extension 4061.

STUDENT EMPLOYMENT. Federal Work-Study Program. Institutional employment. 65% of full-time undergraduates work on campus during school year. Students may expect to earn an average of $600 during school year. Off-campus part-time employment opportunities rated "good."

COMPUTER FACILITIES. 250 IBM/IBM-compatible microcomputers; 50 are networked. Students may access IBM minicomputer/mainframe systems. Residence halls may be equipped with stand-alone microcomputers. Computer facilities are available to all students.

Fees: None.

Hours: 8 AM-10 PM.

GRADUATE CAREER DATA. Graduate school percentages: 2% enter law school. 1% enter medical school. 1% enter graduate business programs. Highest graduate school enrollments: Jackson State U, Mississippi State U, U of Akron, U of Arkansas, U of Memphis, U of Mississippi, Xavier U. Companies and businesses that hire graduates: IBM, Internal Revenue Service.

PROMINENT ALUMNI/AE. Dr. Adolph Harper, physician; Mrs. Lonear Heard-Davis, entrepreneur; Dimaggio Nichols, president, Noble Ford/Mercury; Earvin "Magic" Johnson, former NBA basketball player; Dr. William "Bill" Cosby, comedian and actor.

Saint Augustine's College

Raleigh, NC 27610   **919 516-4000**

Undergraduate profile. 98% Black, 1% White, 1% Other. 51% are state residents; 4% are transfers. Average age of undergraduates is 20.

Enrollment. Undergraduates: 750 men, 1,043 women (full-time). Freshman class: 2,624 applicants, 1,816 accepted, 687 enrolled.

Faculty. 82 full-time, 14 part-time; 70 Black, 17 White, 9 Other. 52% of faculty holds doctoral degree. Student/faculty ratio: 20 to 1.

Test score averages/ranges. Average SAT I scores: 405 verbal, 404 math.

1995-96 Costs. Tuition: $5,897. Room & board: $3,708. Fees, books, misc. academic expenses (school's estimate): $2,098.

PROFILE. Saint Augustine's, founded in 1867, is a church-affiliated, historically Black college. Programs are offered through the Divisions of Business, Education, Humanities, Natural Sciences and Mathematics, and Social Sciences. Its 110-acre campus, including the college chapel named as an historic site by the County Historic Commission, is located in Raleigh.

Accreditation: SACS, ACICS.

Religious orientation: Saint Augustine's College is affiliated with the Episcopal Church; three semesters of religion required.

Library: Collections totaling over 136,000 volumes, 4,724 periodical subscriptions, and 92 microform items.

Athletic facilities: Field house, tennis courts, track, baseball, and soccer fields, weight room.

STUDENT BODY. Freshman profile: Majority of accepted applicants took SAT I. 95% of freshmen come from public schools.

Undergraduate achievement: 52% of entering class graduates. 38% of students who complete a degree program go on to graduate study.

Foreign students: 125 students are from out of the country. Countries represented include Ethiopia, Iran, Liberia, Venezuela, and Zaire; 23 in all.

PROGRAMS OF STUDY. Degrees: B.A., B.S.

Majors: Accounting, Aerospace Engineering, Art, Biological/Agricultural Engineering, Biology, Business Administration, Business Education, Business/Management, Chemical Engineering, Chemistry, Civil Engineering, Communications Media, Computer Science, Criminal Justice, Early Childhood Education, Economics, Electrical Engineering, Elementary Education, English, French, Health/Physical Education, History/Government, Industrial Hygiene/Safety, Industrial Mathematics, Intermediate Education, Materials Engineering, Mathematics, Mechanical Engineering, Medical Technology, Modern Foreign Languages, Music, Physical Therapy, Physics, Political Science/Pre-Law, Pre-Medicine, Psychology, Social Studies, Sociology/Social Welfare, Spanish, Urban Affairs.

Distribution of degrees: The majors with the highest enrollments are business, sociology/social welfare, and computer science; chemistry, mathematics, and biology have the lowest.

Requirements: General education requirement.

Academic regulations: Minimum 2.0 GPA must be maintained.

Special: Curriculum is half liberal arts with the rest equally divided into teacher education and career-related fields. Undergraduate Record Exam and English Comprehensive Exam required of juniors; oral and written comprehensive exam required of seniors. Dual degrees. Independent study. Cooperative education programs. Preprofessional programs in law, medicine, veterinary science, pharmacy, dentistry, theology, laboratory technology, nursing, physical therapy, and social work. 3-2 engineering program with North Carolina State U. Member of Raleigh Consortium of Colleges; cross-registration possible. Exchange program with Shaw U. Teacher certification in early childhood, elementary, and secondary education. Study abroad in England. ROTC. AFROTC at North Carolina State U.

Honors: Honors program.

Academic Assistance: Remedial reading and math.

STUDENT LIFE. Housing: First-time freshmen must live on campus. Women's and men's dorms. School-owned/operated apartments. 63% of students live in college housing.

Social atmosphere: Students gather on the mall, in the college union, and on the quadrangle. Influential campus groups include Greeks, athletes, and the African-American Student Forum. Homecoming, Greek Roll-Out shows, sports events, the coronation of the college queen, and Partners in the Arts performances are favorite campus events. According to the editor of the student newspaper, "Students generally support school-oriented activities."

Services and counseling/handicapped student services: Placement services. Health service. Counseling services for military and veteran students. Personal counseling. Career and academic guidance services. Religious counseling.

Campus organizations: Undergraduate student government. Student newspaper (Pen, published once/month). Yearbook. Radio and TV stations. Black Accountants Association, National Society of Black Engineers. Concert band, choral club, music guild, drama and photography clubs, Falcon

Club, pep squad, debating, business education group, Pershing Rifles, Student National Education group. Eight fraternities, no chapter houses; five sororities, no chapter houses. 6% of men join a fraternity. 8% of women join a sorority.

Religious organizations: Canterbury Club, Lay Readers Group.

Foreign student organizations: International Student Club.

ATHLETICS. Physical education requirements: Two semesters of physical education required. **Intercollegiate competition:** 12% of students participate. Baseball (M), basketball (M,W), cheerleading (W), cross-country (M,W), golf (M), softball (W), tennis (M), track (indoor) (M,W), track (outdoor) (M,W), track and field (indoor) (M,W), track and field (outdoor) (M,W), volleyball (W). Member of Central Intercollegiate Athletic Association, NCAA Division II.

Intramural and club sports: 4% of students participate. Intramural basketball, flag football, softball, table tennis, volleyball. Men's club soccer.

ADMISSIONS. Academic basis for candidate selection (in order of priority): Secondary school record, standardized test scores, class rank, school's recommendation, essay.

Nonacademic basis for candidate selection: Character and personality are emphasized. Extracurricular participation and particular talent or ability are important. Alumni/ae relationship is considered.

Requirements: Graduation from secondary school is required; GED is accepted. 18 units and the following program of study are required: 4 units of English, 3 units of math, 2 units of lab science, 2 units of social studies, 7 units of academic electives. Minimum combined SAT I score of 700, rank in top quarter of secondary school class, and minimum 2.0 GPA required. SAT I is required; ACT may be substituted. Campus visit and interview recommended. Off-campus interviews available with admissions and alumni representatives.

Procedure: Take SAT I or ACT by August 1 of 12th year. Application deadline is March 15. Notification of admission on rolling basis. $25 room deposit, refundable until July 1. Freshmen accepted for all terms.

Special programs: Admission may be deferred one semester. Concurrent enrollment program.

Transfer students: Transfer students accepted for all terms. In fall 1993, 4% of all new students were transfers into all classes. 160 transfer applications were received, 100 were accepted. Application deadline is March 15 for fall; October 15 for spring. Minimum 2.0 GPA recommended. Lowest course grade accepted is "C." Maximum number of transferable credits is 90 semester hours. At least 30 semester hours must be completed at the college to receive degree.

Admissions contact: Wanzo F. Hendrix, M.Soc.Work, Director of Admissions. 919 516-4011.

FINANCIAL AID. Available aid: Pell grants, SEOG, state grants, school scholarships, private grants, ROTC scholarships, athletic scholarships, and United Negro College Fund. Perkins Loans (NDSL), Stafford Loans (GSL), state loans, and school loans. Tuition Plan Inc. and deferred payment plan.

Financial aid statistics: In 1993-94, 88% of all undergraduate aid applicants received aid; 78% of freshman aid applicants. Average amounts of aid awarded freshmen: Scholarships and grants, $1,500; loans, $1,000.

Supporting data/closing dates: FAFSA/FAF: Priority filing date is April 30. School's own aid application: Priority filing date is April 30. Notification of awards on rolling basis.

Financial aid contact: Sherri Avent, M.B.A., Director of Financial Aid. 919 516-4130.

STUDENT EMPLOYMENT. Federal Work-Study Program. Institutional employment. 15% of full-time undergraduates work on campus during school year. Students may expect to earn an average of $2,000 during school year. Off-campus part-time employment opportunities rated "excellent."

COMPUTER FACILITIES. 14 microcomputers. Computers are available only to students enrolled in lab courses.

Fees: None.

GRADUATE CAREER DATA. Highest graduate school enrollments: Clark Atlanta U, Columbia U, Howard U, Ohio State U, Michigan State U, New York U, Tennessee State U. 30% of graduates choose careers in business and industry. Companies and businesses that hire graduates: armed services, IBM, government agencies.

PROMINENT ALUMNI/AE. Hannah Diggs, Oklahoma secretary of state; Dr. J.G. Gordon, chief of radiology, Bowman-Gray Hospital; Ralph Campbell, North Carolina state auditor.

Saint Paul's College

Lawrenceville, VA 23868   804 848-3111

Undergraduate profile. 93% Black, 6% White, 1% Other. 76% are state residents; 13% are transfers. Average age of undergraduates is 20.

Enrollment. Undergraduates: 249 men, 429 women (full-time). Freshman class: 660 applicants, 504 accepted, 228 enrolled.

Faculty. 32 full-time, 12 part-time; 18 Black, 13 White, 13 Other. 37% of faculty holds doctoral degree. Student/faculty ratio: 13 to 1.

Test score averages/ranges. Average SAT I scores: 310 verbal, 320 math.

1995-96 Costs. Tuition: $6,158. Room & board: $3,834. Fees, books, misc. academic expenses (school's estimate): $600.

PROFILE. Saint Paul's, founded in 1888, is a private, church-affiliated, multipurpose, historically Black college. Its 75-acre campus is located in Lawrenceville, 60 miles south of Richmond.

Accreditation: SACS.

Religious orientation: Saint Paul's College is affiliated with the Protestant Episcopal Church; three semesters of religion/theology required. Attendance is mandatory for chapel one service/week.

Library: Collections totaling over 55,000 volumes, 225 periodical subscriptions, and 30,093 microform items.

Special facilities/museums: Language lab.

Athletic facilities: Gymnasium.

STUDENT BODY. Freshman profile: 1% of freshmen who took SAT I scored 600 or over on math; 1% scored 500 or over on verbal, 4% scored 500 or over on math; 19% scored 400 or over on verbal, 17% scored 400 or over on math; 51% scored 300 or over on verbal, 54% scored 300 or over on math. Majority of accepted applicants took SAT I.

Undergraduate achievement: 58% of fall 1993 freshmen returned for fall 1994 term. 12% of entering class graduates. 15% of students who complete a degree program immediately go on to graduate study.

Foreign students: 11 students are from out of the country. Countries represented include Ghana, Ivory Coast, Liberia, Nigeria, and the West Indies; six in all.

PROGRAMS OF STUDY. Degrees: B.A., B.S., B.S.Ed.

Majors: Accounting, Aquaculture/Acquatic Science, Biology, Business Administration, Business Education, Computer Science, Criminal Justice, Early Childhood Education, Elementary Education, English, Environmental Science, General Office Procedures, General Science, General Studies, Management, Marketing, Mathematics, Organizational Management, Political Science, Social Sciences, Sociology.

Distribution of degrees: The majors with the highest enrollments are sociology, business administration, and political science; English, social sciences, and elementary education have the lowest.

Requirements: General education requirement.

Academic regulations: Minimum 2.0 GPA must be maintained.

Special: Minors offered in some majors and in chemistry, communication, economics, and history. Independent study. Internships. Cooperative education programs. Preprofessional programs in medicine and theology. 2-2 criminal justice program. Washington Semester. Exchange program with Eastern Mennonite U. Teacher certification in early childhood, elementary, and secondary education. Certification in specific subject areas. Exchange program abroad in England (Whitelands Coll). ROTC.

Honors: Honors program. Honor societies.

Academic Assistance: Remedial reading, writing, math, and study skills. Nonremedial tutoring.

STUDENT LIFE. Housing: Freshmen and sophomores must live on campus. Women's and men's dorms. Off-campus privately-owned housing. 55% of students live in college housing.
Social atmosphere: Students gather at the Can-Do Club, Dino's Restaurant, and Meljo's Club. Greeks, the student government, the Science and Math Club, and the NAACP are influential groups on campus. Favorite campus events include Homecoming, Spring Fling, and basketball games. The student newspaper describes the campus atmosphere as close-knit. Campus groups organize and sponsor many well-attended events, including movies, concerts, and talent shows.
Services and counseling/handicapped student services: Placement services. Health service. Day care. Counseling services for military students. Birth control, personal, and psychological counseling. Career and academic guidance services. Religious counseling. Physically disabled student services. Learning disabled services. Notetaking services. Tape recorders. Tutors. Reader services for the blind.
Campus organizations: Undergraduate student government. Student newspaper. Yearbook. Choral society, dance troupe, Players' Guild, Lecture and Concert Series, art club, varsity club, Visiting Artists/Scholars Series, English, political science, and science/math clubs, 19 organizations in all. Four fraternities, three chapter houses; four sororities, no chapter houses. 7% of men join a fraternity. 10% of women join a sorority.
Religious organizations: Canterbury Club, Bible study group.
Foreign student organizations: International student organization.

ATHLETICS. Physical education requirements: Two semesters of physical education required.
Intercollegiate competition: 2% of students participate. Baseball (M), basketball (M,W), cheerleading (M,W), cross-country (M,W), golf (M,W), softball (W), tennis (M,W), track (indoor) (M,W), track (outdoor) (M,W), track and field (indoor) (M,W), track and field (outdoor) (M,W), volleyball (W). Member of Central Intercollegiate Athletic Association, NCAA Division II.
Intramural and club sports: 1% of students participate. Intramural basketball, flag football, volleyball, weightlifting.

ADMISSIONS. Academic basis for candidate selection (in order of priority): Secondary school record, standardized test scores, class rank, school's recommendation, essay.
Nonacademic basis for candidate selection: Character and personality and extracurricular participation are emphasized. Alumni/ae relationship is important. Particular talent or ability is considered.
Requirements: Graduation from secondary school is required; GED is accepted. 16 units and the following program of study are required: 4 units of English, 2 units of math, 2 units of science, 2 units of social studies, 6 units of electives. Minimum combined SAT I score of 700, rank in top half of secondary school class or recommendation from principal or guidance counselor, and minimum 2.0 GPA required. Conditional admission possible for applicants not meeting standard requirements. SAT I is required; ACT may be substituted. Campus visit and interview recommended. Off-campus interviews available with an admissions representative.
Procedure: Notification of admission on rolling basis. $50 nonrefundable tuition deposit. $50 refundable room deposit. Freshmen accepted for all terms.
Special programs: Credit and/or placement may be granted through CEEB Advanced Placement exams for scores of 3 or higher. Credit and/or placement may be granted through CLEP general and subject exams. Credit may be granted for military experience. Placement may be granted through challenge exams. Concurrent enrollment program.
Transfer students: Transfer students accepted for all terms. In fall 1994, 13% of all new students were transfers into all classes. 114 transfer applications were received, 59 were accepted. Application deadline is rolling for fall; rolling for spring. Minimum 2.0 GPA required. Lowest course grade accepted is "C." At least 30 semester hours must be completed at the college to receive degree.
Admissions contact: Mary Ransom, Director of Admissions/Recruitment. 804 848-3984.

FINANCIAL AID. Available aid: Pell grants, SEOG, state scholarships and grants, school scholarships and grants, private scholarships and grants, ROTC scholarships, academic merit scholarships, athletic scholarships, aid for undergraduate foreign students, and United Negro College Fund. Perkins Loans (NDSL), PLUS, Stafford Loans (GSL), and unsubsidized Stafford Loans. Deferred payment plan and family tuition reduction.

Financial aid statistics: 12% of aid is not need-based. In 1994-95, 90% of all undergraduate aid applicants received aid; 85% of freshman aid applicants. Average amounts of aid awarded freshmen: Scholarships and grants, $2,000; loans, $2,000.

Supporting data/closing dates: FAFSA: Priority filing date is March 30; deadline is August 12. School's own aid application: Priority filing date is March 30; accepted on rolling basis; deadline is August 12. State aid form: Accepted on rolling basis. Income tax forms: Priority filing date is March 30; deadline is August 12. Notification of awards begins April 15.

Financial aid contact: Samuel W. Wade, Director of Financial Aid. 804 848-4505.

STUDENT EMPLOYMENT. Federal Work-Study Program. Institutional employment. 46% of full-time undergraduates work on campus during school year. Students may expect to earn an average of $1,300 during school year. Off-campus part-time employment opportunities rated "fair."

COMPUTER FACILITIES. 50 IBM/IBM-compatible microcomputers. Students may access IBM minicomputer/mainframe systems, Internet. Client/LAN operating systems include DOS. Computer facilities are available to all students.

Fees: Computer fee is included in tuition/fees.

GRADUATE CAREER DATA. Highest graduate school enrollments: Ohio State U, Old Dominion U, , U of Virginia, Virginia State U. 75% of graduates choose careers in business and industry. Companies and businesses that hire graduates: Schools, state and federal governments, Winn-Dixie.

PROMINENT ALUMNI/AE. Dr. Elbanks Gilbert, radiologist; Dr. Irma Freeman, dentist; Dr. Carolyn Hines, entrepreneur.

Savannah State College

Savannah, GA 31404   **912 356-2186**

Undergraduate profile: 91.9% Black, .7% Asian/Pacific Islander, .3% Hispanic, .1% Native American, 7% White. 90% are state residents. Average age of undergraduates is 23.

Enrollment. Undergraduates: 1,249 men, 1,510 women (full-time). Freshman class: 1,689 applicants, 1,504 accepted, 726 enrolled.

Faculty. 145 full-time; 58 part-time. 52% of faculty holds doctoral degree. Student/faculty ratio: 19 to 1.

Test score averages/ranges. Average SAT I scores: 319 verbal, 361 math. Average ACT scores: 18 composite.

1995-96 Costs. Tuition: $1,498 (state residents), $4,704 (out-of-state). Room & board: $2,710. Fees, books, misc. academic expenses (school's estimate): $1,071.

PROFILE. Savannah State is a public, multipurpose, historically black college. Founded in 1890, it adopted coeducation in 1921. Programs are offered through the Schools of Business, Humanities and Social Sciences, and Science and Technology. Its 165-acre campus is located in Savannah.

Accreditation: SACS. Professionally accredited by the Accreditation Board for Engineering and Technology, Inc., the Council on Social Work Education.

Religious orientation: Savannah State College is nonsectarian; no religious requirements.

Library: Collections totaling 173,702 volumes, 757 periodical subscriptions, and 500,211 microform items. On-line catalog of audiovisual items.

Athletic facilities: Gymnasium, baseball and practice fields, track, stadium.

STUDENT BODY. Freshman profile: Majority of accepted applicants took SAT I.

Undergraduate achievement: 70% of fall 1993 freshmen returned for fall 1994 term.

Foreign students: 48 students are from out of the country. Countries represented include the Bahamas, Ethiopia, Kuwait, Nigeria, Pakistan, and the Virgin Islands; 18 in all.

PROGRAMS OF STUDY. Degrees: B.A., B.Bus.Admin., B.S., B.Soc.Work.

Majors: Accounting, Biology, Chemistry, Civil Engineering Technology, Computer Science Technology, Criminal Justice, Electronics Engineering Technology, English Language/Literature, Environmental Studies, History, Information Systems, International Business, Management, Marine Biology, Marketing, Mass Communications, Mathematics, Mechanical Engineering Technology, Music, Political Science, Recreation, Social Work, Sociology.

Distribution of degrees: The majors with the highest enrollments are management, accounting, and criminal justice; English language/literature, music, and environmental studies have the lowest.

Requirements: General education requirement.

Academic regulations: Freshmen must maintain minimum 1.8 GPA; sophomores, juniors, seniors, 2.0 GPA.

Special: Minors offered in several majors and in art, child development, computer science, disadvantaged/handicapped families, electronics/physics, engineering technology, English, French, German, gerontology, hotel management, naval science, psychology, religious/ philosophical studies, and Spanish. Associate degrees offered. Double majors. Dual degrees. Independent study. Accelerated study. Internships. Cooperative education programs. ROTC and NROTC.

Honors: Honors program.

Academic Assistance: Nonremedial tutoring.

STUDENT LIFE. Housing: Freshmen, sophomores, and juniors must live on campus. Women's and men's dorms. School-owned/operated apartments. 37% of students live in college housing.

Services and counseling/handicapped student services: Placement services. Health service. Counseling services for military, veteran, and older students. Personal counseling. Career and academic guidance services.

Campus organizations: Undergraduate student government. Student newspaper (Tiger's Roar, published once/month). Literary magazine. Yearbook. Radio station. Band, choral society, concert choir, gospel choir, special-interest groups. Five fraternities, no chapter houses; four sororities, no chapter houses.

ATHLETICS. Physical education requirements: None.

Intercollegiate competition: 4% of students participate. Baseball (M), basketball (M,W), cheerleading (W), cross-country (W), football (M), tennis (W), track (outdoor) (M), volleyball (W). Member of NCAA Division II, Southeastern Intercollegiate Athletic Conference.

Intramural and club sports: 1% of students participate. Intramural basketball, flag football, softball.

ADMISSIONS. Academic basis for candidate selection (in order of priority): Standardized test scores, secondary school record.

Requirements: Graduation from secondary school is required; GED is accepted. The following program of study is recommended: 4 units of English, 3 units of math, 3 units of science, 2 units of foreign language, 3 units of social studies, 3 units of electives. Minimum combined SAT I score of 750 (composite ACT score of 19) and minimum 2.0 GPA required. Conditional admission possible for applicants not meeting standard requirements. Learning Support Program for applicants not normally admissible. SAT I or ACT is required. Admissions interview recommended. Off-campus interviews available with an admissions representative.

Procedure: Take SAT I or ACT by December 10 of 12th year. Visit college for interview by May 1 of 12th year. Suggest filing application by March 1; deadline is 20 days before registration. Notification of admission on rolling basis. Reply is required by May 1. $50 refundable room deposit. Freshmen accepted for all terms.

Special programs: Credit and/or placement may be granted through CEEB Advanced Placement exams for scores of 3 or higher. Credit may be granted through CLEP general and subject exams. Credit and placement may be granted for military experience. Early entrance/early admission program. Concurrent enrollment program.

Transfer students: Transfer students accepted for all terms. Minimum 2.0 GPA required. Lowest course grade accepted is "D."

Admissions contact: Roy Jackson, Ph.D., Director of Admissions. 912 356-2181.

FINANCIAL AID. Available aid: Pell grants, SEOG, state scholarships and grants, school scholarships, private scholarships and grants, ROTC scholarships, academic merit scholarships, and athletic scholarships. Perkins Loans (NDSL), state loans, school loans, and private loans.

Financial aid statistics: In 1994-95, 95% of all undergraduate aid applicants received aid; 95% of freshman aid applicants.

Supporting data/closing dates: FAFSA/FAF: Priority filing date is July 18. School's own aid application: Deadline is July 18. Notification of awards on rolling basis.

Financial aid contact: Ron Higgs, Director of Financial Aid. 912 356-2253.

STUDENT EMPLOYMENT. Federal Work-Study Program. 45% of full-time undergraduates work on campus during school year. Students may expect to earn an average of $900 during school year. Freshmen are discouraged from working during their first term. Off-campus part-time employment opportunities rated "good."

COMPUTER FACILITIES. IBM/IBM-compatible and Apple/Macintosh microcomputers. Client/LAN operating systems include DOS. Computer facilities are available to all students.

Fees: None.

Hours: 8 AM-10 PM.

Selma University

Selma, AL 36701

334 872-2533

Undergraduate profile. 94% Black, 6% Other. 50% are transfers.

Enrollment. Undergraduates: 77 men, 67 women (full-time). Freshman class: 150 applicants, 75 accepted.

Faculty. 13% of faculty holds highest degree in specific field.

Test score averages/ranges. N/A.

1995-96 Costs. Tuition: $4,260. Room & board: $3,745. Fees, books, misc. academic expenses (school's estimate): $250.

PROFILE. Selma, founded in 1878 as a coed institution, is a private, church-affliated, traditionally Black liberal arts university. Its 25-acre campus is located in Selma, 50 miles from Montgomery.

Accreditation: SACS.

Religious orientation: Selma University is affiliated with the Alabama Baptist State Convention; two units of religion/theology required. Attendance is mandatory for chapel three times/week.

STUDENT BODY. Freshman profile: 75% of freshmen come from public schools.

PROGRAMS OF STUDY. Degrees: B.A., B.S.

Majors: Business Administration, Computer Science, General Studies, Religious Education, Theological Studies.

Requirements: General education requirement.

Special: Associate degrees offered. Self-designed majors. Preprofessional programs in medicine. ROTC.

Honors: Honor societies.

Academic Assistance: Remedial reading, math, and study skills.

STUDENT LIFE. Housing: Women's and men's dorms. 90% of students live in college housing.

Services and counseling/handicapped student services: Personal counseling. Career guidance services. Learning disabled services.

Campus organizations: Undergraduate student government. Student newspaper. Yearbook. Choral group, drama, music ensembles. Two fraternities, no chapter houses; 10 sororities, no chapter houses. 50% of men join a fraternity. 55% of women join a sorority.

Religious organizations: Baptist Student Union.

ATHLETICS. Physical education requirements: Three semester hours of physical education required.

Intercollegiate competition: Baseball (M), basketball (M), volleyball (M). Member of NJCAA.

Intramural and club sports: Intramural basketball, softball, table tennis, volleyball.

ADMISSIONS. Requirements: Graduation from secondary school is recommended. GED is accepted. No specific distribution of secondary school units required. Open admissions policy. Applicants with deficient high school records or low test scores must take remedial courses. ACT is required; SAT I may be substituted.

Procedure: Notification of admission on rolling basis. $125 nonrefundable tuition deposit. $50 room deposit, partially refundable. Freshmen accepted for all terms.

Transfer students: Transfer students accepted for fall term. In fall 1994, 50% of all new students were transfers into all classes. 250 transfer applications were received. Minimum 2.0 GPA recommended. Lowest course grade accepted is "C." At least 25 semester hours must be completed at the university to receive degree.

Admissions contact: Estella Davis-Baynes, Director of Admissions. 334 872-2533.

FINANCIAL AID.

Supporting data/closing dates: FAFSA: Priority filing date is September 15; accepted on rolling basis. Notification of awards begins August 23.

Financial aid contact: Brenda Cheatham, Director of Financial Aid. 334 874-4827.

COMPUTER FACILITIES. 55 IBM/IBM-compatible microcomputers; four are networked. Students may access Hewlett-Packard, IBM minicomputer/mainframe systems. Client/LAN operating systems include DOS, Windows NT, Microsoft. Computer facilities are available to all students.

Fees: $25 computer fee per semester.

Shaw University
Raleigh, NC 27601   919 546-8220

Undergraduate profile. 95% Black, 4% White, 1% Other. Average age of undergraduates is 26. 65% are state residents; 26% are transfers.

Enrollment. Undergraduates: 945 men, 1,313 women (full-time). Freshman class: 2,460 applicants, 1,333 accepted, 568 enrolled.

Faculty. 100 full-time, 174 part-time; 137 Black, 82 White, 55 Other. 71% of faculty holds doctoral degree. Student/faculty ratio: 13 to 1.

Test score averages/ranges. Range of ACT scores of middle 50%: 14-15 composite.

1995-96 Costs. Tuition: $5,946. Room & board: $3,824. Fees, books, misc. academic expenses (school's estimate): $850.

PROFILE. Shaw, founded in 1865, is a private, church-affiliated, liberal arts university. Its 18-acre campus is located in downtown Raleigh.

Accreditation: SACS.

Religious orientation: Shaw University is affiliated with the Baptist Church; no religious requirements.

Library: Collections totaling 121,813 volumes, 500 periodical subscriptions, and 6,920 microform items.

Special facilities/museums: TV and film production facilities.

Athletic facilities: Gymnasium, student union activity room, baseball and softball fields, tennis courts.

STUDENT BODY. Freshman profile: Majority of accepted applicants took SAT I. 98% of freshmen come from public schools.

Undergraduate achievement: 60% of fall 1993 freshmen returned for fall 1994 term. 34% of entering class graduates. 19% of students who complete a degree program immediately go on to graduate study.

Foreign students: 40 students are from out of the country. Countries represented include the Bahamas, Bermuda, Ethiopia, Gambia, Israel, and Jordan; nine in all.

PROGRAMS OF STUDY. Degrees: B.A., B.S.

Majors: Accounting, Adaptive Physical Education/Therapeutic Recreation, Biology, Business Administration, Business Management, Chemistry, Computer Studies, Criminal Justice, Early Childhood Education, English, Intermediate Education, International Studies, Mathematics, Music,

Psychology, Public Administration, Radio/Television/Film, Religious Education/Pre-Theology, Secondary Education, Sociology, Speech Pathology/Audiology, Theatre Arts.

Distribution of degrees: The majors with the highest enrollments are business, criminal justice, and radio/television/film; English and mathematics have the lowest.

Requirements: General education requirement.

Academic regulations: Freshmen must maintain minimum 1.5 GPA; sophomores, 1.85 GPA; juniors, 1.95 GPA; seniors, 2.0 GPA.

Special: Center for Alternative Programs in Education for nontraditional students. Associate degrees offered. Double majors. Independent study. Internships. Cooperative education programs. Member of Cooperating Raleigh Colleges. Cross-registration with Meredith Coll, North Carolina State U, Peace Coll, St. Augustine's Coll, and St. Mary's Coll. Teacher certification in elementary, secondary, and special education. Certification in specific subject areas. ROTC. AFROTC at North Carolina State U.

Honors: Honor societies.

STUDENT LIFE. Housing: Freshmen must live on campus. Women's and men's dorms. 47% of students live in college housing.

Services and counseling/handicapped student services: Placement services. Health service. Testing service. Career and academic guidance services. Learning disabled services.

Campus organizations: Undergraduate student government. Student newspaper (Shaw Journal, published four times/year). Yearbook. Black Scientists of America. Radio station. Bands, choir, choral society, ensembles, Shaw Players, Unique Horizon Dancers, debating, academic groups. 11 fraternities, no chapter houses; four sororities, no chapter houses.

Religious organizations: Several religious groups.

ATHLETICS. Physical education requirements: One semester of physical education required.

Intercollegiate competition: 5% of students participate. Baseball (M), basketball (M,W), cross-country (M,W), softball (W), tennis (M,W), track (indoor) (M,W), track (outdoor) (M,W), volleyball (W). Member of Central Intercollegiate Athletic Association, NCAA Division II.

Intramural and club sports: 21% of students participate. Intramural basketball, bowling, flag football, softball, table tennis, tennis.

ADMISSIONS. Academic basis for candidate selection (in order of priority): Secondary school record, class rank, school's recommendation, standardized test scores.

Nonacademic basis for candidate selection: Character and personality and alumni/ae relationship are important. Extracurricular participation and geographical distribution are considered.

Requirements: Graduation from secondary school is recommended; GED is accepted. 18 units and the following program of study are required: 3 units of English, 2 units of math, 2 units of science, 2 units of history, 9 units of academic electives. Minimum 2.0 GPA required. Upward Bound Program for applicants not normally admissible; summer preparatory program continues through freshman year with tutorials and special classes. SAT I or ACT is recommended.

Procedure: Take SAT I or ACT by fall of 12th year. Application deadline is August 10. Notification of admission on rolling basis. $20 nonrefundable room deposit. Freshmen accepted for all terms.

Special programs: Admission may be deferred. Credit and/or placement may be granted through CLEP general and subject exams. Early entrance/early admission program.

Transfer students: Transfer students accepted for all terms. In fall 1994, 26% of all new students were transfers into all classes. 511 transfer applications were received, 341 were accepted. Lowest course grade accepted is "C." Maximum number of transferable credits is 70 semester hours from a two-year school and 90 semester hours from a four-year school. At least 30 semester hours must be completed at the university to receive degree.

Admissions contact: Alfonza Carter, Director of Admissions. 919 546-8275.

FINANCIAL AID. Available aid: Pell grants, SEOG, state scholarships and grants, school scholarships and grants, private scholarships and grants, athletic scholarships, and United Negro College Fund. Perkins Loans (NDSL), PLUS, Stafford Loans (GSL), state loans, and unsubsidized Stafford Loans. Tuition Plan Inc., AMS, and deferred payment plan.

Financial aid statistics: 25% of aid is not need-based. In 1993-94, 95% of all undergraduate aid applicants received aid; 90% of freshman aid applicants. Average amounts of aid awarded freshmen: Scholarships and grants, $6,000; loans, $2,625.

Supporting data/closing dates: FAFSA: Priority filing date is April 1; deadline is August 1. FAF: Priority filing date is June 15. State aid form: Priority filing date is January 1; deadline is March 15. Income tax forms: Priority filing date is April 1; accepted on rolling basis. Notification of awards on rolling basis.

Financial aid contact: Sharon Oliver, Director of Financial Aid. 919 546-8241.

STUDENT EMPLOYMENT. Federal Work-Study Program. Institutional employment. 65% of full-time undergraduates work on campus during school year. Students may expect to earn an average of $1,000 during school year. Off-campus part-time employment opportunities rated "excellent."

COMPUTER FACILITIES. 60 IBM/IBM-compatible and Apple/Macintosh microcomputers; 3 are networked. Students may access IBM, SUN minicomputer/mainframe systems, Internet. Client/LAN operating systems include DOS.

Fees: None.

Hours: 8 AM-5 PM (M-F).

GRADUATE CAREER DATA. 43% of graduates choose careers in business and industry.

PROMINENT ALUMNI/AE. James E. Cheek, past president, Howard U; Willie E. Gary, attorney; Wendell Sommerville, executive secretary, Lott Curey foreign mission.

Sojourner-Douglass College

Baltimore, MD 21205   **410 276-0306**

Undergraduate profile. 99% Black. Average age of undergraduates is 32.

Enrollment. Undergraduates: 262 (full-time). Freshman class: 72 enrolled.

Faculty. 67 full-time. 17% of faculty holds highest degree in specific field.

Test score averages/ranges. N/A.

1995-96 Costs. Tuition: $5,100. Housing: None. Fees, books, misc. academic expenses (school's estimate): $450.

PROFILE. Sojourner-Douglass, founded in 1980, is a private liberal arts college. It is located in Baltimore.

Accreditation: MSACS.

Religious orientation: Sojourner-Douglass College is nonsectarian; no religious requirements.

PROGRAMS OF STUDY. Degrees: B.A.

Majors: Accounting, Business Administration/Management, Business Economics, Counseling Psychology, Criminal Justice Studies, Early Childhood Education, Elementary Education, Health Care Administration, Public Administration, Social Work.

Requirements: General education requirement.

Academic regulations: Freshmen must maintain minimum 2.0 GPA.

Special: Independent study. Accelerated study. Cooperative education programs.

Honors: Honors program.

STUDENT LIFE. Housing: Commuter campus; no student housing.

Services and counseling/handicapped student services: Day care. Personal counseling. Career guidance services. Learning disabled services.

Campus organizations: Undergraduate student government. Student newspaper.

ATHLETICS. Physical education requirements: None.

ADMISSIONS. Requirements: Graduation from secondary school is recommended. No specific distribution of secondary school units required. Admissions interview required.

Procedure: Notification of admission on rolling basis. Freshmen accepted for all fall terms.

Special programs: Credit and placement may be granted through challenge exams.

FINANCIAL AID. Supporting data/closing dates: FAFSA: Accepted on rolling basis. Notification of awards on rolling basis.

South Carolina State University

Orangeburg, SC 29117   **803 536-7000**

Undergraduate profile. 96.3% Black, .4% Asian-American, 3.3% White. 84% are state residents. Average age of undergraduates is 21.

Enrollment. Undergraduates: 1,561 men, 2,046 women (full-time). Freshman class: 1,556 applicants, 1,269 accepted, 615 enrolled. Graduate enrollment: 223 men, 566 women.

Faculty. 217 full-time; 135 Black, 46 White, 36 Other. 62% of faculty holds doctoral degree. Student/faculty ratio: 19 to 1.

Test score averages/ranges. Average SAT I scores: 354 verbal, 397 math.

1995-96 Costs. Tuition: $2,500 (state residents), $4,980 (out-of-state). Room & board: $2,986. Fees, books, misc. academic expenses (school's estimate): $700.

PROFILE. South Carolina State, founded in 1896, is a public, multipurpose college. Programs are offered through the Schools of Arts and Sciences, Business, Education, Engineering Technologies, Home Economics, and Graduate Studies. Its 147-acre campus is located in Orangeburg, 40 miles east of Columbia.

Accreditation: SACS. Professionally accredited by the Accreditation Board for Engineering and Technology, Inc., the American Home Economics Association.

Religious orientation: South Carolina State University is nonsectarian; no religious requirements.

Library: Collections totaling 1,337 periodical subscriptions, 654,907 microform items, and 34 CD-ROMs.

Special facilities/museums: Museum, planetarium, language lab.

Athletic facilities: Gymnasium, stadium, basketball and tennis courts, golf course, track, athletic fields.

STUDENT BODY. Freshman profile: 1% of freshmen who took SAT I scored 600 or over on verbal, 1% scored 600 or over on math; 4% scored 500 or over on verbal, 10% scored 500 or over on math; 23% scored 400 or over on verbal, 46% scored 400 or over on math; 82% scored 300 or over on verbal, 95% scored 300 or over on math. Majority of accepted applicants took SAT I. 98% of freshmen are from public schools.

Foreign students: 40 students are from out of the country. Countries represented include the Bahamas, Brazil, Cape Verde, India, Nigeria, and Portugal; 21 in all.

PROGRAMS OF STUDY. Degrees: B.A., B.S.

Majors: Accounting, Agribusiness, Art, Art Education, Biology, Business Economics, Business Education, Chemistry, Civil Engineering Technology, Computer Science, Criminal Justice, Drama, Early Childhood Education, Electrical Engineering Technology, Elementary Education, English, English Education, Food/Nutrition, Foreign Language Education, French, Health/Physical Education, History, Home Economics, Home Economics Education, Industrial Education, Industrial Technology, Management, Marketing, Mathematics, Mathematics Education, Mechanical Engineering Technology, Music, Music Education, Music Merchandising, Nursing, Nutritional Science, Physics, Political Science, Pre-Law, Printmaking, Psychology, Secondary Education, Social Studies Education, Social Work, Sociology, Spanish, Special Education, Speech Pathology/Audiology.

Distribution of degrees: The majors with the highest enrollments are business/management, education, and engineering technologies; foreign languages and visual/performing arts have the lowest.

Requirements: General education requirement.

Special: Minors offered in many majors and in Black studies and German. Courses offered in broadcasting, geography, humanities, philosophy, physical sciences, and speech arts. Internships. Cooperative education programs. Preprofessional programs in law, medicine, veterinary science, dentistry, optometry, and agriculture. Teacher certification in elementary, secondary, and special education. Study abroad in Spain (U of Madrid). ROTC and AFROTC.

Honors: Honors program.

Academic Assistance: Remedial reading, writing, and math. Nonremedial tutoring.

STUDENT LIFE. Housing: Women's and men's dorms. On-campus married-student housing. 62% of students live in college housing.

Social atmosphere: The Student Center is a popular on-campus gathering spot. On-campus social life is influenced by the Student Union Board, the Student Christian Association, and the Student Alumni Relations Association. Homecoming, baseball and football games are the most popular events of the school year.

Services and counseling/handicapped student services: Placement services. Health service. Chaplains. Counseling services for military, veteran, and older students. Birth control, personal, and psychological counseling. Career and academic guidance services.

Campus organizations: Undergraduate student government. Student newspaper (Collegian). Yearbook. Radio station. NAACP. College, jazz, and concert bands, chorale, mixed octet, Henderson Davis Players, Music Educators Association, Houston Engineers Society, Council for Exceptional Children, science club, Young Democrats, student publications, service and special-interest groups, departmental organizations. Four fraternities, no chapter houses; four sororities, no chapter houses.

Religious organizations: Student Christian Association, Newman Club, United Methodist Student Movement.

Foreign student organizations: International Student Association.

ATHLETICS. Physical education requirements: Four semester hours of physical education required.

Intercollegiate competition: 1% of students participate. Basketball (M,W), cross-country (M,W), football (M), golf (M), softball (W), tennis (M,W), track and field (indoor) (M,W), track and field (outdoor) (M,W), volleyball (W). Member of Mid-Eastern Athletic Conference, NCAA Division I, NCAA Division I-AA for football.

Intramural and club sports: 75% of students participate. Intramural badminton, basketball, cheerleading, cross-country, flag football, fun run, softball, step aerobics, tennis, volleyball, weight training, wrestling.

ADMISSIONS. Academic basis for candidate selection (in order of priority): Secondary school record, standardized test scores, class rank, school's recommendation.

Nonacademic basis for candidate selection: Character and personality, extracurricular participation, particular talent or ability, and alumni/ae relationship are considered.

Requirements: Graduation from secondary school is required; GED is accepted. 16 units and the following program of study are required: 4 units of English, 3 units of math, 2 units of lab science, 2 units of foreign language, 2 units of social studies, 1 unit of history, 2 units of electives including 1 unit of academic electives. Rank in top half of secondary school class required. Portfolio required of art program applicants. Audition required of music program applicants. Provisional admission for applicants not meeting standard requirements. Student Support Services Program for applicants not normally admissible. SAT I is required; ACT may be substituted. Campus visit and interview recommended. Off-campus interviews available with an alumni representative.

Procedure: Take SAT I or ACT by winter of 12th year. Application deadline is July 31. Notification of admission on rolling basis. $35 nonrefundable tuition deposit. $25 nonrefundable room deposit. Freshmen accepted for all terms.

Special programs: Admission may be deferred one semester. Credit and/or placement may be granted through CEEB Advanced Placement exams for scores of 3 or higher. Credit and placement may be granted through challenge exams.

Transfer students: Transfer students accepted for all terms. In fall 1994, 366 transfer applications were received, 299 were accepted. Application deadline is July 31 for fall; November 30 for spring.

Minimum 2.0 GPA required. Lowest course grade accepted is "C." At least 30 credits must be completed at the university to receive degree.

Admissions contact: Dorothy L. Brown, M.A., Ed.D., Acting Director of Admissions and Recruitment. 803 536-7185, 803 536-7186.

FINANCIAL AID. Available aid: Pell grants, SEOG, Federal Nursing Student Scholarships, school scholarships, private scholarships, ROTC scholarships, academic merit scholarships, and athletic scholarships. Perkins Loans (NDSL), PLUS, Stafford Loans (GSL), NSL, private loans, and unsubsidized Stafford Loans. AMS and deferred payment plan. Veterans Administration loans. State loans.

Financial aid statistics: Average amounts of aid awarded freshmen: Scholarships and grants, $1,400; loans, $2,625.

Supporting data/closing dates: FAFSA: Priority filing date is May 1; accepted on rolling basis. Notification of awards begins June 15.

Financial aid contact: Margaret Black, Director of Financial Aid. 803 536-7067.

STUDENT EMPLOYMENT. Federal Work-Study Program. Institutional employment. Students may expect to earn an average of $1,360 during school year. Freshmen are discouraged from working during their first term.

COMPUTER FACILITIES. 300 IBM/IBM-compatible and Apple/Macintosh microcomputers. Students may access AT&T, Digital, Hewlett-Packard, IBM, UNISYS minicomputer/mainframe systems. Client/LAN operating systems include Apple/Macintosh, DOS, UNIX/XENIX/AIX, DEC, LocalTalk/AppleTalk. Some computer lab use restricted to students in specific courses.
Fees: None.

GRADUATE CAREER DATA. Graduate school percentages: 2% enter law school. 2% enter medical school. 2% enter graduate business programs. 11% enter graduate arts and sciences programs. 32% of graduates choose careers in business and industry. Companies and businesses that hire graduates: NationsBank, First Union Bank, Colonial Life, U.S. Dept. of Energy, Wal-Mart, U.S. Dept. of Labor, U.S. Dept. of Interior, Bi-Lo, Farmers Home.

PROMINENT ALUMNI/AE. Ernest Finney, chief justice, South Carolina supreme court; Matthew Perry, federal judge; Brig. Gen. Clifford Stanley, U.S. Marine Corps; Benjamin Payton, president, Tuskegee U; Benjamin E. Mayes, president emeritus, Morehouse Coll.

Southern University at New Orleans
New Orleans, LA 70126   504 286-5314

Undergraduate profile. 89% Black, 1% Asian-American, 1% Hispanic, 6% White, 3% Other.
Enrollment. Undergraduates: 1,100 men, 2,200 women (full-time). Freshman class: 950 applicants, 950 accepted, 530 enrolled. Graduate enrollment: 40 men, 160 women.
Faculty. 126 full-time. 60% of faculty holds doctoral degree.
Test score averages/ranges. N/A.
1995-96 Costs. Tuition: $1,662 (state residents), $3,426 (out-of-state). Housing: None. Fees, books, misc. academic expenses (school's estimate): $800.

PROFILE. Southern University, founded in 1956, is a public, comprehensive institution. Programs are offered through the Divisions of Business, Education, Humanities, Science, and Social Science. Its 17-acre campus is located in a residential section of New Orleans.

Accreditation: SACS. Professionally accredited by the Council on Social Work Education.

Religious orientation: Southern University at New Orleans is nonsectarian; no religious requirements.

STUDENT BODY. Freshman profile: 99% of accepted applicants took ACT. 98% of freshmen come from public schools.

Foreign students: 70 students are from out of the country. Nine countries represented in all.

PROGRAMS OF STUDY.

Degrees: B.A., B.S.

Majors: Accounting, Art, Biology, Business Administration, Chemistry, Economics, Elementary Education, English, French, Health/Physical Education, History, Mathematics, Office Administration, Physics, Political Science, Psychology, Secondary Education, Social Work, Sociology, Spanish.

Special: Minors offered in most majors and in finance, management, and marketing. Freshmen remain in Division of Freshman Studies until 31 semester hour credits have been earned. Primary emphasis in education placed on preparing inner-city school teachers. Associate degrees offered. Double majors. Dual degrees. Cooperative education programs. Preprofessional programs in medicine, veterinary science, pharmacy, optometry, allied health, engineering, medical technology, and nursing. 3-1 medical technology program. Cross-registration with U of New Orleans and Delgado Junior Coll. Teacher certification in elementary and secondary education. ROTC.

Honors: Honors program.

STUDENT LIFE. Housing: Commuter campus; no student housing.

Services and counseling/handicapped student services: Placement services. Health service. Testing center. Personal counseling. Career and academic guidance services. Learning disabled services.

Campus organizations: Undergraduate student government. Lyceum Committee, academic groups, special-interest groups. Four fraternities, no chapter houses; four sororities, no chapter houses. 10% of men join a fraternity. 12% of women join a sorority.

Religious organizations: Denominational religious groups.

ATHLETICS. Physical education requirements: Four semester hours of health/physical education required.

ADMISSIONS. Academic basis for candidate selection (in order of priority): Standardized test scores, secondary school record.

Requirements: Graduation from secondary school is required; GED is accepted. No specific distribution of secondary school units required. English, math, science, social studies, and physical education units recommended. ACT is required.

Procedure: Take ACT by fall of 12th year. Notification of admission on rolling basis. Freshmen accepted for all terms.

Special programs: Credit may be granted through CEEB Advanced Placement. Credit may be granted through CLEP general and subject exams. Credit may be granted through DANTES and challenge exams and for military experience. Early entrance/early admission program. Concurrent enrollment program.

Transfer students: Transfer students accepted for all terms. Application deadline is 30 days prior to registration for fall; 30 days prior to registration for spring. Lowest course grade accepted is "C." Maximum number of transferable credits is 93 semester hours.

Admissions contact: Melvin L. Hodges, Director of Admissions.

FINANCIAL AID. Available aid: Pell grants, SEOG, and aid for undergraduate foreign students. Legislative scholarships. Stafford Loans (GSL).

Supporting data/closing dates: FAFSA: Priority filing date is April 1; accepted on rolling basis. Verification Form: Priority filing date is April 1.

Financial aid contact: Gerald Williams, Director of Financial Aid.

STUDENT EMPLOYMENT. Federal Work-Study Program.

Southern University and Agricultural and Mechanical College

Baton Rouge, LA 70813   504 771-4500

Undergraduate profile. 95.4% Black, .6% Asian-American, .2% Hispanic, 2.7% White, 1.1% Other. 77% are state residents. Average age of undergraduates is 20.

Enrollment. Undergraduates: 3,385 men, 4,398 women (full-time). Freshman class: 4,060 applicants, 3,451 accepted, 2,480 enrolled. Graduate enrollment: 478 men, 807 women.

Faculty. 415 Black, 75 White, 62 Other. 51% of faculty holds doctoral degree. Student/faculty ratio: 20 to 1.

Test score averages/ranges. Average ACT scores: 16 English, 16 math, 17 composite.

1995-96 Costs. Tuition: $2,028 (state residents), $4,808 (out-of-state). Room: $1,508. Board: $1,444. Fees, books, misc. academic expenses (school's estimate): $500.

PROFILE. Southern University and A&M College, founded in 1880, is a public, comprehensive institution. Programs are offered through the Colleges of Agriculture, Arts and Humanities, Business, Education, Engineering, Home Economics, and Science; the Schools of Law and Nursing; and the Graduate School. Its 884-acre campus is located in Baton Rouge.

Accreditation: SACS. Professionally accredited by the Accreditation Board for Engineering and Technology, Inc., the Accrediting Council on Education in Journalism and Mass Communication, the American Dietetic Association, the American Speech-Language-Hearing Association, the Computing Sciences Accreditation Board, the Council on Social Work Education, the National Architecture Accrediting Board, the National Association of Schools of Music, the National Council for Accreditation of Teacher Education, the National League for Nursing.

Religious orientation: Southern University and Agricultural and Mechanical College is nonsectarian; no religious requirements.

Library: Collections totaling 713,868 volumes, 2,301 periodical subscriptions, 375,698 microform items, 419 CD-ROMs, and 2,935 audiovisual items.

Special facilities/museums: Jazz institute.

Athletic facilities: Gymnasiums, weight room, track, basketball and tennis courts, baseball and football fields.

STUDENT BODY. Freshman profile: 6% of freshmen who took ACT scored 24 or over on English, 4% scored 24 or over on math, 3% scored 24 or over on composite; 36% scored 18 or over on English, 29% scored 18 or over on math, 34% scored 18 or over on composite; 90% scored 12 or over on English, 97% scored 12 or over on math, 99% scored 12 or over on composite; 100% scored 6 or over on English, 100% scored 6 or over on math, 100% scored 6 or over on composite. 75% of freshmen come from public schools.

Undergraduate achievement: 57% of fall 1993 freshmen returned for fall 1994 term. 5% of entering class graduates. 21% of students who complete a degree program go on to graduate study within one year.

Foreign students: 22 countries represented in all.

PROGRAMS OF STUDY. Degrees: B.A., B.Arch., B.Mus., B.S.

Majors: Accounting, Agricultural Economics, Animal Science, Apparel/Textiles/Related Arts, Architecture, Biology, Chemistry, Child Development, Civil Engineering, Computer Science, Early Childhood Education, Economics, Electrical Engineering, Electrical Engineering Technology, Electronic Engineering Technology, Elementary School Education, English, Fine Arts, French, History, Human Nutrition/Food, Management, Marketing, Mass Communications, Mathematics, Mechanical Engineering, Mechanical Engineering Technology, Music, Nursing, Physics, Plant Science, Political Science, Psychology, Rehabilitation Services, Secondary Education, Social Work, Sociology, Soil Science, Spanish, Special Education, Speech Communications, Speech Pathology/Audiology, Theater Arts, Therapeutic Recreation/Leisure Studies, Urban Forestry, Vocational Agriculture Education, Vocational Business Education.

Distribution of degrees: The majors with the highest enrollments are accounting, management, and computer science; music, plant science, and animal science have the lowest.

Requirements: General education requirement.

Academic regulations: Minimum 1.5 GPA must be maintained.

Special: Associate degrees offered. Dual degrees. Independent study. Cooperative education programs. Graduate school at which qualified undergraduates may take graduate-level courses. Preprofessional programs in law, medicine, veterinary science, and dentistry. Dual degree programs with Jackson State U and Xavier U. Cross-registration with Louisiana State U at Baton Rouge. Teacher certification in elementary and secondary education. ROTC and NROTC.

Honors: Honors program. Honor societies.

Academic Assistance: Remedial reading, writing, math, and study skills. Nonremedial tutoring.

STUDENT LIFE. Housing: Freshmen under age 21 must live on campus. On-campus married-student housing. 33% of students live in college housing.

Services and counseling/handicapped student services: Placement services. Health service. Women's center. Counseling services for military students. Psychological counseling. Career and academic guidance services. Physically disabled student services. Learning disabled services. Notetaking services. Tape recorders. Tutors.

Campus organizations: Undergraduate student government. Student newspaper (Southern Digest, published once/week). Literary magazine. Yearbook. Choirs, glee clubs, chorale, orchestras, band, departmental organizations, debating club, special-interest groups. Four fraternities, no chapter houses; four sororities, no chapter houses. 2% of men join a fraternity. 4% of women join a sorority.

Religious organizations: Several religious associations.

ATHLETICS. Physical education requirements: Two semesters of physical education required.

Intercollegiate competition: 3% of students participate. Baseball (M), basketball (M,W), cross-country (M,W), football (M), golf (M), tennis (M,W), track (indoor) (M,W), track (outdoor) (M,W), track and field (indoor) (M,W), track and field (outdoor) (M,W), volleyball (W). Member of NCAA Division I, NCAA Division I-AA for football, Southwestern Athletic Conference.

Intramural and club sports: 80% of students participate. Intramural badminton, bait casting, basketball, croquet, flag football, fly fishing, frisbee, golf, horseshoes, paddle tennis, soccer, softball, swimming, table tennis, tennis, track and field, volleyball, weight lifting.

ADMISSIONS.

Requirements: Graduation from secondary school is recommended; GED is accepted. The following program of study is recommended: 4 units of English, 3 units of math, 3 units of science, 3 units of foreign language, 3 units of social studies, 1 unit of history. Open admissions policy. Exams on the equivalent of 15 units of secondary school work required of applicants not meeting standard requirements. SAT I or ACT is required.

Procedure: Take SAT I or ACT by January of 12th year. Visit college for interview by January of 12th year. Notification of admission on rolling basis. $50 refundable room deposit. Freshmen accepted for all terms.

Special programs: Credit may be granted through CEEB Advanced Placement. Credit may be granted through CLEP general and subject exams. Placement may be granted through challenge exams. Early entrance/early admission program.

Transfer students: Transfer students accepted for all terms. Application deadline is July 1 for fall; November 1 for spring. Lowest course grade accepted is "D." Maximum number of transferable credits is 64 semester hours from a two-year school and 93 semester hours from a four-year school.

Admissions contact: Henry Bellaire, M.S., Director of Admissions. 504 771-2430.

FINANCIAL AID. Available aid: Pell grants, SEOG, state scholarships and grants, school scholarships, academic merit scholarships, and athletic scholarships. University participates in College Board College Scholarship Service. PLUS, Stafford Loans (GSL), and unsubsidized Stafford Loans.

Financial aid statistics: 10% of aid is not need-based. In 1994-95, 96% of all undergraduate aid applicants received aid; 88% of freshman aid applicants. Average amounts of aid awarded freshmen: Scholarships and grants, $2,028; loans, $2,000.

Supporting data/closing dates: FAFSA/FAF: Priority filing date is April 17. Notification of awards on rolling basis.

Financial aid contact: Cynthia Tarver, Director of Financial Aid. 504 771-2790.

STUDENT EMPLOYMENT. Federal Work-Study Program. Institutional employment. 30% of full-time undergraduates work on campus during school year. Students may expect to earn an average of $500 during school year. Off-campus part-time employment opportunities rated "good."

COMPUTER FACILITIES. IBM/IBM-compatible and Apple/Macintosh microcomputers. Students may access BITNET, Internet. Computer facilities are available to all students.

Fees: None.

GRADUATE CAREER DATA. Graduate school percentages: 1% enter law school. 2% enter medical school. 1% enter dental school. 3% enter graduate business programs. Highest graduate school enrollments: Georgia Tech, Louisiana State U.

Southwestern Christian College

Terrell, TX 75160   **214 524-3341**

Undergraduate profile. N/A.

Enrollment. Undergraduates: 116 men, 96 women (full-time). Freshman class: 104 applicants, 104 accepted, 104 enrolled.

Faculty. 17 full-time; 3 part-time.

Test score averages/ranges. N/A.

1995-96 Costs. Tuition: $7,676. Room & board: $2,793. Fees, books, misc. academic expenses (school's estimate): $460.

PROFILE. Southwestern Christian, established in 1949, is a private, church-affliated liberal arts college.

Accreditation: SACS.

Religious orientation: Southwestern Christian College is affiliated with the Church of Christ; no religious requirements.

Athletic facilities: Gymnasium, tennis courts.

PROGRAMS OF STUDY. Degrees: B.A., B.S.

Majors: Religious Education, Theological Studies.

Requirements: General education requirement.

Special: Associate degrees offered. Independent study. Internships.

STUDENT LIFE. Housing: Women's and men's dorms.

Services and counseling/handicapped student services: Personal counseling. Career guidance services. Learning disabled services.

Campus organizations: Undergraduate student government. Student newspaper. Yearbook. Choral groups, jazz band, drama, music ensembles, pep band.

ATHLETICS. Physical education requirements: None.

Intercollegiate competition: 20% of students participate. Basketball (M,W), cheerleading (M,W), track and field (outdoor) (M,W). Member of NJCAA.

Intramural and club sports: 30% of students participate. Intramural basketball, flag football, softball.

ADMISSIONS. Requirements: Graduation from secondary school is recommended. No specific distribution of secondary school units required. Open admissions policy. Admissions interview recommended.

Procedure: Application deadline is July 31. Notification of admission on rolling basis. Freshmen accepted for fall term only.

Special programs: Admission may be deferred. Credit and placement may be granted through challenge exams. Early entrance/early admission program.

FINANCIAL AID. Supporting data/closing dates: FAFSA: Deadline is July 15. Notification of awards begins July 15.

Spelman College

Atlanta, GA 30314   404 681-3643

Undergraduate profile. 99% Black, 1% Other. 21% are state residents; 7% are transfers. Average age of undergraduates is 20.
Enrollment. 1,933 women (full-time). Freshman class: 3,650 applicants, 1,377 accepted, 448 enrolled.
Faculty. 134 full-time, 75 part-time; 90 Black, 30 White, 14 Other. 87% of faculty holds doctoral degree. Student/faculty ratio: 15 to 1.
Test score averages/ranges. Average SAT I scores: 1010 combined. Average ACT scores: 23 composite.
1995-96 Costs. Tuition: $7,550. Room & board: $5,890. Fees, books, misc. academic expenses (school's estimate): $1,825.

PROFILE. Spelman, founded in 1881, is a private, historically Black, liberal arts college for women. Its 32-acre campus is located one mile from downtown Atlanta.

Accreditation: SACS. Professionally accredited by the National Association of Schools of Music, the National Council for Accreditation of Teacher Education.

Religious orientation: Spelman College is nonsectarian; no religious requirements.

Library: Collections totaling 404,991 volumes, 1,739 periodical subscriptions, and 385,538 microform items.

Special facilities/museums: Nursery-elementary school, language lab, electron microscope.

Athletic facilities: Gymnasium, bowling lanes, swimming pool, badminton, basketball, tennis, and volleyball courts.

STUDENT BODY. Freshman profile: 80% of accepted applicants took SAT I; 20% took ACT. 84% of freshmen come from public schools.

Undergraduate achievement: 91% of fall 1993 freshmen returned for fall 1994 term. 69% of entering class graduates. 41% of students who complete a degree program immediately go on to graduate study.

Foreign students: 24 students are from out of the country. Countries represented include African countries, the Bahamas, Bermuda, and the Dominican Republic; six in all.

PROGRAMS OF STUDY. Degrees: B.A., B.S.

Majors: Art, Biochemistry, Biology, Chemistry, Child Development, Computer Sciences, Drama, Economics, Engineering, English, French, History, Independent Major, Mathematics, Music, Natural Sciences, Philosophy, Physics, Political Science, Psychology, Religion, Sociology, Spanish.

Distribution of degrees: The majors with the highest enrollments are psychology, English, and economics; religion, French, and philosophy have the lowest.

Requirements: General education requirement.

Academic regulations: Freshmen must maintain minimum 1.8 GPA; sophomores, juniors, seniors, 2.0 GPA.

Special: Minors offered in several majors and in communication studies, dance, international studies, management and organization, and women's studies. Social welfare program. Freshman studies program offers pilot interdisciplinary core curriculum. Self-designed majors. Double majors. Dual degrees. Internships. Preprofessional programs in law, medicine, pharmacy, and dentistry. 3-2 engineering programs with Auburn U, Boston U, Georgia Tech, and Rochester U. Member of Atlanta University Center Consortium. Washington Semester. New York Semester. Exchange programs with Mills Coll, Mount Holyoke Coll, Pomona Coll, Simmons Coll, Smith Coll, Vassar Coll, and Wellesley Coll. Premedical program with Boston U. Teacher certification in early childhood, elementary, and secondary education. Study abroad in numerous countries. ROTC and NROTC at Morehouse Coll. AFROTC at Georgia Tech.

Honors: Honors program.

Academic Assistance: Remedial reading, math, and study skills. Nonremedial tutoring.

STUDENT LIFE. Housing: All honors students must live on campus freshman year. Women's dorms. 59% of students live in college housing.

Social atmosphere: Popular gathering spots include the Lower Manley Student Center Plaza and Friday Market. Student Government Association, sororities, and AST (African Sisterhood) have widespread influence on student life. Eagerly anticipated social events include Homecoming Week, Founder's Week, Celebration in Black, Howard vs. Morehouse football game, and Upperclass Women Week. "There is a lot to do," reports the editor of the student newspaper. "Although we are a small private college, we are part of a larger university system. We are within walking distance of three other colleges/universities. We are also five minutes from the downtown Atlanta area."

Services and counseling/handicapped student services: Placement services. Health service. Women's center. Day care. Office of Freshman Studies. Counseling services for older students. Birth control, personal, and psychological counseling. Career and academic guidance services. Religious counseling. Physically disabled student services. Learning disabled services. Notetaking services. Tape recorders. Tutors. Reader services for the blind.

Campus organizations: Undergraduate student government. Student newspaper (Spotlight, published bimonthly). Literary magazine. Yearbook. Chorus, glee club, jazz band, dance theatres, tour guides, tutoring groups, debate group, departmental and political groups, service and special-interest groups. Five sororities, no chapter houses. 8% of women join a sorority.

Religious organizations: Several religious groups.

Foreign student organizations: International Student Club.

ATHLETICS. Physical education requirements: Two semesters of physical education required.

Intercollegiate competition: 5% of students participate. Basketball (W), tennis (W), track and field (outdoor) (W), volleyball (W).

Intramural and club sports: 5% of students participate. Intramural badminton, basketball, soccer, softball, swimming, tennis, volleyball.

ADMISSIONS. Academic basis for candidate selection (in order of priority): Secondary school record, standardized test scores, essay, school's recommendation, class rank.

Nonacademic basis for candidate selection: Extracurricular participation is important. Particular talent or ability, geographical distribution, and alumni/ae relationship are considered.

Requirements: Graduation from secondary school is required; GED is accepted. 15 units and the following program of study are required: 4 units of English, 2 units of math, 2 units of science including 1 unit of lab, 2 units of foreign language, 2 units of social studies, 2 units of electives. 3 units of math, 3 units of science, 3 units of foreign language are recommended. SAT I or ACT is required. Campus visit recommended.

Procedure: Take SAT I or ACT by December of 12th year. Visit college by January of 12th year. Application deadline is February 1. Notification of admission by March 15. Reply is required by May 1. $50 tuition deposit, refundable until July 1. $50 room deposit. Freshmen accepted for all terms.

Special programs: Admission may be deferred one year. Credit may be granted through CEEB Advanced Placement for scores of 3 or higher. Credit may be granted through CLEP subject exams. Credit and placement may be granted through challenge exams. Early decision program. In fall 1994, 440 applied for early decision and 189 were accepted. Deadline for applying for early decision is November 15. Early entrance/early admission program. Concurrent enrollment program.

Transfer students: Transfer students accepted for all terms. In fall 1994, 7% of all new students were transfers into all classes. 199 transfer applications were received, 69 were accepted. Application deadline is February 1 for fall; November 1 for spring. Minimum 2.0 GPA required. Lowest course grade accepted is "C." Maximum number of transferable credits is 90 semester hours. At least 32 semester hours must be completed at the college to receive degree.

Admissions contact: Victoria Valle, Director of Admissions and Orientation Services. 404 681-3643, extension 2188.

FINANCIAL AID. Available aid: Pell grants, SEOG, state grants, school grants, private scholarships and grants, ROTC scholarships, academic merit scholarships, and aid for undergraduate foreign students. Perkins Loans (NDSL), PLUS, and Stafford Loans (GSL). Deferred payment plan.

Financial aid statistics: In 1994-95, 76% of all undergraduate aid applicants received aid.

Supporting data/closing dates: FAFSA: Deadline is April 1. School's own aid application: Deadline is April 1. Notification of awards begins April 2.
Financial aid contact: Shirley Scott, M.S., Director of Financial Aid. 404 681-3643, extension 1471.
STUDENT EMPLOYMENT. Federal Work-Study Program. Institutional employment. 25% of full-time undergraduates work on campus during school year. Students may expect to earn an average of $1,500 during school year. Off-campus part-time employment opportunities rated "fair."
COMPUTER FACILITIES. IBM/IBM-compatible microcomputers. Computer facilities are available to all students.
Fees: None.
Hours: 8 AM-10 PM.
PROMINENT ALUMNI/AE. Marian Wright Edelman, founder and president, Children's Defense Fund; Alice Walker, author; Esther Rolle, actress; Varnette Honeywood, artist; Rolanda Watts, newscaster; Deborah Prolo-Stith, Massachusetts public health commissioner; Col. Marchelite Jordan, first woman commander of a U.S. Air Force base.

Stillman College

Tuscaloosa, AL 35403   **205 349-4240**

Undergraduate profile: 97% Black, 2% White, 1% Other. 73% are state residents; 6% are transfers. Average age of undergraduates is 20.
Enrollment. Undergraduates: 293 men, 612 women (full-time). Freshman class: 664 applicants, 557 accepted, 185 enrolled.
Faculty. 56 full-time, 15 part-time; 35 Black, 36 White, 7 Other. 54% of faculty holds doctoral degree. Student/faculty ratio: 12 to 1.
Test score averages/ranges. Average ACT scores: 17 English, 16 math, 17 composite.
1995-96 Costs. Tuition: $5,200. Room & board: $3,100. Fees, books, misc. academic expenses (school's estimate): $550.

PROFILE. Stillman is a church-affiliated, predominantly black, liberal arts college. Founded in 1876, it adopted coeducation in 1899. Its 100-acre campus is located in Tuscaloosa, 60 miles from Birmingham.
Accreditation: SACS.
Religious orientation: Stillman College is affiliated with the Presbyterian Church (USA); five semesters of religion required. Regular attendance is mandatory for chapel, assemblies, and convocations.
Library: Collections totaling 103,530 volumes, 350 periodical subscriptions, and 572 CD-ROMs.
Athletic facilities: Gymnasium, softball field, tennis courts.
STUDENT BODY. Freshman profile: 32% of freshmen who took ACT scored 18 or over on composite; 96% scored 12 or over on composite; 100% scored 6 or over on composite. Majority of accepted applicants took ACT. 99% of freshmen come from public schools.
Undergraduate achievement: 70% of fall 1993 freshmen returned for fall 1994 term. 22% of entering class graduated. 16% of students who complete a degree program immediately go on to graduate study.
Foreign students: Eight students are from out of the country. Countries represented include Nigeria and St. Kitts; six in all.
PROGRAMS OF STUDY. Degrees: B.A., B.S.
Majors: Biology, Business, Chemistry, Communications, Computer Science, Elementary Education, English, Health/Physical Education, History, Interdisciplinary Studies, International Studies, Mathematics, Music, Physics, Recreation Management, Religion/Philosophy, Sociology.
Distribution of degrees: The majors with the highest enrollments are business, biology, and education; English and physics have the lowest.
Requirements: General education requirement.

Academic regulations: Freshmen must maintain minimum 1.6 GPA; sophomores, 1.8 GPA; juniors, 2.0 GPA.

Special: Minors offered in all majors (except elementary education) and in art, foreign languages, political science, and psychology. Certificat program in gerontology. Double majors. Dual degrees. Independent study. Internships. Cooperative education programs. Preprofessional programs in law and medicine. 3-2 nursing program. Combined degree programs in engineering, occupational therapy, and social work. Exchange program with Alma Coll, Marietta Coll, U of Alabama at Birmingham, and Whitworth Coll. Teacher certification in elementary and secondary education. Certification in specific subject areas. ROTC at U of Alabama.

Honors: Honors program.

Academic Assistance: Remedial reading, writing, and math.

STUDENT LIFE. Housing: Students may live on or off campus. Women's and men's dorms. School-owned/operated apartments. Cooperative dorms. 68% of students live in college housing.

Social atmosphere: Some popular gathering spots for students are the College Student Center and the Greek Square. The Student Government Association, Delta Sigma Theta, and the basketball team are influential groups on campus. Among the popular events of the year are Founder's Day, Homecoming, Black History Month, Martin Luther King Convocation, Matriculation Convocation, basketball games and social forums. According to the student newspaper, "Most students on campus enjoy recreational activities such as basketball, playing cards, video games, and other sports. They also spend a good deal of time in the various computer centers."

Services and counseling/handicapped student services: Placement services. Health service. Counseling services for older students. Birth control and personal counseling. Career and academic guidance services. Religious counseling. Physically disabled student services. Tape recorders. Tutors. Reader services for the blind.

Campus organizations: Undergraduate student government. Student newspaper (Tiger's Paw, published once/month). Yearbook. Radio station. Band, choir, veterans club, women's social club, academic clubs. Five fraternities, no chapter houses; four sororities, no chapter houses.

Religious organizations: Christian Student Association.

Foreign student organizations: Intercultural Club.

ATHLETICS. Physical education requirements: Two semesters of physical education required. ROTC fulfills requirement.

Intercollegiate competition: 4% of students participate. Basketball (M,W), cross-country (M), tennis (M,W), track and field (outdoor) (M,W), volleyball (W). Member of NCAA Division III.

Intramural and club sports: 10% of students participate. Intramural basketball, billiards, bowling, softball, swimming, tennis, touch football.

ADMISSIONS. Academic basis for candidate selection (in order of priority): Secondary school record, standardized test scores, class rank, school's recommendation.

Nonacademic basis for candidate selection: Character and personality and geographical distribution are emphasized. Extracurricular participation and alumni/ae relationship are important.

Requirements: Graduation from secondary school is required; GED is accepted. 15 units and the following program of study are required: 4 units of English, 1 unit of math, 1 unit of science, 1 unit of social studies, 1 unit of history, 7 units of electives. 2 units of math, 2 units of science, and 2 units of social studies are recommended. Minimum 2.0 GPA recommended. Conditional admission for applicants with minimum 1.6 GPA. SAT I or ACT is recommended.

Procedure: Take SAT I or ACT by December of 12th year. Suggest filing application by March 15; no deadline. Notification of admission on rolling basis. Reply is required by June 30. $50 nonrefundable room deposit. Freshmen accepted for all terms.

Special programs: Admission may be deferred. Credit and/or placement may be granted through CEEB Advanced Placement exams. Credit and/or placement may be granted through CLEP general and subject exams. Credit may be granted for life experience. Early entrance/early admission program. Concurrent enrollment program.

Transfer students: Transfer students accepted for all terms. In fall 1994, 6% of all new students were transfers into all classes. 153 transfer applications were received, 64 were accepted. Application deadline is June 30 for fall; October 15 for spring. Lowest course grade accepted is "C."
Admissions contact: Barbara K. Smith, M.A., Director of Admissions. 205 349-4240.

FINANCIAL AID. Available aid: Pell grants, SEOG, state grants, school scholarships and grants, private scholarships and grants, and United Negro College Fund. Perkins Loans (NDSL), PLUS, Stafford Loans (GSL), state loans, school loans, private loans, and unsubsidized Stafford Loans.
Financial aid statistics: 15% of aid is not need-based. In 1994-95, 90% of all undergraduate aid applicants received aid; 90% of freshman aid applicants. Average amounts of aid awarded freshmen: Scholarships and grants, $3,031; loans, $2,100.
Supporting data/closing dates: FAFSA: Priority filing date is June 15. School's own aid application: Priority filing date is June 15. State aid form: Deadline is September 15. Income tax forms: Priority filing date is June 15. Notification of awards on rolling basis.
Financial aid contact: Joseph Davis, M.A., Director of Financial Aid. 205 349-4240.

STUDENT EMPLOYMENT. Federal Work-Study Program. Institutional employment. 35% of full-time undergraduates work on campus during school year. Students may expect to earn an average of $700 during school year. Off-campus part-time employment opportunities rated "fair."

COMPUTER FACILITIES. 100 IBM/IBM-compatible and Apple/Macintosh microcomputers; 50 are networked. Students may access Digital minicomputer/mainframe systems. Client/LAN operating systems include Apple/Macintosh, DOS, DEC, Novell. Computer facilities are available to all students.
Fees: $20 computer fee per course.
Hours: Microcomputers: 8 AM-5 PM; minicomputers: 8 AM-8 PM (M-Sa), 4-8 PM (Su).

GRADUATE CAREER DATA. Highest graduate school enrollments: Alabama State U, U of Alabama, U of Alabama at Birmingham.

PROMINENT ALUMNI/AE. Dr. Haywood Strickland, past director of grant management, United Negro College Fund; Coy Williamson, entrepreneur, health care services; Michael Figures, Alabama state senator.

Talladega College

Talladega, AL 35160   205 362-0206

Undergraduate profile. 96% Black, 1% Hispanic, 3% White. 63% are state residents; 1% are transfers. Average age of undergraduates is 21.
Enrollment. Undergraduates: 334 men, 549 women (full-time). Freshman class: 2,633 applicants, 1,042 accepted, 328 enrolled.
Faculty. 55 full-time, 18 part-time; 39 Black, 25 White, 9 Other. 48% of faculty holds doctoral degree. Student/faculty ratio: 18 to 1.
Test score averages/ranges. Average SAT I scores: 778 combined. Average ACT scores: 17 composite.
1995-96 Costs. Tuition: $5,666. Room: $1,424. Board: $1,540. Fees, books, misc. academic expenses (school's estimate): $768.

PROFILE. Talladega is a private, historically Black, liberal arts college. Founded in 1867, it adopted coeducation in 1880. Its 135-acre campus is located in Talladega, 50 miles east of Birmingham.
Accreditation: SACS. Professionally accredited by the Council on Social Work Education.
Religious orientation: Talladega College is affiliated with the United Church of Christ; no religious requirements.
Library: Collections totaling over 95,000 volumes, 330 periodical subscriptions, 1,250 microform items, and seven CD-ROMs.
Special facilities/museums: Art gallery.

Athletic facilities: Gymnasium, baseball field, basketball and tennis courts, swimming pool, golf driving range.

STUDENT BODY. Freshman profile: 1% of freshmen who took ACT scored 30 or over on composite; 12% scored 24 or over on composite; 44% scored 18 or over on composite; 99% scored 12 or over on composite; 100% scored 6 or over on composite. 15% of accepted applicants took SAT I; 67% took ACT. 86% of freshmen come from public schools.

Undergraduate achievement: 54% of fall 1993 freshmen returned for fall 1994 term. 22% of entering class graduates. 37% of students who complete a degree program go on to graduate study.

Foreign students: Five students are from out of the country. Countries represented include Bermuda; one in all.

PROGRAMS OF STUDY. Degrees: B.A., B.Mus.

Majors: Biology, Business Administration, Chemistry, Computer/Information Sciences, Economics, English, History, Mathematics, Music, Music Education, Music Performance, Physics, Psychology, Public Administration, Rehabilitation Education Services, Social Work, Sociology.

Distribution of degrees: The majors with the highest enrollments are business administration, biology, and English; music and mathematics have the lowest.

Requirements: General education requirement.

Academic regulations: Minimum 2.0 GPA must be maintained.

Special: Courses offered in art, communications, criminal justice, French, German, journalism, marine sciences, philosophy, political science, religion, secondary education, and Spanish. Students are admitted into General Division and move into concentrated major field after two years of basic study. Double majors. Dual degrees. Internships. Preprofessional programs in law, medicine, dentistry, allied health fields, and nursing. Teacher certification in secondary education. Certification in specific subject areas. ROTC at Jacksonville State U.

Honors: Honors program. Honor societies.

Academic Assistance: Remedial reading, writing, math, and study skills. Nonremedial tutoring.

STUDENT LIFE. Housing: Women's and men's dorms. School-owned/operated apartments. 86% of students live in college housing.

Services and counseling/handicapped student services: Career and academic guidance services. Physically disabled student services. Learning disabled services. Tape recorders. Tutors.

Campus organizations: Undergraduate student government. Student newspaper (Talladega Student Star). Yearbook. Black Musician Association. Annual fine arts festival, choir and string groups, jazz ensemble, debate society, Little Theatre, biology, German, and math clubs, social work club, pre-alumni group, departmental and special-interest groups, 32 organizations in all. Four fraternities, no chapter houses; three sororities, no chapter houses. 18% of men join a fraternity. 45% of women join a sorority.

Religious organizations: Baptist Student Union, Album of Faith.

ATHLETICS. Physical education requirements: Two semesters of physical education required.

Intercollegiate competition: 20% of students participate. Baseball (M), basketball (M,W), cheerleading (M,W), cross-country (M,W), golf (M), tennis (M,W), track (indoor) (M,W), track (outdoor) (M,W), track and field (indoor) (M,W), volleyball (W). Member of NAIA, Southern States Conference.

Intramural and club sports: 60% of students participate. Intramural basketball, billiards, flag football, softball, swimming, table tennis, volleyball. Men's club tennis, volleyball. Women's club volleyball.

ADMISSIONS. Academic basis for candidate selection (in order of priority): Secondary school record, standardized test scores, class rank, school's recommendation, essay.

Nonacademic basis for candidate selection: Character and personality and alumni/ae relationship are emphasized. Particular talent or ability is considered.

Requirements: Graduation from secondary school is required; GED is not accepted. 13 units and the following program of study are required: 4 units of English, 2 units of math, 2 units of science, 3 units of social studies, 2 units of academic electives. Minimum composite ACT score of 18 and minimum 2.5 GPA required. Audition required of music program applicants. ACT is required; SAT I may be substituted. Campus visit and interview recommended. Off-campus interviews available with an admissions representative.

Procedure: Take SAT I or ACT by March of 12th year. Suggest filing application by June 15; no deadline. Notification of admission by June 1. Reply is required by August 1. Nonrefundable deposit of one-third of tuition. $50 nonrefundable room deposit. Freshmen accepted for all terms.

Special programs: Admission may be deferred. Credit and/or placement may be granted through CEEB Advanced Placement exams for scores of 3 or higher. Credit and/or placement may be granted through CLEP general and subject exams. Placement may be granted through challenge exams. Credit and placement may be granted through Regents College and ACT PEP exams. Early decision program. Early entrance/early admission program.

Transfer students: Transfer students accepted for all terms. In fall 1994, 1% of all new students were transfers into all classes. Application deadline is rolling for fall; rolling for spring. Minimum 2.0 GPA required. Lowest course grade accepted is "C." Maximum number of transferable credits is 90 semester hours. At least 60 semester hours must be completed at the college to receive degree.

Admissions contact: Monroe Thornton, M.B.A., Director of Admissions. 800 633-2440 (out-of-state), 800 762-2468 (in-state).

FINANCIAL AID. Available aid: Pell grants, SEOG, state grants, school scholarships and grants, private scholarships and grants, academic merit scholarships, athletic scholarships, and aid for undergraduate foreign students. Perkins Loans (NDSL) and Stafford Loans (GSL). AMS and Tuition Management Systems.

Financial aid statistics: 20% of aid is not need-based. In 1994-95, 90% of all undergraduate aid applicants received aid; 90% of freshman aid applicants. Average amounts of aid awarded freshmen: Scholarships and grants, $2,100; loans, $2,420.

Supporting data/closing dates: FAFSA/FAF. School's own aid application: Priority filing date is May 1. Income tax forms: Priority filing date is May 1. Notification of awards on rolling basis.

Financial aid contact: Johnny Byrd, Director of Financial Aid. 205 362-0206, extension 236.

STUDENT EMPLOYMENT. Federal Work-Study Program. Institutional employment. 30% of full-time undergraduates work on campus during school year. Students may expect to earn an average of $500 during school year. Off-campus part-time employment opportunities rated "fair."

COMPUTER FACILITIES. 30 IBM/IBM-compatible microcomputers; all are networked. Students may access Digital, IBM minicomputer/mainframe systems. Client/LAN operating systems include DOS, Novell. Computer facilities are available to all students. **Fees:** None. **Hours:** 8 AM-4:30 PM, 7-10 PM.

GRADUATE CAREER DATA. Graduate school percentages: 5% enter law school. 11% enter medical school. Highest graduate school enrollments: Clark U, Jacksonville State U, U of Alabama. 27% of graduates choose careers in business and industry.

PROMINENT ALUMNI/AE. Eunice W. Johnson, coordinator, Ebony Fashion Fair; J. Mason Davis, attorney, chairperson of Talladega College trustees; Dr. Jewel Plummer Cobb, president, California State U at Fullerton; Arthur Shores, attorney.

Tennessee State University

Nashville, TN 37209-1561   **615 963-5000**

Undergraduate profile. 69% Black, 3% Hispanic, 1% Native American, 27% White. 83% are state residents. Average age of undergraduates is 25.

Enrollment. Undergraduates: 1,949 men, 3,091 women (full-time). Freshman class: 3,566 applicants, 1,919 accepted, 893 enrolled. Graduate enrollment: 468 men, 991 women.

Faculty. 294 full-time. 136 Black, 135 White, 23 Other. 58% of faculty holds doctoral degree. Student/faculty ratio: 25 to 1.

Test score averages/ranges. Average ACT scores: 20 composite.

1995-96 Costs. Tuition: $1,866 (state residents), $5,996 (out-of-state). Room & board: $2,720. Fees, books, misc. academic expenses (school's estimate): $900.

PROFILE. Tennessee State, founded in 1912, is a public, historically Black university. Programs are offered through the Schools of Agriculture and Home Economics, Allied Health Professions, Arts and Sciences, Business, Education, Engineering and Technology, Nursing, and the Graduate School. Its 465-acre main campus is located north of the center of Nashville.

Accreditation: SACS. Professionally accredited by the Accreditation Board for Engineering and Technology, Inc., the American Home Economics Association, the American Medical Association (CAHEA), the Council on Social Work Education, the National Association of Schools of Music, the National Council for Accreditation of Teacher Education.

Religious orientation: Tennessee State University is nonsectarian; no religious requirements.

Library: Collections totaling 420,463 volumes, 1,775 periodical subscriptions, and 657,532 microform items.

Athletic facilities: Sports complex.

STUDENT BODY. Freshman profile: 10% of accepted applicants took SAT I; 90% took ACT. 88% of freshmen come from public schools.

Foreign students: 154 students are from out of the country. Countries represented include the Bahamas, China, India, Jordan, Nigeria, and Saudi Arabia; 40 in all.

PROGRAMS OF STUDY. Degrees: B.A., B.Bus.Admin., B.S., B.S.Nurs.

Majors: Accounting, Administration/Supervision, Aeronautical/Industrial Technology, African Studies, Agricultural Science, Agricultural Sciences, Architectural Engineering, Art, Arts/ Sciences, Biology, Business Administration, Cardiorespiratory Care Sciences, Chemistry, Civil Engineering, Criminal Justice, Criminal Justice Administration, Curriculum/Instruction, Dental Hygiene, Early Childhood Education, Economics, Electrical Engineering, Elementary Education, Engineering, English, Finance, Foreign Languages, General Interdisciplinary Studies, Guidance/ Counseling, Health Care Administration/Planning, Health/Physical Education/Recreation Administration, Health/Physical Education/Recreation Education, History/Geography/Political Science, Home Economics, Home Economics Education, Hotel/Restaurant Administration, Mathematics, Mechanical Engineering, Medical Technology, Music, Music Education, Nursing, Occupational Therapy, Office Management, Physical Therapy, Physics/Mathematics/Computer Science, Psychology, Public Administration, Reading, Social Work/Sociology, Special Education, Speech Communication/Theatre, Speech Pathology/Audiology.

Distribution of degrees: The majors with the highest enrollments are nursing, business administration, and engineering; agricultural sciences, physics/mathematics/computer science, and music have the lowest.

Special: Minors offered. Associate degrees offered. Independent study. Internships. Cooperative education programs. Graduate school at which qualified undergraduates may take graduate-level courses. Preprofessional programs in medicine, veterinary science, dentistry, occupational therapy, physical therapy, and social work. 2-2 pre-dentistry and 3-2 pre-medicine programs with Meharry Medical Coll. 3-1 medical technology program offered with local hospitals. Natural science courses offered at Gulf Coast Research Lab. Teacher certification in elementary, secondary, and special education. Certification in specific subject areas. AFROTC. ROTC and NROTC at Vanderbilt U.

Honors: Phi Beta Kappa. Honors program. Honor societies.

Academic Assistance: Remedial reading, writing, math, and study skills.

STUDENT LIFE. Housing: Students may live on or off campus. Women's and men's dorms. 25% of students live in college housing.

Services and counseling/handicapped student services: Placement services. Health service. Day care. Counseling services for veteran students. Birth control, personal, and psychological counseling. Career and academic guidance services.

Campus organizations: Undergraduate student government. Student newspaper (Meter). Yearbook. Radio station. String ensembles, concert singers, concert and marching bands, choir, jazz group, children's theatre, Players Guild, debate society, athletic, departmental, service, and special-interest groups. Four fraternities, no chapter houses; four sororities, no chapter houses. 1% of men join a fraternity. 1% of women join a sorority.

Religious organizations: Student Christian Association, Baptist Club, Catholic Club.

Foreign student organizations: International Student Organization, African Student Organization.

ATHLETICS. Physical education requirements: Two semesters of physical education required.

Intercollegiate competition: Baseball (M), basketball (M,W), cheerleading (M,W), cross-country (M,W), football (M), golf (M), tennis (M,W), track and field (indoor) (W), track and field (outdoor) (W), volleyball (W). Member of NCAA Division I, NCAA Division I-AA for football, Ohio Valley Conference.

Intramural and club sports: Intramural basketball.

ADMISSIONS. Academic basis for candidate selection (in order of priority): Secondary school record, standardized test scores, class rank, school's recommendation, essay.

Nonacademic basis for candidate selection: Character and personality, particular talent or ability, and alumni/ae relationship are considered.

Requirements: Graduation from secondary school is required; GED is accepted. 14 units and the following program of study are required: 4 units of English, 3 units of math, 2 units of science including 1 unit of lab, 2 units of foreign language, 1 unit of social studies, 1 unit of history, 1 unit of visual/performing arts. Minimum composite ACT score of 19 and minimum 2.25 GPA required. Minimum 2.5 GPA required of out-of-state applicants. Developmental studies program for applicants not normally admissible. ACT is required; SAT I may be substituted.

Procedure: Take SAT I or ACT by November of 12th year. Application deadline is August 1. Notification of admission on rolling basis. $50 nonrefundable room deposit. Freshmen accepted for all terms.

Special programs: Credit may be granted through CEEB Advanced Placement for scores of 4 or higher. Credit may be granted through CLEP subject exams. Credit may be granted through DANTES and challenge exams and for military experience. Placement may be granted through ACT PEP exams.

Transfer students: Transfer students accepted for all terms. In fall 1994, less than 1% of all new students were transfers into all classes. 1,756 transfer applications were received, 1,166 were accepted. Application deadline is August 1 for fall; December 1 for spring. Minimum 2.0 GPA required. Lowest course grade accepted is "C." At least 60 semester hours must be completed at the university to receive degree.

Admissions contact: John Cade, M.S., Dean of Admissions and Records. 615 963-5101.

FINANCIAL AID. Available aid: Pell grants, SEOG, state grants, school scholarships and grants, private scholarships and grants, ROTC scholarships, academic merit scholarships, athletic scholarships, aid for undergraduate foreign students, and United Negro College Fund. Perkins Loans (NDSL), Stafford Loans (GSL), and school loans.

Financial aid statistics: In 1993-94, 75% of all undergraduate aid applicants received aid; 75% of freshman aid applicants. Average amounts of aid awarded freshmen: Scholarships and grants, $400.

Supporting data/closing dates: FAFSA/FAF: Priority filing date is April 1. School's own aid application: Priority filing date is April 1. Notification of awards on rolling basis.

Financial aid contact: Wilson Lee, Jr, M.S., M.P.A., Director of Financial Aid. 615 963-5701.

STUDENT EMPLOYMENT. Federal Work-Study Program. Institutional employment. 20% of full-time undergraduates work on campus during school year. Students may expect to earn an average of $900 during school year. Off-campus part-time employment opportunities rated "excellent."

COMPUTER FACILITIES. 300 IBM/IBM-compatible microcomputers; 150 are networked. Students may access Digital minicomputer/mainframe systems. Client/LAN operating systems include DOS, Microsoft. Computer facilities are available to all students.

Fees: None.

Hours: 8 AM-10 PM.

Texas College

Tyler, TX 75702

903 593-8311

Undergraduate profile. 99% Black, 1% Other. 74% are state residents; 6% are transfers. Average age of undergraduates is 20.

Enrollment. Undergraduates: 296 men, 247 women (full-time). Freshman class: 225 applicants, 205 accepted, 198 enrolled.

Faculty. 25 full-time, 5 part-time. 54% of faculty holds doctoral degree. Student/faculty ratio: 18 to 1.

Test score averages/ranges. Average SAT I scores: 220 verbal, 260 math. Average ACT scores: 15 composite.

1995-96 Costs. Tuition: $4,800. Room & board: $2,430. Fees, books, misc. academic expenses (school's estimate): $620.

PROFILE. Texas College, founded in 1894, is a private, church-affiliated, historically Black college. Its 66-acre campus is located in Tyler, 100 miles east of Dallas.

Accreditation: SACS.

Religious orientation: Texas College is affiliated with the Christian Methodist Episcopal Church; two semesters of religion required.

Library: Collections totaling 80,492 volumes, 130 periodical subscriptions, and 24,513 microform items.

Special facilities/museums: On-campus preschool.

Athletic facilities: Gymnasium, athletic fields.

STUDENT BODY. Freshman profile: Majority of accepted applicants took SAT I. 98% of freshmen come from public schools.

Undergraduate achievement: 67% of fall 1992 freshmen returned for fall 1993 term. 40% of entering class graduates. 70% of students who complete a degree program go on to graduate study within five years.

Foreign students: 24 students are from out of the country. Countries represented include Nigeria.

PROGRAMS OF STUDY. Degrees: B.A., B.S.

Majors: Biology, Business Administration, Business Education, Computer Science, Elementary Education, English, General Science, History, Mathematics, Music, Physical Education, Political Science, Social Science, Social Work, Sociology.

Distribution of degrees: The majors with the highest enrollments are business administration, biology, and physical education; elementary education, music, and English have the lowest.

Academic regulations: Minimum 2.0 GPA required for graduation.

Special: Minors offered in several majors and in art. Double majors. Preprofessional programs in law, medicine, and dentistry. Teacher certification in early childhood, elementary, and secondary education. Certification in specific subject areas.

Honors: Honors program. Honor societies.

Academic Assistance: Remedial reading, writing, math, and study skills. Nonremedial tutoring.

STUDENT LIFE. Housing: All freshmen must live on campus. Women's and men's dorms. 62% of students live in college housing.

Services and counseling/handicapped student services: Placement services. Health service. Personal counseling. Career and academic guidance services. Religious counseling. Learning disabled program/services.

Campus organizations: Undergraduate student government. Yearbook. Choir, national music education meeting, Panhellenic Council, home economics club, humanities club, social science club, Little Theatre, The Steers. Four fraternities, no chapter houses; three sororities, no chapter houses. 10% of men join a fraternity. 25% of women join a sorority.

Religious organizations: Students for Christ.

ATHLETICS. Physical education requirements: Four semesters of physical education required.

Intercollegiate competition: 4% of students participate. Baseball (M), basketball (M,W), cheer-leading (W), softball (W), tennis (M,W), track and field (indoor) (M,W), track and field (outdoor) (M,W), volleyball (W). Member of Interregional Athletic Conference, NAIA.

Intramural and club sports: 3% of students participate.

ADMISSIONS. Academic basis for candidate selection (in order of priority): Secondary school record, standardized test scores, class rank, school's recommendation, essay.

Nonacademic basis for candidate selection: Character and personality and particular talent or ability are important. Extracurricular participation is considered.

Requirements: Graduation from secondary school is required; GED is accepted. 16 units and the following program of study are required: 4 units of English, 2 units of math, 2 units of lab science, 2 units of history, 6 units of academic electives. Academic Reinforcement Lab required of applicants with ACT score below 10. SAT I or ACT recommended. Campus visit and interview recommended.

Procedure: Take SAT I or ACT by November of 12th year. Visit college for interview by spring of 12th year. Suggest filing application by March. Application deadline is August 15. Notification of admission on rolling basis. Freshmen accepted for all terms.

Special programs: Admission may be deferred one year. Early entrance/early admission program.

Transfer students: Transfer students accepted for all terms. In fall 1993, 6% of all new students were transfers into all classes. 42 transfer applications were received, 40 were accepted. Application deadline is August 15 for fall; December 15 for spring. Minimum 2.0 GPA recommended. Lowest course grade accepted is "C." At least 30 semester hours must be completed at the college to receive degree.

Admissions contact: Joseph Morale, Ph.D., Director of Enrollment Management. 903 593-8311, extension 236.

FINANCIAL AID. Available aid: Pell grants, SEOG, school scholarships, private scholarships, academic merit scholarships, athletic scholarships, and United Negro College Fund. Perkins Loans (NDSL) and Stafford Loans (GSL). Deferred payment plan.

Financial aid statistics: Average amounts of aid awarded freshmen: Loans, $2,500.

Supporting data/closing dates: FAFSA. FAF: Deadline is May 31. Notification of awards on rolling basis.

Financial aid contact: Dr. W.C. Champion, Financial Aid Officer. 903 593-8311, extensions 216, 219.

STUDENT EMPLOYMENT. Federal Work-Study Program. 50% of full-time undergraduates work on campus during school year. Students may expect to earn an average of $800 during school year. Freshmen are discouraged from working during their first term. Off-campus part-time employment opportunities rated "good."

COMPUTER FACILITIES. 15 Apple/Macintosh microcomputers. Computer facilities are available to all students. **Fees:** $100 computer fee per semester. **Hours:** 24 hours.

GRADUATE CAREER DATA. Highest graduate school enrollments: U of Texas at Tyler.

Texas Southern University

Houston, TX 77004   713 527-7011

Undergraduate profile. 78% Black, 1% Asian-American, 4% Hispanic, 1% Native American, 4% White, 12% Other. 90% are state residents; 12% are transfers. Average age of undergraduates is 27.

Enrollment. Undergraduates: 2,515 men, 4,173 women (full-time). Freshman class: 3,234 applicants, 2,932 accepted, 2,071 enrolled. Graduate enrollment: 817 men, 1,072 women.

Faculty. 376 full-time, 139 part-time; 133 Black, 67 White, 51 Other. 60% of faculty holds doctoral degree. Student/faculty ratio: 20 to 1.

Test score averages/ranges. N/A.

1995-96 Costs. Tuition: $1,249 (state residents), $5,856 (out-of-state). Room & board: $3,250-$3,320. Fees, books, misc. academic expenses (school's estimate): $800.

PROFILE. Texas Southern, founded in 1947, is a public, historically Black university. Programs are offered through the Colleges of Arts and Sciences, Education, and Pharmacy and Health Sciences; the Graduate School; and the Schools of Business, Law, and Technology. Its 118-acre campus is located in Houston.

Accreditation: SACS. Professionally accredited by the American Bar Association, the American Council on Pharmaceutical Education, the National Council for Accreditation of Teacher Education.

Religious orientation: Texas Southern University is nonsectarian; no religious requirements.

Library: Collections totaling 747,785 volumes, 2,398 periodical subscriptions, and 349,969 microform items.

Special facilities/museums: Excellence in education center, hunger and world peace center, minority institute reserve center.

Athletic facilities: Gymnasiums, athletic complex, tennis courts.

STUDENT BODY. Freshman profile: 90% of freshmen come from public schools.

Undergraduate achievement: 9% of entering class graduates. 25% of students who complete a degree program immediately go on to graduate study.

Foreign students: 290 students are from out of the country. Countries represented include Bangladesh, Hong Kong, Iraq, Nigeria, Saudi Arabia, and Thailand; 40 in all.

PROGRAMS OF STUDY. Degrees: B.A.Ed., B.Bus.Admin., B.F.A., B.S.Comp.Sci., B.S.Ed., B.S.Home Econ., B.S.Indust.Tech., B.S.Med.Tech., B.S.Pharm., B.S.Phys.Ther., B.S.Pub.Aff.

Majors: Accounting, Administration of Justice, Art, Bilingual Education, Biology, Business, Business Education, Chemistry, Communications, Computer Science, Dietetics, Early Childhood Education, Economics, Education, English, French, Health Administration, Health Education, History, Home Economics, Housing Management, Industrial Education, Industrial Technology, Journalism, Law, Mathematics, Medical Records Administration, Medical Technology, Music, Music Education, Office Administration, Pharmacy, Physical Education, Physical Therapy, Physics, Political Science, Psychology, Public Affairs, Public Services, Respiratory Therapy, Social Work, Sociology, Spanish, Speech Communication, Speech Disorders, Technology, Telecommunications, Theatre/Cinema, Transportation.

Distribution of degrees: The majors with the highest enrollments are business, pharmacy, and accounting; art and history have the lowest.

Requirements: General education requirement.

Academic regulations: Freshmen must maintain minimum 1.5 GPA; sophomores, 1.75 GPA; juniors, 2.0 GPA; seniors, 2.0 GPA.

Special: Two-year certificate programs offered. Dual degrees. Cooperative education programs. Preprofessional programs in medicine and dentistry. B.A. in several areas of engineering with Rice U. M.P.A./J.D. and M.B.A./J.D. programs. Teacher certification in early childhood, elementary, secondary, and special education.

Honors: Honors program.

Academic Assistance: Remedial reading, writing, math, and study skills.

STUDENT LIFE. Housing: All freshmen and sophomores must live on campus unless living with family. Women's and men's dorms. Athletic housing.

Social atmosphere: Popular gathering spots for students include the student center, nearby fast food restaurants, and a few nearby soul food cafeterias. Spring Festival and Homecoming Week are among the most popular events of the school year.

Services and counseling/handicapped student services: Placement services. Health service. Counseling services for veteran students. Psychological counseling. Academic guidance services. Religious counseling.

Campus organizations: Undergraduate student government. Student newspaper (TSU Herald, published bimonthly). Yearbook. Radio station. Concert choir, marching band, stage band, debating, theatre. Hispanic Student Association. Four fraternities, no chapter houses; four sororities, no chapter houses. 15% of men join a fraternity. 15% of women join a sorority.

Religious organizations: United Ministries.

Foreign student organizations: International Student Organization, Nigerian Student Association.

ATHLETICS. Physical education requirements: Two semesters of physical education required.
Intercollegiate competition: 3% of students participate. Baseball (M), basketball (M,W), cheerleading (M,W), cross-country (M,W), football (M), golf (M,W), tennis (M,W), track (indoor) (M,W), track (outdoor) (M,W), track and field (indoor) (M,W), track and field (outdoor) (M,W), volleyball (W). Member of NCAA Division I, NCAA Division I-AA for football, Southwestern Athletic Conference.
Intramural and club sports: 45% of students participate. Intramural basketball, pool, skating, softball, tennis, touch football, volleyball. Women's club cheerleading.

ADMISSIONS. Academic basis for candidate selection (in order of priority): Secondary school record, class rank, standardized test scores, essay, school's recommendation.
Nonacademic basis for candidate selection: Character and personality are emphasized. Extracurricular participation is important. Particular talent or ability and alumni/ae relationship are considered.
Requirements: Graduation from secondary school is recommended; GED is accepted. 15 units and the following program of study are recommended: 4 units of English, 2 units of math, 2 units of science, 2 units of social studies. Conditional admission possible for applicants not meeting standard requirements. SAT I or ACT is required.
Procedure: Take SAT I or ACT by spring of 12th year. Suggest filing application by June 15. Application deadline is August 9. Notification of admission by August 31. $126 room deposit, refundable until July 15 for fall; December 20 for spring. Freshmen accepted for all terms.
Special programs: Admission may be deferred one year. Credit may be granted through CLEP subject exams. Credit may be granted for military experience. Concurrent enrollment program.
Transfer students: Transfer students accepted for all terms. In fall 1993, 12% of all new students were transfers into all classes. 819 transfer applications were received, 819 were accepted. Application deadline is August 7 for fall; December 18 for spring. Minimum 2.0 GPA recommended. Lowest course grade accepted is "D."
Admissions contact: Audrey Pearsall, M.B.A., Admissions Coordinator. 713 527-7070.

FINANCIAL AID. Available aid: Pell grants, SEOG, state scholarships and grants, school scholarships and grants, private scholarships, academic merit scholarships, athletic scholarships, and aid for undergraduate foreign students. PLUS, Stafford Loans (GSL), state loans, and school loans.
Financial aid statistics: In 1993-94, 80% of all undergraduate aid applicants received aid; 75% of freshman aid applicants. Average amounts of aid awarded freshmen: Scholarships and grants, $4,000; loans, $2,625.
Supporting data/closing dates: FAFSA/FAF: Deadline is May 1. School's own aid application: Priority filing date is May 1. Income tax forms: Priority filing date is May 1. ACT: Priority filing date is May 1. Notification of awards on rolling basis.
Financial aid contact: Yancy Beavers, M.S., Director of Financial Aid. 713 527-7530.

STUDENT EMPLOYMENT. Federal Work-Study Program. Institutional employment. 50% of full-time undergraduates work on campus during school year. Students may expect to earn an average of $2,000 during school year. Off-campus part-time employment opportunities rated "good."

COMPUTER FACILITIES. IBM/IBM-compatible and Apple/Macintosh microcomputers. Computer facilities are available to all students.
Fees: $15 computer fee per semester; included in tuition/fees.
Hours: 8 AM-11 PM; 24-hour access with modem.

GRADUATE CAREER DATA. Graduate school percentages: 10% enter law school. 2% enter medical school. 1% enter dental school. 20% enter graduate business programs. 55% enter graduate arts and sciences programs. 5% enter theological school/seminary. 20% of graduates choose careers in business and industry.

PROMINENT ALUMNI/AE. Barbara Jordan, U.S. congresswoman; G. Mickey Leland and Craig Washington, U.S. congressmen.

Tougaloo College

Tougaloo, MS 39174

601 977-7700

Undergraduate profile. 100% Black. 83% are state residents; 18% are transfers. Average age of undergraduates is 21.

Enrollment. Undergraduates: 336 men, 726 women (full-time). Freshman class: 3,280 applicants, 589 accepted, 235 enrolled.

Faculty. 68 full-time, 7 part-time; 38 Black, 14 White, 16 Other. 51% of faculty holds doctoral degree. Student/faculty ratio: 16 to 1.

Test score averages/ranges. Average ACT scores: 18 composite.

1995-96 Costs. Tuition: $5,180. Room & board: $2,400. Fees, books, misc. academic expenses (school's estimate): $1,000.

PROFILE. Tougaloo, founded in 1869, is a church-affiliated, historically Black college. Its 1,265-acre campus is located in Tougaloo, just outside Jackson.

Accreditation: SACS.

Religious orientation: Tougaloo College is affiliated with the United Church of Christ; no religious requirements.

Library: Collections totaling over 137,000 volumes, 482 periodical subscriptions, 7,335 microform items, and 15 CD-ROMs.

Special facilities/museums: Art collection.

Athletic facilities: Gymnasium.

STUDENT BODY. Freshman profile: 4% of accepted applicants took SAT I; 96% took ACT. 98% of freshmen come from public schools.

Undergraduate achievement: 74% of fall 1993 freshmen returned for fall 1994 term. 21% of entering class graduates. 59% of students who complete a degree program immediately go on to graduate study.

PROGRAMS OF STUDY. Degrees: B.A., B.S.

Majors: Accounting/Economics, Afro-American Studies, Art, Biology, Chemistry, Early Childhood Education, Economics, Elementary Education, English, English/Journalism, Health/Physical Education, History, Humanities, Mathematics, Mathematics/Computer Science, Music, Physics, Political Science, Psychology, Psychology/Mental Health, Sociology.

Distribution of degrees: The majors with the highest enrollments are economics, political science, and English; art and physics have the lowest.

Requirements: General education requirement.

Academic regulations: Minimum 2.0 GPA must be maintained.

Special: Courses offered in business administration, French, geography, geology, library science, philosophy, religion, special education, and speech/drama. Social Science Advancement Institute conducts intercollegiate seminars, discussion groups, preparatory seminars for graduate study, and tutorials. Associate degrees offered. Double majors. Dual degrees. Independent study. Accelerated study. Pass/fail grading option. Internships. Cooperative education programs. Graduate school at which qualified undergraduates may take graduate-level courses. Preprofessional programs in law, medicine, veterinary science, dentistry, theology, engineering, nursing, lab technology, and social work. 3-1 medical technology programs with Meharry Medical Coll and St. Dominic-Jackson Hospital. 3-2 engineering programs with Brown U, Georgia Tech, Howard U, Tuskegee U, U of Mississippi, and U of Wisconsin at Madison. Cross-registration with Millsaps Coll. Washington Semester. Exchange programs with Bowdoin Coll, Brown U, and Meharry Medical Coll. Teacher certification in early childhood, elementary, and secondary education. Study abroad in African countries and France. ROTC at Jackson State U.

Honors: Honors program.

Academic Assistance: Remedial reading, writing, and math. Nonremedial tutoring.

STUDENT LIFE. Housing: Women's and men's dorms. 51% of students live in college housing.

Services and counseling/handicapped student services: Placement services. Health service. Counseling services for older students. Birth control, personal, and psychological counseling. Career and academic guidance services. Religious counseling. Learning disabled services.

Campus organizations: Undergraduate student government. Student newspaper (Harambee, published once/month). Yearbook. Radio station. Black Expo, Black Unity Coordinating Committee, NAACP. Heroines of Jericho, Operation Somebody Cares, Order of Eastern Stars, Panhellenic Council, pre-alumni, PEPS, education clubs, French Club, departmental groups, dance ensemble, cheerleaders. Four fraternities, no chapter houses; four sororities, no chapter houses. 20% of men join a fraternity. 20% of women join a sorority.

Religious organizations: Baptist Student Union, Crusaders for Christ, United Church of Christ.

Foreign student organizations: Foreign Student Club.

ATHLETICS. Physical education requirements: Two semesters of physical education required.

Intercollegiate competition: 1% of students participate. Basketball (M,W), cheerleading (M,W), cross-country (M,W), golf (M), softball (W), track (indoor) (M), track (outdoor) (M). Member of Gulf Coast Conference, NAIA.

Intramural and club sports: 15% of students participate. Intramural basketball, flag football, softball, tennis, track, volleyball.

ADMISSIONS. Academic basis for candidate selection (in order of priority): Secondary school record, school's recommendation, standardized test scores.

Nonacademic basis for candidate selection: Character and personality, extracurricular participation, particular talent or ability, and alumni/ae relationship are considered.

Requirements: Graduation from secondary school is recommended; GED is accepted. 16 units and the following program of study are required: 3 units of English, 2 units of math, 2 units of science, 2 units of foreign language, 2 units of social studies, 1 unit of history, 4 units of academic electives. Minimum 2.0 GPA required. Algebra and geometry recommended. Portfolio required of art program applicants. Audition required of music program applicants. Upward Bound and special services programs for applicants not normally admissible. SAT I or ACT is required. Admissions interview recommended. Off-campus interviews available with admissions and alumni representatives.

Procedure: Take SAT I or ACT by August of 12th year. Notification of admission on rolling basis. $50 room deposit, refundable until two weeks prior to registration. Freshmen accepted for all terms.

Special programs: Admission may be deferred one year. Credit and/or placement may be granted through CEEB Advanced Placement exams for scores of 4 or higher. Credit and/or placement may be granted through CLEP general and subject exams. Placement may be granted through challenge exams. Early entrance/early admission program.

Transfer students: Transfer students accepted for all terms. In fall 1994, 18% of all new students were transfers into all classes. 123 transfer applications were received, 76 were accepted. Minimum 2.0 GPA required. Lowest course grade accepted is "C." Maximum number of transferable credits is 62 semester hours from a two-year school and 94 semester hours from a four-year school. At least 30 semester hours must be completed at the college to receive degree.

Admissions contact: Washington Cole IV, Director of Admissions. 601 977-7770.

FINANCIAL AID. Available aid: Pell grants, SEOG, state scholarships and grants, school scholarships and grants, private scholarships, academic merit scholarships, athletic scholarships, aid for undergraduate foreign students, and United Negro College Fund. Perkins Loans (NDSL), PLUS, and Stafford Loans (GSL). Deferred payment plan.

Financial aid statistics: 41% of aid is not need-based. In 1994-95, 83% of all undergraduate aid applicants received aid. Average amounts of aid awarded freshmen: Scholarships and grants, $3,301; loans, $1,800.

Supporting data/closing dates: FAFSA: Priority filing date is April 15. School's own aid application: Priority filing date is April 15. Notification of awards on rolling basis.

Financial aid contact: Janis H. Evans, Director of Financial Aid. 601 977-7769.

STUDENT EMPLOYMENT. Federal Work-Study Program. Institutional employment. 10% of full-time undergraduates work on campus during school year. Students may expect to earn an average of $1,050 during school year. Freshmen are discouraged from working during their first term. Off-campus part-time employment opportunities rated "fair."

COMPUTER FACILITIES. IBM/IBM-compatible and Apple/Macintosh microcomputers. Students may access IBM minicomputer/mainframe systems. Computer facilities are available to all students.

Fees: Computer fee is included in tuition/fees.

Hours: 8 AM-midn.

Tuskegee University

Tuskegee, AL 36088

(800) 622-6531

205 727-8011

Undergraduate profile. 95% Black, .4% Asian-American, 2.1% Hispanic, .1% Native American, 1.8% White, .6% Other. 25% are state residents. Average age of undergraduates is 20.

Enrollment. Undergraduates: 1,411 men, 1,579 women (full-time). Freshman class: 2,867 applicants, 1,995 accepted, 713 enrolled. Graduate enrollment: 103 men, 92 women.

Faculty. 262 full-time, 13 part-time; 168 Black, 56 White, 42 Other. 68% of faculty holds doctoral degree. Student/faculty ratio: 13 to 1.

Test score averages/ranges. Average SAT I scores: 355 verbal, 450 math.

1995-96 Costs. Tuition: $7,424. Room & board: $3,750.

PROFILE. Tuskegee, founded in 1881, is a private, comprehensive university. Programs are offered through the College of Arts and Sciences and the Schools of Agriculture and Home Economics, Business, Education, Engineering and Architecture, Nursing and Allied Health, and Veterinary Medicine. Its 5,000-acre campus, located in Tuskegee, has been designated a National Historic Landmark.

Accreditation: SACS. Professionally accredited by the Accreditation Board for Engineering and Technology, Inc., the American Dietetic Association, the Council on Education American Veterinary Medical Association, the Council on Social Work Education, the National Architecture Accrediting Board, the National League for Nursing.

Religious orientation: Tuskegee University is nonsectarian; no religious requirements.

Library: Collections totaling 293,656 volumes, 1,092 periodical subscriptions, and 131,412 microform items.

Special facilities/museums: Agricultural and natural history museum, electron microscopes, two nursery schools.

Athletic facilities: Baseball and football fields, tennis courts, gymnasium.

STUDENT BODY. Freshman profile: 83% of freshmen come from public schools.

Undergraduate achievement: 60% of fall 1993 freshmen returned for fall 1994 term. 23% of entering class graduates.

Foreign students: 132 students are from out of the country. Countries represented include the Bahamas, Dominica, Gambia, Guyana, India, and Kenya; 36 in all.

PROGRAMS OF STUDY. Degrees: B.A., B.Arch., B.S.

Majors: Accounting, Aerospace Engineering, Agribusiness Education, Animal/Poultry Sciences, Architecture, Biology, Business Administration, Chemical Engineering, Chemistry, Computer Sciences, Construction Science/Management, Early Childhood Education, Economics, Electrical Engineering, Elementary Education, English, Extension Education, Fashion Merchandising, Finance, Food/Nutritional Science, General Dietetics, General Science, History, Hospitality Management, Language Arts, Management Science, Marketing, Mathematics, Mechanical Engineering, Medical Technology, Mental Retardation, Nursing, Occupational Therapy, Physical Education, Physics, Plant/Soil Science, Political Science, Psychology, Social Work, Sociology.

Distribution of degrees: The majors with the highest enrollments are electrical engineering, biology, and business administration; medical technology and home economics education have the lowest.

Requirements: General education requirement.

Special: Minors offered in banking/finance, foreign languages, general science, math, prelaw, and premedicine. Courses offered in art, geography, music, and social science. Honors program includes seminars, summer readings, sophomore and senior comprehensive exams, and senior thesis. Dual degrees. Pass/fail grading option. Internships. Cooperative education programs. Graduate school at which qualified undergraduates may take graduate-level courses. Preprofessional programs in law, medicine, veterinary science, and dentistry. 3-2 programs in engineering. Member of Alabama Center of Higher Education. Teacher certification in elementary, secondary, and vo-tech education. Certification in specific subject areas. ROTC and AFROTC.

Honors: Honors program. Honor societies.

Academic Assistance: Remedial reading, writing, math, and study skills. Nonremedial tutoring.

STUDENT LIFE. Housing: All freshmen, sophomores, and first-year transfer students must live on campus unless living with family. Women's and men's dorms. Off-campus privately-owned housing. On-campus married-student housing. 55% of students live in college housing.

Services and counseling/handicapped student services: Placement services. Health service. Day care. Counseling services for military and veteran students. Birth control and personal counseling. Career and academic guidance services.

Campus organizations: Undergraduate student government. Student newspaper (Campus Digest, published once/month). Yearbook. Chapel orchestra, choir, men's and women's glee clubs, marching and concert bands, Little Theatre, professional and special-interest groups. Four fraternities, no chapter houses; four sororities, no chapter houses. 6% of men join a fraternity. 5% of women join a sorority.

ATHLETICS. Physical education requirements: Two semesters of physical education required.

Intercollegiate competition: 5% of students participate. Baseball (M), basketball (M,W), cross-country (M,W), football (M), tennis (M,W), track and field (outdoor) (M,W), volleyball (W). Member of NCAA Division II, Southern Intercollegiate Athletic Conference.

Intramural and club sports: 10% of students participate. Intramural basketball, flag football, slow-pitch softball, volleyball.

ADMISSIONS. Academic basis for candidate selection (in order of priority): Standardized test scores, secondary school record, class rank, school's recommendation, essay.

Nonacademic basis for candidate selection: Character and personality are emphasized. Extracurricular participation and particular talent or ability are considered.

Requirements: Graduation from secondary school is required; GED is not accepted. 16 units and the following program of study are required: 4 units of English, 3 units of math, 2 units of science, 3 units of social studies, 4 units of electives. Minimum combined SAT I score of 800 and minimum 2.0 GPA required; combined SAT I score of 900 and 2.5 GPA recommended. National League of Nursing exam required of nursing program applicants. Conditional admission possible for applicants not meeting standard requirements. SAT I is required; ACT may be substituted. SAT II recommended.

Procedure: Suggest filing application by March 31. Application deadline is April 15. Notification of admission on rolling basis. $300 nonrefundable room deposit. Freshmen accepted for all terms.

Special programs: Admission may be deferred one year. Placement may be granted through CEEB Advanced Placement exams. Credit and/or placement may be granted through CLEP general and subject exams. Credit and placement may be granted through challenge exams and for military and life experience. Early entrance/early admission program.

Transfer students: Transfer students accepted for all terms. Application deadline is July 15 for fall; November 31 for spring. Minimum 2.0 GPA required. Lowest course grade accepted is "C." Maximum number of transferable credits is 30 semester hours. At least 30 semester hours must be completed at the university to receive degree.

Admissions contact: Vory Billups, Associate Director of Admissions. 205 727-8500.

FINANCIAL AID. Available aid: Pell grants, SEOG, Federal Nursing Student Scholarships, state scholarships and grants, school scholarships and grants, private scholarships and grants, ROTC scholarships, academic merit scholarships, athletic scholarships, and United Negro College Fund. Perkins Loans (NDSL), PLUS, Stafford Loans (GSL), NSL, Health Professions Loans, state loans, and unsubsidized Stafford loans. Knight Tuition Plans, deferred payment plan, and family tuition reduction.

Financial aid statistics: 35% of aid is not need-based. In 1994-95, 93% of all undergraduate aid applicants received aid; 88% of freshman aid applicants. Average amounts of aid awarded freshmen: Scholarships and grants, $3,000.

Pete Spears - 1
334-727-8421

Supporting data/closing dates: FAFSA/FAF: Deadline is March 31. School's own aid application: Deadline is March 31. Notification of awards begins April 1.

Financial aid contact: Barbara Blair, Director of Financial Aid. 205 727-8210, 205 727-8201.

STUDENT EMPLOYMENT. Federal Work-Study Program. 65% of full-time undergraduates work on campus during school year. Students may expect to earn an average of $1,540 during school year. Off-campus part-time employment opportunities rated "good."

COMPUTER FACILITIES. 75 IBM/IBM-compatible microcomputers; 25 are networked. Students may access Digital minicomputer/mainframe systems. Computer facilities are available to all students.

Fees: Computer fee is included in tuition/fees.

Hours: 24 hours.

GRADUATE CAREER DATA. Graduate school percentages: 1% enter law school. 2% enter medical school. 3% enter graduate business programs. 7% enter graduate arts and sciences programs. Highest graduate school enrollments: Indiana U, Tuskegee U, UCLA. 29% of graduates choose careers in business and industry.

PROMINENT ALUMNI/AE. Gen. Daniel James, U.S. Air Force; R.D. Morrison, president emeritus, Alabama A&M U; Lionel Richie, singer-songwriter.

University of Arkansas at Pine Bluff

Pine Bluff, AR 71601-2799   **501 543-8000**

Undergraduate profile. 85.6% Black, .3% Asian-American, .3% Hispanic, 13.8% White. 88% are state residents. Average age of undergraduates is 19.

Enrollment. Undergraduates: 1,211 men, 1,736 women (full-time). Freshman class: 1,109 applicants, 1,095 accepted, 792 enrolled. Graduate enrollment: 15 men, 112 women.

Faculty. 167 full-time, 26 part-time; 116 Black, 29 White, 22 Other. 54% of faculty holds doctoral degree. Student/faculty ratio: 19 to 1.

Test score averages/ranges. Average SAT I scores: 364 verbal, 377 math. Average ACT scores: 16 English, 16 math, 16 composite.

1995-96 Costs. Tuition: $1,608 (state residents), $3,720 (out-of-state). Room & board: $3,000. Fees, books, misc. academic expenses (school's estimate): $675.

PROFILE. U Arkansas at Pine Bluff is a public, multipurpose, land-grant institution. It was founded as a Normal school in 1873, became a four-year college in 1933, and merged with the University of Arkansas in 1972. Its 295-acre campus is located in Pine Bluff, 38 miles south of Little Rock.

Accreditation: NCACS. Professionally accredited by the American Home Economics Association, the National Association of Schools of Music, the National Council for Accreditation of Teacher Education, the National League for Nursing.

Religious orientation: University of Arkansas at Pine Bluff is nonsectarian; no religious requirements.

Library: Collections totaling 113,658 volumes, 810 periodical subscriptions, 96,255 microform items, and 562 government documents.

Special facilities/museums: Fine arts gallery, child care center, 240-acre farm.

Athletic facilities: Swimming pool, racquetball and tennis courts, gymnastic and weight rooms.

STUDENT BODY. Freshman profile: Majority of accepted applicants took ACT.

Undergraduate achievement: 66% of fall 1993 freshmen returned for fall 1994 term.

PROGRAMS OF STUDY. Degrees: B.A., B.S.

Majors: Accounting, Agricultural Economics, Agricultural Education, Agronomy, Animal Science, Art Education, Art Functional, Automotive Technology Management, Biology, Business Administration, Business Education, Chemistry, Child Development, Community Recreation, Computer Science, Criminal Justice, Early Childhood Development, Economics, Educational Media, Elementary Education, English, English Education, Fashion Merchandising, Fisheries Biology,

Food Sciences/Human Nutrition, Health/Physical Education, History, Home Economics Education, Industrial Arts Education, Industrial Technology, Law Enforcement, Mathematics, Mathematics Education, Music, Music Education, Nursing, Physics, Political Science, Pre-Engineering, Psychology, Regulatory Science/Agriculture, Regulatory Science/Environmental Biology, Regulatory Science/Industrial Health/Safety, Science Education, Social Science Education, Social Sciences, Social Welfare, Sociology, Special Education, Speech/Drama, Speech/Dramatic Arts Education, Trade/Industrial Education.

Distribution of degrees: The majors with the highest enrollments are business administration, criminal justice, and accounting; animal science, physics, and English have the lowest.

Requirements: General education requirement.

Academic regulations: Freshmen must maintain minimum 1.65 GPA; sophomores, 1.83 GPA; juniors, 1.96 GPA; seniors, 2.0 GPA.

Special: Associate degrees offered. Double majors. Internships. Preprofessional programs in law, medicine, engineering, medical technology, and nursing. Teacher certification in early childhood, elementary, secondary, special education, and vo-tech education. ROTC.

Honors: Honors program.

Academic Assistance: Remedial reading, writing, math, and study skills. Nonremedial tutoring.

STUDENT LIFE. Housing: Students may live on or off campus. Women's and men's dorms. 27% of students live in college housing.

Services and counseling/handicapped student services: Placement services. Health service. Day care. Counseling services for military, veteran, and older students. Personal and psychological counseling. Career and academic guidance services.

Campus organizations: Undergraduate student government. Student newspaper. Yearbook. Choir, military and marching bands, speech and drama club, Lyceum Program, home town clubs. Four fraternities, no chapter houses; four sororities, no chapter houses. 5% of men join a fraternity. 2% of women join a sorority.

Religious organizations: Several religious groups.

ATHLETICS. Physical education requirements: Two semesters of physical education required.

Intercollegiate competition: 2% of students participate. Basketball (M,W), cheerleading (M,W), cross-country (M,W), football (M), golf (M), track (indoor) (M,W), track (outdoor) (M,W), track and field (indoor) (M,W), track and field (outdoor) (M,W). Member of NAIA.

Intramural and club sports: 40% of students participate. Intramural basketball, football, racquetball, softball, swimming, tennis, track.

ADMISSIONS. Academic basis for candidate selection (in order of priority): Secondary school record, class rank, standardized test scores, school's recommendation.

Nonacademic basis for candidate selection: Character and personality are important. Extracurricular participation and alumni/ae relationship are considered.

Requirements: Graduation from secondary school is required; GED is accepted. The following program of study is required: 4 units of English, 3 units of math, 2 units of lab science, 2 units of foreign language, 1 unit of social studies, 2 units of history, 2 units of electives. Minimum composite ACT score of 19 and minimum "C" grade average required. Conditional admission possible for applicants not meeting standard requirements. ACT is required. Campus visit recommended. Off-campus interviews available with an admissions representative.

Procedure: Take ACT by February of 12th year. Suggest filing application by fall. Application deadline is July 25. Notification of admission on rolling basis. $25 refundable room deposit. Freshmen accepted for all terms.

Special programs: Admission may be deferred. Credit and/or placement may be granted through CLEP general and subject exams. Early entrance/early admission program. Concurrent enrollment program.

Transfer students: Transfer students accepted for all terms. In fall 1994, 496 transfer applications were received, 408 were accepted. Minimum 2.0 GPA recommended. Maximum number of transferable credits is 68 semester hours.

Admissions contact: Kwurly M. Floyd, M.Ed., Registrar. 501 543-8492, 800 264-6585.

FINANCIAL AID. Available aid: Pell grants, SEOG, state scholarships, school scholarships, private scholarships and grants, ROTC scholarships, academic merit scholarships, and athletic scholarships. Perkins Loans (NDSL), PLUS, Stafford Loans (GSL), and school loans. Tuition Plan Inc.
Financial aid statistics: 24% of aid is not need-based. In 1994-95, 89% of all undergraduate aid applicants received aid; 85% of freshman aid applicants. Average amounts of aid awarded freshmen: Loans, $2,000.
Supporting data/closing dates: FAFSA/FAF: Priority filing date is April 15. School's own aid application. Income tax forms: Priority filing date is May 15; accepted on rolling basis. Notification of awards begins in February.
Financial aid contact: Ray Watley, Director of Financial Aid. 501 543-8301, 800 264-6523.
STUDENT EMPLOYMENT. Federal Work-Study Program. Institutional employment. 40% of full-time undergraduates work on campus during school year. Students may expect to earn an average of $600 during school year. Off-campus part-time employment opportunities rated "good."
COMPUTER FACILITIES. 27 IBM/IBM-compatible microcomputers. Students may access Digital minicomputer/mainframe systems. Residence halls may be equipped with stand-alone microcomputers. Computer facilities are available to all students. **Fees:** None. **Hours:** 7:30 AM-10 PM (M-F); 9 AM-5 PM (Sa).

University of Maryland Eastern Shore

Princess Anne, MD 21853   **410 651-2200**

Undergraduate profile. 75% Black, 1% Asian-American, 1% Hispanic, 20% White, 3% Other. 74% are state residents; 15% are transfers. Average age of undergraduates is 22.

Enrollment. Undergraduates: 1,235 men, 1,194 women (full-time). Freshman class: 2,473 applicants, 1,663 accepted, 763 enrolled. Graduate enrollment: 105 men, 129 women.

Faculty. 131 full-time, 57 part-time; 80 Black, 94 White, 14 Other. 57% of faculty holds doctoral degree. Student/faculty ratio: 18 to 1.

Test score averages/ranges. Average SAT I scores: 353 verbal, 391 math.

1995-96 Costs. Tuition: $2,855 (state residents), $7,536 (out-of-state). Room & board: $4,030. Fees, books, misc. academic expenses (school's estimate): $700.

PROFILE. U Maryland Eastern Shore is a public, multipurpose institution. It was founded in 1886, became a state college in 1948, and gained university status in 1970. Programs are offered through the Schools of Agricultural Sciences, Arts and Sciences, and Professional Studies. Its 540-acre campus is located in Princess Anne, 15 miles from Salisbury.
Accreditation: MSACS. Professionally accredited by the American Council for Construction Education.
Religious orientation: University of Maryland Eastern Shore is nonsectarian; no religious requirements.
Library: Collections totaling over 146,200 volumes, 1,396 periodical subscriptions, and 109,728 microform items.
Special facilities/museums: Art museum, performing arts center, college farm, academic center.
Athletic facilities: Gymnasium, swimming pool, tennis courts, track, playing fields, stadium.
STUDENT BODY. Freshman profile: 1% of freshmen who took SAT I scored 700 or over on math; 3% scored 600 or over on math; 5% scored 500 or over on verbal, 14% scored 500 or over on math; 28% scored 400 or over on verbal, 42% scored 400 or over on math; 76% scored 300 or over on verbal, 88% scored 300 or over on math. 95% of accepted applicants took SAT I; 5% took ACT. 90% of freshmen come from public schools.
Undergraduate achievement: 72% of fall 1993 freshmen returned for fall 1994 term. 13% of entering class graduates.
Foreign students: 101 students are from out of the country. Countries represented include Bermuda, Cameroon, Ethiopia, Jamaica, Liberia, and Trinidad; 41 in all.
PROGRAMS OF STUDY. Degrees: B.A., B.Gen.Studies, B.S.

Majors: Accounting, Agribusiness, Agricultural Education, Agriculture, Agriculture Education, Airway Science, Art Education, Biology, Biology Education, Business Administration, Business Education, Chemistry, Computer Science, Construction Management Technology, Criminal Justice, Electrical/Electronics Engineering, English, Environmental Science, Home Economics, Hotel/Restaurant Management, Industrial Arts Education, Mathematics, Music Education, Physical Education, Rehabilitation Services, Social Sciences, Sociology, Special Education.

Distribution of degrees: The majors with the highest enrollments are business and criminal justice; physical education has the lowest.

Requirements: General education requirement.

Academic regulations: Minimum 2.0 GPA required for graduation.

Special: Minors offered in many majors and in economics, French, German, physics, and political science. Courses offered in geography, philosophy, photography, psychology, Russian, and Spanish. General agriculture students may concentrate in agribusiness, agriscience, animal science, conservation, food and dairy processing, forestry, mechanization, plant science, poultry husbandry, or veterinary science. Department of Experimental Studies offers numerous workshops, institutes, and programs. Center for Interdisciplinary Studies. Honors program with preprofessional tracks in allied health fields, community planning, dentistry, law, medicine, nursing, pharmacy, and social work guarantees admission into corresponding professional school of U of Maryland. Self-designed majors. Double majors. Dual degrees. Independent study. Accelerated study. Pass/fail grading option. Internships. Cooperative education programs. Graduate school at which qualified undergraduates may take graduate-level courses. Preprofessional programs in law, medicine, veterinary science, pharmacy, and dentistry. 2-2 engineering program and numerous one-year transfer programs with U of Maryland at College Park. 3-1 medical technology program. Cross-registration with Salisbury State U. Hotel/Restaurant Management Semester, NASA program, study possible at Wallops Island, Va., other off-campus study opportunities in marine research. Teacher certification in elementary, secondary, and special education. ROTC at Salisbury State U.

Honors: Honors program.

Academic Assistance: Remedial reading, writing, math, and study skills. Nonremedial tutoring.

STUDENT LIFE. Housing: Students may live on or off campus. Coed, women's, and men's dorms. School-owned/operated apartments. Hospitality House for hotel majors. 54% of students live in college housing.

Services and counseling/handicapped student services: Placement services. Health service. Counseling services for military and veteran students. Birth control, personal, and psychological counseling. Career and academic guidance services. Physically disabled student services. Learning disabled program/services. Notetaking services. Tape recorders. Tutors.

Campus organizations: Undergraduate student government. Student newspaper (Hawk Flyer, published once/quarter). Yearbook. Radio station. Black Awareness Movement, NAACP. Drama club, music and athletic groups, Future Agriculturalists of America, Veteran's Tutorial Program, departmental and service groups, special-interest groups. Five fraternities, no chapter houses; four sororities, no chapter houses. 20% of men join a fraternity. 30% of women join a sorority.

Foreign student organizations: International Student Organization, Caribbean Club.

ATHLETICS. Physical education requirements: Three semesters of physical education required.

Intercollegiate competition: 8% of students participate. Baseball (M), basketball (M,W), cheerleading (M,W), cross-country (M,W), soccer (M), softball (W), tennis (M,W), track (indoor) (M,W), track (outdoor) (M,W), track and field (indoor) (M,W), track and field (outdoor) (M,W), volleyball (W). Member of Mid Eastern Athletic Conference, NCAA Division I.

Intramural and club sports: 12% of students participate. Intramural basketball, flag football, softball, swimming, tennis, volleyball.

ADMISSIONS. Academic basis for candidate selection (in order of priority): Secondary school record, class rank, standardized test scores, school's recommendation, essay.

Nonacademic basis for candidate selection: Particular talent or ability is emphasized. Character and personality, extracurricular participation, and alumni/ae relationship are important.

Requirements: Graduation from secondary school is required; GED is accepted. 20 units and the following program of study are required: 4 units of English, 3 units of math, 2 units of lab science, 2 units of foreign language, 3 units of social studies, 6 units of electives. Minimum 2.5 GPA and combined SAT I score of 750 recommended. In-state applicants who have secondary school diploma and minimum "C" grade average may be admitted on basis of predictive index weighing GPA and SAT I scores. Specific requirements for music and engineering program applicants. Audition required of music program applicants. Summer College Readiness required for applicants not normally admissable. SAT I or ACT is required. Campus visit and interview recommended. Off-campus interviews available with admissions and alumni representatives.

Procedure: Take SAT I or ACT by April of 12th year. Visit college for interview by April 20 of 12th year. Suggest filing application by April. Application deadline is in May. Notification of admission on rolling basis. $25 tuition deposit, refundable until June 1. $100 room deposit, refundable until June 1. Reply is required by May 1. Freshmen accepted for all terms.

Special programs: Admission may be deferred one year. Credit may be granted through CEEB Advanced Placement for scores of 4 or higher. Credit and/or placement may be granted through CLEP general and subject exams. Early decision program. In fall 1993, 20 applied for early decision and 10 were accepted. Deadline for applying for early decision is in April. Early entrance/early admission program. Concurrent enrollment program.

Transfer students: Transfer students accepted for all terms. In fall 1994, 15% of all new students were transfers into all classes. 391 transfer applications were received, 255 were accepted. Application deadline is in April for fall; in December for spring. Minimum 2.0 GPA required. Lowest course grade accepted is "C." Maximum number of transferable credits is 60 semester hours. At least 30 semester hours must be completed at the university to receive degree.

Admissions contact: Rochell Peoples, Ed.D., Assistant Vice President for Enrollment Management. 410 651-6410.

FINANCIAL AID. Available aid: Pell grants, SEOG, state scholarships and grants, school scholarships and grants, private scholarships and grants, academic merit scholarships, and athletic scholarships. Perkins Loans (NDSL), PLUS, Stafford Loans (GSL), and school loans. Tuition Plan Inc. and AMS.

Financial aid statistics: In 1993-94, 85% of all undergraduate aid applicants received aid; 89% of freshman applicants. Average amounts of aid awarded freshmen: Loans, $1,500.

Supporting data/closing dates: FAFSA/FAF: Priority filing date is April 15. Notification of awards begins in April.

Financial aid contact: Dorothy Body, M.A., Director of Financial Aid. 410 651-6172.

STUDENT EMPLOYMENT. Federal Work-Study Program. Institutional employment. 30% of full-time undergraduates work on campus during school year. Students may expect to earn an average of $800 during school year. Freshmen are discouraged from working during their first term. Off-campus part-time employment opportunities rated "fair."

COMPUTER FACILITIES. 80 IBM/IBM-compatible microcomputers. Residence halls may be equipped with modems. Computer facilities are available to all students. **Fees:** None.

University of the District of Columbia
Washington, DC 20008 　　　　　　　　　　　　　　　　　　　　**202 274-5000**

Undergraduate profile. 81% Black, 2% Asian-American, 3% Hispanic, 3% White, 11% Other. 95% are state residents; 10% are transfers. Average age of undergraduates is 29.

Enrollment. Undergraduates: 1,563 men, 1,972 women (full-time). Freshman class: 4,602 applicants, 3,657 accepted, 1,980 enrolled. Graduate enrollment: 250 men, 345 women.

Faculty. 284 full-time, 196 part-time; 157 Black, 80 White, 47 Other. 60% of faculty holds doctoral degree. Student/faculty ratio: 13 to 1.

Test score averages/ranges. N/A.

1995-96 Costs. Tuition: $1,008 (state residents), $4,032 (out-of-state). Housing: None. Fees, books, misc. academic expenses (school's estimate): $645.

PROFILE. The University of the District of Columbia, founded in 1976, is a public university. Programs are offered through the Colleges of Business and Public Management; Education and Human Ecology; Liberal and Fine Arts; Life Sciences; and Physical Science, Engineering, and Technology. Its 21-acre campus is located in Washington, D.C.

Accreditation: MSACS. Professionally accredited by the Accreditation Board for Engineering and Technology, Inc.

Religious orientation: University of the District of Columbia is nonsectarian; no religious requirements.

Library: Collections totaling 522,123 volumes, 1,983 periodical subscriptions, and 605,281 microform items. Records, tapes and CDs.

Special facilities/museums: Theatre, greenhouse.

Athletic facilities: Gymnasium, swimming pool, racquetball and tennis courts, weight room, exercise rooms, athletic field.

STUDENT BODY. Freshman profile: 90% of freshmen come from public schools.

Undergraduate achievement: 25% of fall 1993 freshmen returned for fall 1994 term. 25% of entering class graduates. 10% of students who complete a degree program immediately go on to graduate study.

Foreign students: 2,496 students are from out of the country. Countries represented include Cameroon, Ethiopia, Gambia, Kenya, Nigeria, and Trinidad/Tobago; 133 in all.

PROGRAMS OF STUDY. Degrees: B.A., B.Bus.Admin., B.Mus.Ed., B.Pub.Admin., B.S.

Majors: Accounting, Administration of Justice, Anthropology, Art Education, Biology, Business Education, Business Management, Chemistry, Civil Engineering, Clothing/Textiles, Community/Urban Planning, Computer Information/Systems Science, Computer Science, Construction Engineering, Early Childhood Education, Economics, Electrical Engineering, Electromechanical Systems Engineering Technology, Elementary Education, Emergency Medical Services, English, Environmental Science, Family Living/Child Development, Finance, Fire Science Administration, Food/Nutrition, Food Science, French, General Home Economics, Geography, Geoscience, Health Education, History, Home Economics Education, Leisure Studies, Marketing, Mass Media Arts, Mathematics, Mechanical Engineering, Media Library Technology, Music, Music Education, Office Administration, Ornamental Horticulture, Philosophy, Physical Education, Physics, Political Science, Printing Management, Procurement/Public Contracting, Public Management, Secondary Education, Social Work, Sociology, Spanish, Special Education, Speech/Language Pathology, Studio Art, Theater Arts, Urban Studies, Water Quality.

Distribution of degrees: The majors with the highest enrollments are business and education; social sciences have the lowest.

Requirements: General education requirement.

Academic regulations: Minimum 2.3 GPA required for graduation.

Special: Associate degrees offered. Double majors. Independent study. Internships. Cooperative education programs. Graduate school at which qualified undergraduates may take graduate-level courses. Member of Consortium of Universities of the Washington Metropolitan Area. Teacher certification in early childhood, elementary, and special education. ROTC and AFROTC at Howard U. NROTC at Naval Science Inst.

Honors: Honors program.

Academic Assistance: Remedial reading and math.

STUDENT LIFE. Housing: Commuter campus; no student housing.

Services and counseling/handicapped student services: Placement services. Health service. Day care. Counseling services for veteran and older students. Career and academic guidance services. Physically disabled student services. Learning disabled services. Tutors. Reader services for the blind.

Campus organizations: Undergraduate student government. Student newspaper (Trilogy, published once/month). Yearbook. Radio station. Arts ensemble, departmental groups, jazz ensemble, marching band, The Voices chorale, music interest group, music senate, political science organization, modern dance group, special-interest organizations. Three fraternities, no chapter houses; three sororities, no chapter houses. 5% of men join a fraternity. 5% of women join a sorority.

ATHLETICS. Physical education requirements: 1-1/2 semesters of physical education required. **Intercollegiate competition:** 5% of students participate. Basketball (M,W), cheerleading (W), cross-country (M,W), soccer (M), tennis (M,W), volleyball (W). Member of Independent, NCAA Division II.

Intramural and club sports: 10% of students participate. Intramural basketball, flag football, racquetball, softball, swimming, table tennis, tennis, weight training. Women's club swimming.

ADMISSIONS. Academic basis for candidate selection (in order of priority): Secondary school record.

Requirements: Graduation from secondary school is required; GED is accepted. No specific distribution of secondary school units required. Open admissions policy for graduates of accredited secondary schools or the equivalent. Portfolio required of art program applicants. Audition required of music program applicants. Conditional admission possible for applicants not meeting standard requirements. Campus visit and interview recommended. No off-campus interviews.

Procedure: Suggest filing application by June 1. Application deadline is August 1. Notification of admission on rolling basis. Freshmen accepted for all terms.

Special programs: Admission may be deferred one year. Placement may be granted through CEEB Advanced Placement exams for scores of 4 or higher. Credit may be granted through CLEP general and subject exams. Early decision program. Early entrance/early admission program. Concurrent enrollment program.

Transfer students: Transfer students accepted for all terms. In fall 1994, 10% of all new students were transfers into all classes. Application deadline is June 14 for fall; November 15 for spring. Minimum 2.0 GPA required. Lowest course grade accepted is "C." At least 60 semester hours must be completed at the university to receive degree.

Admissions contact: Sandra Dolphin, M.A., Director of Admissions and Recruitment. 202 274-5060.

FINANCIAL AID. Available aid: Pell grants, SEOG, state grants, school scholarships and grants, private scholarships, academic merit scholarships, and athletic scholarships. Perkins Loans (NDSL), PLUS, school loans, and private loans. Direct Federal Student Loans. Deferred payment plan.

Financial aid statistics: 7% of aid is not need-based. In 1994-95, 34% of all undergraduate aid applicants received aid; 40% of freshman aid applicants. Average amounts of aid awarded freshmen: Scholarships and grants, $500.

Supporting data/closing dates: FAFSA: Priority filing date is March 15; accepted on rolling basis. FAF. School's own aid application. Notification of awards on rolling basis.

Financial aid contact: Kenneth Howard, M.A., Director of Financial Aid. 202 274-6059.

STUDENT EMPLOYMENT. Federal Work-Study Program. Institutional employment. 1% of full-time undergraduates work on campus during school year. Students may expect to earn an average of $1,000 during school year. Off-campus part-time employment opportunities rated "good."

COMPUTER FACILITIES. 100 IBM/IBM-compatible microcomputers. Students may access Digital, IBM minicomputer/mainframe systems. Client/LAN operating systems include DOS, OS/2. Computer facilities are available to all students.

Fees: None.

Hours: 24 hours.

GRADUATE CAREER DATA. Graduate school percentages: 1% enter law school. 1% enter medical school. 1% enter dental school. 3% enter graduate business programs. 15% of graduates choose careers in business and industry. Companies and businesses that hire graduates: IBM, Kodak, Naval Air Systems Command, Xerox, Washington D.C. and federal governments.

PROMINENT ALUMNI/AE. Maggie Taylor, director of community services, HUD Office of Contracts; Marilyn Thornton, executive director, Arts D.C.; Warren E. Connley, aerospace engineer, Naval Air Systems Command.

University of the Virgin Islands

Charlotte Amalie, VI 00802   **809 776-9200**

Undergraduate profile. 75% Black, 1% Asian-American, 3% Hispanic, 1% Native American, 5% White, 15% Other. Average age of undergraduates is 21.

Enrollment. Undergraduates: 344 men, 864 women (full-time). Freshman class: 711 applicants, 551 accepted, 321 enrolled. Graduate enrollment: 54 men, 215 women.

Faculty. 112 full-time; 151 part-time. 56% of faculty holds doctoral degree. Student/faculty ratio: 12 to 1.

Test score averages/ranges. N/A.

1995-96 Costs. Tuition: $1,816 (state residents), $5,448 (out-of-state). Room & board: $2,425. Fees, books, misc. academic expenses (school's estimate): $1,046.

PROFILE. The University of the Virgin Islands, founded in 1962, is a public institution. Its 175-acre campus is located three miles west of downtown Charlotte Amalie on the island of St. Thomas.

Accreditation: MSACS. Professionally accredited by the National League for Nursing.

Religious orientation: University of the Virgin Islands is nonsectarian; no religious requirements.

Library: Collections totaling 103,131 volumes, 1,020 periodical subscriptions, and 79,069 microform items.

Special facilities/museums: Caribbean and African art collection.

Athletic facilities: Golf course, tennis courts, swimming pool, volleyball and basketball courts, track, softball field.

STUDENT BODY. Freshman profile: 90% of accepted applicants took SAT I. 70% of freshmen come from public schools.

Foreign students: 289 students are from out of the country. Countries represented include Anguilla, Antigua, Dominica, Nevis, and St. Kitts; 10 in all.

PROGRAMS OF STUDY. Degrees: B.A., B.S.

Majors: Accounting, Biology, Business Administration, Caribbean Studies, Chemistry, Chemistry/Physics, Elementary Education, English, Humanities, Marine Biology, Mathematics, Music Education, Nursing, Psychology, Social Sciences, Social Welfare Services, Spanish, Speech Communications/Theatre Arts, Vocational Education.

Distribution of degrees: The majors with the highest enrollments are elementary education, business administration, and accounting; Caribbean studies, humanities, and marine biology have the lowest.

Requirements: General education requirement.

Special: Associate degrees offered. Internships. Graduate school at which qualified undergraduates may take graduate-level courses. Member of National Student Exchange (NSE).

Academic Assistance: Remedial reading, writing, math, and study skills. Nonremedial tutoring.

STUDENT LIFE. Housing: Students may live on or off campus. Women's and men's dorms. 25% of students live in college housing.

Social atmosphere: Favorite student gathering spots include the Student Activities Center and Club Z Greenhouse. Among the groups with the most widespread influence on campus social life are the Black Heritage Club, the Baptist Student Union, the French Club, the Debate Club, the Soccer Club, FBLA, and Phi Beta Lamba. Highlights of the school year include Charter Day, Black History Month, Homecoming, the UVI Carnival Entry, the Miss UVI Queen selection, cultural series, and intramural sporting events in which dorms compete in tennis, basketball, volleyball, and netball. As one UVI student notes: "The social life on campus is quite good. Students often gather outside dorms to 'lime' (hang out). The cultural life is diverse because students attend UVI from most of the Caribbean as well as other countries."

Services and counseling/handicapped student services: Placement services. Health service. Personal counseling. Career and academic guidance services.

Campus organizations: Undergraduate student government. Yearbook. Band, chorus, musical ensemble, Spanish club, photography club, Carnival Committee.

ATHLETICS. Physical education requirements: Four semesters of physical education required. **Intramural and club sports:** Intramural basketball, soccer, volleyball.

ADMISSIONS. Academic basis for candidate selection (in order of priority): Secondary school record, school's recommendation, essay.

Requirements: Graduation from secondary school is required; GED is accepted. 19 units and the following program of study are required: 4 units of English, 2 units of math, 2 units of science, 1 unit of foreign language, 1 unit of social studies, 1 unit of history, 8 units of electives including 6 units of academic electives. Minimum 2.0 GPA required. Provisional admission possible for applicants not meeting standard requirements. SAT I or ACT is required. Campus visit and interview recommended. No off-campus interviews.

Procedure: Take SAT I or ACT by April 15 of 12th year. Visit college for interview by March 15 of 12th year. Suggest filing application by February 1. Application deadline is April 15. Notification of admission on rolling basis. $50 room deposit, refundable until three weeks prior to start of semester. Freshmen accepted for all terms.

Special programs: Admission may be deferred one year. Credit and/or placement may be granted through CEEB Advanced Placement exams for scores of 3 or higher. Credit may be granted through CLEP subject exams. Credit may be granted through ACT PEP exams. Early entrance/early admission program. Concurrent enrollment program.

Transfer students: Transfer students accepted for all terms. In fall 1993, 188 transfer applications were received, 138 were accepted. Minimum 2.0 GPA required. Lowest course grade accepted is "C." Maximum number of transferable credits is 90 semester hours. At least 30 semester hours must be completed at the university to receive degree.

Admissions contact: Judith W. Edwin, Ed.D., Director of Admissions. 809 776-9200, extension 1247.

FINANCIAL AID. Available aid: Pell grants, SEOG, state scholarships and grants, school scholarships and grants, private scholarships, and academic merit scholarships. Perkins Loans (NDSL), Stafford Loans (GSL), state loans, and school loans. Short-term loans.

Supporting data/closing dates: FAFSA. FAF: Deadline is March 15.

Financial aid contact: Lynn McConnell, Ed.D., Director of Financial Aid. 809 776-9200, extension 1261.

STUDENT EMPLOYMENT. Federal Work-Study Program. Institutional employment. 18% of full-time undergraduates work on campus during school year. Students may expect to earn an average of $1,300 during school year. Off-campus part-time employment opportunities rated "fair."

COMPUTER FACILITIES. 100 IBM/IBM-compatible and Apple/Macintosh microcomputers. Computer facilities are available to all students.

Fees: $20 computer fee per semester.

Hours: 8 AM-9:45 PM (M-Th); 8 AM-6 PM (F-Su).

Virginia State University

Petersburg, VA 23806-2096   804 524-5000

Undergraduate profile. 94% Black, 4% White, 2% Other. 62% are state residents; 13% are transfers.

Enrollment. Undergraduates: 1,296 men, 1,682 women (full-time). Freshman class: 2,881 applicants, 2,626 accepted, 818 enrolled. Graduate enrollment: 210 men, 480 women.

Faculty. 168 full-time, 49 part-time; 10 Black, 51 White, 16 Other. 60% of faculty holds doctoral degree. Student/faculty ratio: 24 to 1.

Test score averages/ranges. Average SAT I scores: 680 combined.

1995-96 Costs. Tuition: $1,951 (state residents), $5,960 (out-of-state). Room & board: $4,845. Fees, books, misc. academic expenses (school's estimate): $1,805.

PROFILE. Virginia State, founded in 1882, is a public, comprehensive, historically Black university. Programs are offered through the Schools of Agriculture, Business Administration, Education, Humanities and Social Sciences, and Natural Sciences. Its 246-acre campus is located in Petersburg, 25 miles south of Richmond.

Accreditation: SACS.

Religious orientation: Virginia State University is nonsectarian; no religious requirements.

Library: Collections totaling 261,030 volumes, 1,147 periodical subscriptions, 599,627 microform items, and 79,027 audiovisual items.

Athletic facilities: Gymnasium, stadium, swimming pool, weight and wrestling rooms, tennis courts, baseball and softball fields.

STUDENT BODY. Freshman profile: 2% of freshmen who took SAT I scored 500 or over on verbal, 5% scored 500 or over on math; 17% scored 400 or over on verbal, 28% scored 400 or over on math; 71% scored 300 or over on verbal, 83% scored 300 or over on math. Majority of accepted applicants took SAT I.

Undergraduate achievement: 69% of fall 1993 freshmen returned for fall 1994 term. 24% of entering class graduates.

Foreign students: 10 students are from out of the country. Countries represented include Bermuda, China, Ghana, Indonesia, Korea, and Kuwait.

PROGRAMS OF STUDY. Degrees: B.A., B.A.Soc.Work, B.F.A., B.Info.Sys., B.Mus., B.S.

Majors: Accounting, Administrative Systems Management, Agriculture/Agricultural Science, Art/Commercial Art/Design, Biology, Chemistry, Economics/Finance, Engineering Technology, English/English Education, Geology, Health/Physical Education, History/History Education, Home Economics/Business, Hotel/Restaurant/Institutional Management, Industrial/Technology Education, Information Systems/Decision Sciences, Interdisciplinary Studies, International Studies, Management, Marketing, Mathematics, Music, Physics, Political Science, Psychology, Public Administration, Social Work, Sociology.

Distribution of degrees: The majors with the highest enrollments are sociology, management, and accounting; geology, chemistry, and physics have the lowest.

Requirements: General education requirement.

Academic regulations: Minimum 2.0 GPA must be maintained.

Special: Courses offered in drama, geography, journalism, non-Western studies, and speech. Double majors. Dual degrees. Internships. Preprofessional programs in law, medicine, pharmacy, dentistry, theology, allied health fields, business, nursing, and physical therapy. 3-2 math/engineering program with Old Dominion U. Member of National Student Exchange Program (NSEP). Teacher certification in early childhood, elementary, secondary, and special education. Study abroad in Puerto Rico and the Virgin Islands. ROTC.

Honors: Phi Beta Kappa. Honors program.

STUDENT LIFE. Housing: Women's and men's dorms. 33% of students live in college housing.

Social atmosphere: On campus, students frequent Foster Hall and Jones Dining Hall. Sororities and fraternities, Big Brothers/Big Sisters, New Generations Ministries, and the Trojan Cheerleaders are influential on student life. The CIAA basketball tournament and Homecoming are highlights of the school year.

Services and counseling/handicapped student services: Placement services. Health service. Counseling services for military and veteran students. Personal counseling. Career and academic guidance services. Religious counseling. Learning disabled services.

Campus organizations: Undergraduate student government. Student newspaper (Virginia Statesman, published once/two weeks). Yearbook. Radio station. Choir, dance band, concert and marching bands, ROTC band, orchestra, debating, drama club, Theatre Guild, Orchesis Dance Group, academic, service, and special-interest groups, 65 organizations in all. Four fraternities, no chapter houses; four sororities, no chapter houses. 9% of men join a fraternity. 10% of women join a sorority.

Religious organizations: Baptist Student Union, Interfaith Council, Muslim Students Association, New Generation Campus Ministries.

Foreign student organizations: International Student Association, Caribbean Student Association.

ATHLETICS. Physical education requirements: Four semester hours of physical education required.

Intercollegiate competition: 15% of students participate. Baseball (M), basketball (M,W), cheerleading (W), cross-country (M,W), football (M), tennis (M), track and field (indoor) (M,W), track and field (outdoor) (M,W). Member of Central Intercollegiate Athletic Association, NCAA Division II.

Intramural and club sports: 10% of students participate. Intramural basketball, flag football, softball, volleyball.

ADMISSIONS. Academic basis for candidate selection (in order of priority): Secondary school record, standardized test scores, class rank, school's recommendation, essay.

Nonacademic basis for candidate selection: Character and personality and particular talent or ability are important. Extracurricular participation and alumni/ae relationship are considered.

Requirements: Graduation from secondary school is required; GED is accepted. 12 units and the following program of study are required: 4 units of English, 2 units of math, 2 units of science, 2 units of foreign language, 2 units of social studies. 4 units of electives recommended. Minimum 2.0 GPA recommended. Qualifying exams required of music program applicants. Conditional admission possible for applicants not meeting standard requirements. SAT I is required; ACT may be substituted. Campus visit and interview recommended. Off-campus interviews available with admissions and alumni representatives.

Procedure: Take SAT I or ACT by November of 12th year. Visit college for interview by April of 12th year. Suggest filing application by May 1; no deadline. Notification of admission on rolling basis. $150 refundable room deposit. Freshmen accepted for all terms.

Special programs: Admission may be deferred one semester. Credit may be granted through CEEB Advanced Placement for scores of 3 or higher. Credit and/or placement may be granted through CLEP general and subject exams. Credit may be granted for military and life experience. Concurrent enrollment program.

Transfer students: Transfer students accepted for all terms. In fall 1994, 13% of all new students were transfers into all classes. 405 transfer applications were received, 220 were accepted. Application deadline is May 1 for fall; October 1 for spring. Minimum 2.0 GPA required. Lowest course grade accepted is "C." At least 30 semester hours must be completed at the university to receive degree.

Admissions contact: Gary E. Knight, M.Ed., Director of Admissions. 804 524-5902.

FINANCIAL AID. Available aid: Pell grants, SEOG, state scholarships and grants, school scholarships, private scholarships and grants, ROTC scholarships, academic merit scholarships, and athletic scholarships. Perkins Loans (NDSL), PLUS, and state loans.

Supporting data/closing dates: FAFSA/FAF: Priority filing date is March 30. School's own aid application: Priority filing date is March 30. Income tax forms: Priority filing date is March 30. Notification of awards begins April 1.

Financial aid contact: Henry Debose, Director of Financial Aid. 804 524-5990.

STUDENT EMPLOYMENT. Federal Work-Study Program. Institutional employment. 16% of full-time undergraduates work on campus during school year. Students may expect to earn an average of $1,650 during school year. Freshmen are discouraged from working during their first term. Off-campus part-time employment opportunities rated "good."

COMPUTER FACILITIES. 200 IBM/IBM-compatible and Apple/Macintosh microcomputers; 60 are networked. Students may access IBM minicomputer/mainframe systems. Client/LAN operating systems include Novell. Computer facilities are available to all students.
Fees: None.
Hours: 8 AM-midn. (M-F); 8 AM-5 PM (Sa, Su).

GRADUATE CAREER DATA. Companies and businesses that hire graduates: AT&T, Chase Manhattan Bank, Sears, Wal-Mart, K-Mart.

PROMINENT ALUMNI/AE. James H. Coleman, Jr., New Jersey state supreme court justice; Camilla Williams, opera singer; Billy Taylor, jazz pianist.

Virginia Union University

Richmond, VA 23220   **804 257-5600**

Undergraduate profile. 99% Black, 1% Other. 54% are state residents; 5% are transfers. Average age of undergraduates is 22.

Enrollment. Undergraduates: 533 men, 751 women (full-time). Freshman class: 1,449 applicants, 1,338 accepted, 459 enrolled. Graduate enrollment: 137 men, 59 women.

Faculty. 87 full-time, 38 part-time; 77 Black, 32 White, 16 Other. 35% of faculty holds doctoral degree. Student/faculty ratio: 15 to 1.

Test score averages/ranges. Average SAT I scores: 320 verbal, 346 math. Range of SAT I scores of middle 50%: 300-399 verbal, 300-399 math.

1995-96 Costs. Tuition: $7,760. Room & board: $3,638. Fees, books, misc. academic expenses (school's estimate): $959.

PROFILE. Virginia Union, founded in 1865, is a church-affiliated, historically Black university. Programs are offered through the College of Liberal Arts and Sciences and the Graduate School of Theology. Its 55-acre campus is located in Richmond.

Accreditation: SACS.

Religious orientation: Virginia Union University is affiliated with the American Baptist Convention; one semester of religion required. Attendance is mandatory for chapel and convocations 20 times/year.

Library: Collections totaling 143,847 volumes, 308 periodical subscriptions, and 62,355 microform items.

Special facilities/museums: Museum of African art, language lab.

STUDENT BODY. Freshman profile: 3% of freshmen who took SAT I scored 500 or over on math; 10% scored 400 or over on verbal, 16% scored 400 or over on math; 67% scored 300 or over on verbal, 76% scored 300 or over on math. 78% of accepted applicants took SAT I.

Undergraduate achievement: 47% of fall 1993 freshmen returned for fall 1994 term. 13% of entering class graduates.

Foreign students: Eight students are from out of the country.

PROGRAMS OF STUDY. Degrees: B.A., B.S., B.Soc.Work.

Majors: Accounting, Biology, Biology Education, Business Administration, Chemistry, Chemistry Education, Criminology, English, English Education, English Language Arts, French, French rEducation, History Education, History/Political Science, Journalism, Mathematics, Mathematics Education, Music, Music Education, Philosophy/Religion, Psychology, Psychology/Human Exceptionalities, Social Work, Sociology, Speech/Drama.

Distribution of degrees: The majors with the highest enrollments are business administration, history/political science, and English language arts; philosophy/religion has the lowest.

Requirements: General education requirement.

Academic regulations: Minimum 2.0 GPA must be maintained.

Special: Minors offered in banking, computer science, criminal justice, gerontology, and pre-law. Dual degrees. Graduate school at which qualified undergraduates may take graduate-level courses. Preprofessional programs in law, medicine, pharmacy, dentistry, chemical research, journalism, library science, medical technology, scientific aid, and theology. 3-3 law program with St. John's U. 3-2 engineering programs with Howard U, U of Iowa, and U of Michigan. Member of Capital Area Training. Teacher certification in early childhood, elementary, middle/junior high, secondary, and special education. Certification in specific subject areas.

Honors: Honors program.

Academic Assistance: Remedial reading and study skills. Nonremedial tutoring.

STUDENT LIFE. Housing: Coed, women's, and men's dorms. 51% of students live in college housing.

Social atmosphere: The Henderson Center is a favorite hang-out. The Student Government Association has widespread influence on campus life. Favorite on-campus events include basketball and football games, homecoming, Gold Bowl, and graduation.

Services and counseling/handicapped student services: Placement services. Health service. Testing service. Counseling services for older students. Birth control, personal, and psychological counseling. Career and academic guidance services.

Campus organizations: Undergraduate student government. Student newspaper (Informer, published once/month). Yearbook. Choir, band, University Players, athletic, departmental, and special-interest groups, 45 organizations in all. Two fraternities, no chapter houses; four sororities, no chapter houses. 40% of men join a fraternity. 40% of women join a sorority.

Religious organizations: Charisma Fellowship.

Foreign student organizations: International Student Organization.

ATHLETICS. Physical education requirements: One semester of physical education required.

Intercollegiate competition: Basketball (M,W), cheerleading (M,W), cross-country (M,W), football (M), golf (M), softball (W), tennis (M), track and field (indoor) (M,W), track and field (outdoor) (M,W), volleyball (W). Member of NCAA Division II.

ADMISSIONS. Academic basis for candidate selection (in order of priority): Secondary school record, standardized test scores, class rank, school's recommendation, essay.

Nonacademic basis for candidate selection: Character and personality, extracurricular participation, and particular talent or ability are important. Alumni/ae relationship is considered.

Requirements: Graduation from secondary school is required; GED is accepted. 16 units and the following program of study are required: 4 units of English, 3 units of math, 2 units of science, 2 units of foreign language, 2 units of social studies, 3 units of electives. Minimum combined SAT I score of 700, rank in top half of secondary school class, and 2.0 GPA required. Audition required of music program applicants. Conditional admission possible for applicants not meeting standard requirements. SAT I is required; ACT may be substituted. Campus visit and interview recommended. Off-campus interviews available with an admissions representative.

Procedure: Take SAT I or ACT by March of 12th year. Suggest filing application by March 1. Application deadline is August 15. Notification of admission on rolling basis. $25 nonrefundable tuition deposit. $110 room deposit, refundable until June 1. Freshmen accepted for all terms.

Special programs: Admission may be deferred one year. Credit and/or placement may be granted through CEEB Advanced Placement exams for scores of 3 or higher. Credit may be granted through CLEP general and subject exams. Placement may be granted through Regents College and ACT PEP exams. Credit and placement may be granted for life experience. Deadline for applying for early decision is January 31. Concurrent enrollment program.

Transfer students: Transfer students accepted for all terms. In fall 1994, 5% of all new students were transfers into all classes. 106 transfer applications were received, 95 were accepted. Application deadline is March 1 for fall; November 1 for spring. Minimum 2.0 GPA required. Lowest course grade accepted is "C." Maximum number of transferable credits is 60 semester hours. At least 30 semester hours must be completed at the university to receive degree.

Admissions contact: Gil M. Powell, Director of Admissions. 804 257-5881.

FINANCIAL AID. Available aid: Pell grants, SEOG, state grants, school scholarships, private scholarships, academic merit scholarships, athletic scholarships, and United Negro College Fund. Perkins Loans (NDSL), PLUS, Stafford Loans (GSL), and unsubsidized Stafford Loans. Deferred payment plan.

Financial aid statistics: 10% of aid is not need-based. In 1994-95, 80% of all undergraduate aid applicants received aid; 100% of freshman aid applicants. Average amounts of aid awarded freshmen: Scholarships and grants, $1,505.

Supporting data/closing dates: FAFSA: Priority filing date is May 15. School's own aid application: Priority filing date is May 15; accepted on rolling basis. State aid form: Deadline is July 31. Notification of awards begins in May.

Financial aid contact: Phenie Golatt, Director of Financial Aid. 804 257-5882.

STUDENT EMPLOYMENT. Federal Work-Study Program. 34% of full-time undergraduates work on campus during school year. Off-campus part-time employment opportunities rated "good."

COMPUTER FACILITIES. 114 IBM/IBM-compatible, Apple/Macintosh, and RISC-/UNIX-based microcomputers; 55 are networked. Students may access Digital minicomputer/mainframe systems. Client/LAN operating systems include Apple/Macintosh, DOS, UNIX/XENIX/AIX, Windows NT, Novell. Computer facilities are available to all students.
Fees: None.
Hours: 9 AM-4:30 PM; some evening hours.
GRADUATE CAREER DATA. 60% of graduates choose careers in business and industry. Companies and businesses that hire graduates: federal government.
PROMINENT ALUMNI/AE. Henry Marsh, senator, Commonwealth of Virginia; L. Douglas Wilder, first elected African-American governor; Dr. Jean Harris Ellis, first African-American graduate of Medical Coll of Virginia; Charles Oakley, professional athlete, New York Knicks.

Voorhees College

Denmark, SC 29042   **803 793-3351**

Undergraduate profile. 98% Black, 1% Hispanic, 1% White. 75% are state residents; 12% are transfers. Average age of undergraduates is 19.
Enrollment. Undergraduates: 298 men, 405 women (full-time). Freshman class: 1,465 applicants, 1,006 accepted, 188 enrolled.
Faculty. 47 full-time, 2 part-time; 27 Black, 10 White, 10 Other. 40% of faculty holds doctoral degree. Student/faculty ratio: 20 to 1.
Test score averages/ranges. Average SAT I scores: 320 verbal, 350 math.
1995-96 Costs. Tuition: $4,600. Room & board: $2,602. Fees, books, misc. academic expenses (school's estimate): $400.

PROFILE. Voorhees, founded in 1897, is a church-affiliated, historically Black college. Its 350-acre campus is located in Denmark, 55 miles south of Columbia.

Accreditation: SACS.
Religious orientation: Voorhees College is affiliated with the Episcopal Church; one semester of religion/theology required. Attendance is mandatory for chapel and convocations 12 times/year.
Library: Collections totaling over 110,000 volumes and 400 periodical subscriptions. Archives. Media center.
Athletic facilities: Gymnasium, baseball and softball fields, tennis courts, track and field.
STUDENT BODY. Freshman profile: 2% of freshmen who took SAT I scored 500 or over on verbal, 2% scored 500 or over on math; 17% scored 400 or over on verbal, 12% scored 400 or over on math; 52% scored 300 or over on verbal, 52% scored 300 or over on math. 70% of accepted applicants took SAT I; 5% took ACT. 95% of freshmen come from public schools.
Undergraduate achievement: 58% of fall 1993 freshmen returned for fall 1994 term. 35% of entering class graduates. 10% of students who complete a degree program immediately go on to graduate study.
Foreign students: Two students are from out of the country. Countries represented include Bangladesh and Liberia; two in all.
PROGRAMS OF STUDY. Degrees: B.A., B.S.
Majors: Accounting, Biology, Business Administration, Computer Science, Criminal Justice, Early Childhood, Elementary Education, English, English Education, Health/Recreation, Mathematics, Mathematics Education, Organizational Management, Physical Education, Political Science, Sociology.
Distribution of degrees: The majors with the highest enrollments are sociology, criminal justice, and business administration; English, mathematics, and political science have the lowest.
Requirements: General education requirement.
Academic regulations: Freshmen must maintain minimum 1.65 GPA; sophomores, 1.75 GPA; juniors, 2.0 GPA; seniors, 2.0 GPA.

Special: Management Institute and Saturday/evening classes available. Internships. Cooperative education programs. Preprofessional programs in law, medicine, engineering, and nursing. 2-3 nursing program with Clemson U. 2-3 engineering programs with Clemson U and U of South Carolina. Teacher certification in early childhood, elementary, and secondary education. Certification in specific subject areas. ROTC at South Carolina State U.

Honors: Honors program. Honor societies.

Academic Assistance: Remedial reading, writing, math, and study skills.

STUDENT LIFE. Housing: Students may live on or off campus. Women's and men's dorms. 79% of students live in college housing.

Services and counseling/handicapped student services: Placement services. Health service. Counseling services for veteran students. Personal and psychological counseling. Career and academic guidance services. Religious counseling. Physically disabled student services. Tape recorders. Tutors.

Campus organizations: Undergraduate student government. Student newspaper (Vista, published twice/semester). Yearbook. Concert choir, Players Guild, residence house councils, Young African Thinkers Club, E.E. Wright Culture Club, White Rose Club, 30 organizations in all. Four fraternities, no chapter houses; four sororities, no chapter houses. 5% of men join a fraternity. 10% of women join a sorority.

Religious organizations: Sunday school.

ATHLETICS. Physical education requirements: Two semesters of physical education required.

Intercollegiate competition: 2% of students participate. Baseball (M), basketball (M,W), cheerleading (M,W), cross-country (M,W), softball (W), track (outdoor) (M,W), track and field (outdoor) (M,W), volleyball (W). Member of EIAC, NAIA.

Intramural and club sports: 1% of students participate. Intramural basketball, flag football, softball, volleyball.

ADMISSIONS. Academic basis for candidate selection (in order of priority): Secondary school record, class rank, school's recommendation, standardized test scores, essay.

Nonacademic basis for candidate selection: Character and personality are emphasized. Particular talent or ability is important. Extracurricular participation is considered.

Requirements: Graduation from secondary school is required; GED is accepted. 20 units and the following program of study are required: 4 units of English, 3 units of math, 2 units of science, 2 units of foreign language, 1 unit of social studies, 1 unit of history, 7 units of electives. Automatic admission for applicants with minimum combined SAT I score of 600 (composite ACT score of 16) and minimum 2.0 GPA. Conditional admission possible for applicants not meeting standard requirements. Excel Program for applicants not normally admissible. SAT I or ACT is recommended. Campus visit and interview recommended. Off-campus interviews available with admissions and alumni representatives.

Procedure: Take SAT I or ACT by May of 12th year. Visit college for interview by May of 12th year. Suggest filing application by April 1. Application deadline is August 1. Notification of admission on rolling basis. Reply is required by August 16. $25 nonrefundable room deposit. Freshmen accepted for all terms.

Special programs: Admission may be deferred one year. Credit may be granted through CEEB Advanced Placement for scores of 3 or higher. Credit and/or placement may be granted through CLEP general and subject exams. Credit may be granted for life experience. Credit and placement may be granted through challenge exams and for military experience.

Transfer students: Transfer students accepted for all terms. In fall 1994, 12% of all new students were transfers into all classes. 65 transfer applications were received, 50 were accepted. Application deadline is rolling for fall; rolling for spring. Minimum 2.0 GPA recommended. Lowest course grade accepted is "C." Maximum number of transferable credits is 100 credits. At least 33 credits must be completed at the college to receive degree.

Admissions contact: Roe Berter W. Kemp, M.Ed., Director of Admissions. 803 793-3351, extension 7301.

FINANCIAL AID. Available aid: Pell grants, SEOG, state grants, school scholarships and grants, private scholarships, ROTC scholarships, academic merit scholarships, and United Negro College Fund. Perkins Loans (NDSL), PLUS, and Stafford Loans (GSL). Deferred payment plan.

Financial aid statistics: 15% of aid is not need-based. In 1994-95, 98% of all undergraduate aid applicants received aid; 98% of freshman applicants. Average amounts of aid awarded freshmen: Scholarships and grants, $2,300; loans, $2,625.

Supporting data/closing dates: FAFSA. FAF: Priority filing date is April 15; accepted on rolling basis. School's own aid application: Priority filing date is April 15; deadline is August 15. State aid form: Priority filing date is January 30; deadline is June 30. Income tax forms: Priority filing date is January 31; deadline is April 15. Notification of awards begins April 30.

Financial aid contact: Lavenia Freeman, M.Ed., Director of Financial Aid. 803 793-3351, extension 7290.

STUDENT EMPLOYMENT. Federal Work-Study Program. 30% of full-time undergraduates work on campus during school year. Students may expect to earn an average of $1,292 during school year. Off-campus part-time employment opportunities rated "fair."

COMPUTER FACILITIES. 130 IBM/IBM-compatible and Apple/Macintosh microcomputers; 60 are networked. Students may access IBM minicomputer/mainframe systems. Residence halls may be equipped with stand-alone microcomputers. Client/LAN operating systems include Apple/Macintosh, DOS, OS/2, Windows NT, Novell. Computer facilities are available to all students.

Fees: None.

Hours: 11 hours/day.

GRADUATE CAREER DATA. Graduate school percentages: 10% enter law school. 10% enter medical school. 5% enter dental school. 30% enter graduate business programs. 40% enter graduate arts and sciences programs. 5% enter theological school/seminary. Highest graduate school enrollments: Clark Atlanta U, Iowa State U, Ohio State U, South Carolina State U, U of Florida, U of South Carolina. 15% of graduates choose careers in business and industry. Companies and businesses that hire graduates: IBM, South Carolina Department of Social Services, South Carolina Department of Corrections, public schools.

PROMINENT ALUMNI/AE. Prezell Robinson, past president, St. Augustine's Coll; Jerry Screen, attorney; Lenny Springs, senior vice president, First Union Bank.

West Virginia State College

Institute, WV 25112-1000   304 766-3000

Undergraduate profile. 13% Black, 1% Asian-American, 86% White. 95% are state residents; 7% are transfers. Average age of undergraduates is 26.

Enrollment. Undergraduates: 2,043 men, 2,476 women (full-time). Freshman class: 2,843 applicants, 2,812 accepted, 1,211 enrolled.

Faculty. 146 full-time, 93 part-time; 24 Black, 109 White, 6 Other. 26% of faculty holds doctoral degree. Student/faculty ratio: 20 to 1.

Test score averages/ranges. Average ACT scores: 18 English, 16 math, 18 composite.

1995-96 Costs. Tuition: $2,050 (state residents), $4,864 (out-of-state). Room: $1,650-$1,700. Board: $1,800. Fees, books, misc. academic expenses (school's estimate): $500.

PROFILE. West Virginia State was founded in 1891 as a Black public college. Programs are offered through the Divisions of Arts and Humanities, Business Administration and Economics, Natural Science and Mathematics, Professional Studies, and Social Sciences. Its 88-acre campus is located in Institute, eight miles from downtown Charleston.

Accreditation: NCACS. Professionally accredited by the Accreditation Board for Engineering and Technology, Inc., the American Medical Association (CAHEA), the Council on Social Work Education, the National Council for Accreditation of Teacher Education.

Religious orientation: West Virginia State College is nonsectarian; no religious requirements.

Library: Collections totaling 10,793 volumes, 631 periodical subscriptions, and 29,409 microform items.

Special facilities/museums: On-campus day-care center, art gallery, ROTC Hall of Fame, Sports Hall of Fame.

Athletic facilities: Football stadium, gymnasium, basketball and tennis courts, baseball and softball fields, bowling, weight room, swimming pool, track.

STUDENT BODY. Freshman profile: 100% of accepted applicants took ACT. 99% of freshmen come from public schools.

Foreign students: 18 students are from out of the country. Countries represented include Iran, Jamaica, Jordan, and Lebanon.

PROGRAMS OF STUDY. Degrees: B.A., B.S.

Majors: Accounting, American Studies, Applied Mathematics, Architectural Industrial Technology, Art, Art Education, Biology, Biology Education, Board of Regents, Building Construction, Business Administration, Business Education, Business Principles Education, Chemistry, Chemistry Education, Communication, Computer Science, Computer Science Application, Corrections, Criminal Justice, Early Childhood Education, Economics, Education, Elementary Education, Elementary Education/Subject Specialization, English, English Education, Finance, General Science Education, Health Physics, History, Management, Marketing, Mathematics, Mathematics Education, Mental Retardation, Music Education, Nuclear Medicine, Physical Education, Political Science, Psychology, Recreation, Recreation Administration, Safety Education, Secondary Education, Secretarial, Social Studies Education, Social Work, Sociology, Therapeutic Recreation, Writing.

Distribution of degrees: The majors with the highest enrollments are business, criminal justice, and education; economics, sociology, and recreation have the lowest.

Requirements: General education requirement.

Academic regulations: Freshmen must maintain minimum 1.9 GPA; sophomores, juniors, seniors, 2.0 GPA.

Special: Minors offered in several majors and in French, music, safety management, security/loss prevention, and Spanish. Associate degrees offered. Double majors. Independent study. Internships. Cooperative education programs. Graduate school at which qualified undergraduates may take graduate-level courses. Preprofessional programs in law, veterinary science, pharmacy, dentistry, optometry, agriculture, engineering, forestry, and nursing. Washington Semester. Teacher certification in early childhood, elementary, secondary, and special education. ROTC.

Honors: Honors program. Honor societies.

Academic Assistance: Remedial reading, writing, and math. Nonremedial tutoring.

STUDENT LIFE. Housing: All unmarried students under age 21 must live on campus unless living near campus with relatives. Women's and men's dorms. School-owned/operated apartments. On-campus married-student housing. 7% of students live in college housing.

Services and counseling/handicapped student services: Placement services. Health service. Day care. Counseling services for military students. Birth control and personal counseling. Academic guidance services. Religious counseling. Physically disabled student services. Learning disabled services. Tutors.

Campus organizations: Undergraduate student government. Student newspaper (Yellow Jacket, published once/week). Literary magazine. Yearbook. TV station. Access Awareness Council, NAACP. College Players, jazz band, choir, departmental groups, College Ambassadors, Women's Group, 44 organizations in all. Six fraternities, no chapter houses; three sororities, no chapter houses. 1% of men join a fraternity. 1% of women join a sorority.

Religious organizations: College Students for Christ, Fellowship of Christian Athletes.

Foreign student organizations: International Student Organization.

ATHLETICS. Physical education requirements: One semester of physical education required.

Intercollegiate competition: 3% of students participate. Baseball (M), basketball (M,W), cheerleading (W), football (M), softball (W), track and field (outdoor) (M,W). Member of NAIA, NCAA Division II.

Intramural and club sports: 13% of students participate. Intramural basketball, bowling, flag football, softball, swimming, tennis, volleyball.

ADMISSIONS. Academic basis for candidate selection (in order of priority): Secondary school record, standardized test scores, class rank, essay, school's recommendation.

Nonacademic basis for candidate selection: Particular talent or ability is emphasized. Character and personality are important. Extracurricular participation and alumni/ae relationship are considered.

Requirements: Graduation from secondary school is required; GED is accepted. 14 units and the following program of study are required: 4 units of English, 2 units of math, 2 units of science, 2 units of foreign language, 3 units of social studies, 1 unit of history. Minimum 2.0 GPA required. Minimum composite ACT score of 17 required of out-of-state applicants. ACT is required; SAT I may be substituted. Campus visit recommended.

Procedure: Take SAT I or ACT by fall of 12th year. Suggest filing application by March 1. Application deadline is August 11. Notification of admission on rolling basis. $50 refundable room deposit. Freshmen accepted for all terms.

Special programs: Admission may be deferred. Credit and/or placement may be granted through CEEB Advanced Placement exams. Credit and/or placement may be granted through CLEP general and subject exams. Early decision program. Early entrance/early admission program. Concurrent enrollment program.

Transfer students: Transfer students accepted for all terms. In fall 1994, 7% of all new students were transfers into all classes. 445 transfer applications were received, 442 were accepted. Application deadline is August 11 for fall; March 1 for spring. Minimum 2.0 GPA required. Lowest course grade accepted is "C." Maximum number of transferable credits is 72 semester hours. At least 30 semester hours must be completed at the college to receive degree.

Admissions contact: Robin L. Green, M.A., Director of Admissions. 304 766-3221.

FINANCIAL AID. Available aid: Pell grants, SEOG, state grants, school scholarships, private scholarships, ROTC scholarships, academic merit scholarships, and athletic scholarships. Perkins Loans (NDSL), PLUS, and Stafford Loans (GSL). Deferred payment plan.

Supporting data/closing dates: FAFSA. FAF: Priority filing date is March 1. School's own aid application: Priority filing date is March 1. Notification of awards on rolling basis.

Financial aid contact: Fred D. Black, Director of Financial Aid. 304 766-3131.

STUDENT EMPLOYMENT. Federal Work-Study Program. Institutional employment. Students may expect to earn an average of $1,300 during school year. Off-campus part-time employment opportunities rated "excellent."

COMPUTER FACILITIES. 400 IBM/IBM-compatible and Apple/Macintosh microcomputers. Residence halls may be equipped with stand-alone microcomputers, networked terminals. Computer facilities are available to all students. **Fees:** None.

PROMINENT ALUMNI/AE. Dr. Perry Julian, arthritis and glaucoma researcher; Dr. Leon Sullivan, founder, Opportunities Industrialization Centers and leader of the anti-apartheid movement in the U.S.; Dr. Vincent Reed, vice president, *Washington Post*; Lou Myers, actor; Dr. L. Eudora Pettigrew, president, SUNY College at Old Westbury.

Wilberforce University

Wilberforce, OH 45384   513 376-2911

Undergraduate profile. 100% Black. 34% are state residents; 7% are transfers. Average age of undergraduates is 19.

Enrollment. Undergraduates: 314 men, 571 women (full-time). Freshman class: 1,223 applicants, 1,021 accepted, 388 enrolled.

Faculty. 51 full-time; 11 part-time. 22% of faculty holds highest degree in specific field. Student/faculty ratio: 14 to 1.

Test score averages/ranges. Average ACT scores: 18 composite.

1995-96 Costs. Tuition: $6,940. Room & board: $3,900. Fees, books, misc. academic expenses (school's estimate): $880.

PROFILE. Wilberforce, founded in 1856, is a church-affiliated, historically Black university. Its 125-acre campus is located in Wilberforce, 18 miles from Dayton.

Accreditation: NCACS.

Religious orientation: Wilberforce University is affiliated with the African Methodist Episcopal Church; no religious requirements.

Library: Collections totaling over 58,000 volumes, 335 periodical subscriptions and 200 microform items.

Special facilities/museums: African Methodist Church archives.

Athletic facilities: Gymnasium, tennis courts; soccer field.

STUDENT BODY. Freshman profile: Majority of accepted applicants took ACT.

Foreign students: Seven students are from out of the country. Countries represented include Malawi and Nigeria; two in all.

PROGRAMS OF STUDY. Degrees: B.A., B.S.

Majors: Accounting, Biology, Business Administration/Management, Business Economics, Chemical Engineering, Chemistry, Civil Engineering, Communications, Comparative Literature, Computer Information Systems, Economics, Engineering, Finance, Fine Art, Health Care Administration, Information Sciences/Systems, Liberal Studies, Marketing, Mathematics, Mechanical Engineering, Music, Political Science, Psychology, Sociology.

Requirements: General education requirement.

Special: Dual degrees. Internships. Cooperative education programs. Preprofessional programs in law and medicine. 3-2 computer science and engineering programs with U of Dayton. 3-2 engineering program with U of Cincinnati. 3-3 prelaw program with St. John's U. Member of Southwestern Ohio Council for Higher Education. Teacher certification in secondary education. Certification in specific subject areas. ROTC at Central State U. AFROTC at Wright State U.

Honors: Honors program.

Academic Assistance: Nonremedial tutoring.

STUDENT LIFE. Housing: All first-year students must live on campus. Women's and men's dorms. School-owned/operated apartments. Off-campus privately-owned housing. On-campus married-student housing. Townhouses. 84% of students live in college housing.

Services and counseling/handicapped student services: Placement services. Health service. Counseling services for minority and veteran students. Personal counseling. Career and academic guidance services.

Campus organizations: Undergraduate student government. Student newspaper (Mirror, published twice/month). Literary magazine. Yearbook. Radio station. Choir, Business League, prealumni groups, Black Male Coalition, Gentlemen of the Court. Four fraternities, no chapter houses; four sororities, no chapter houses. 20% of men join a fraternity. 20% of women join a sorority.

Religious organizations: Alpha Omega, Interfaith Alliance.

ATHLETICS. Physical education requirements: Two semesters of physical education required.

Intercollegiate competition: 10% of students participate. Basketball (M,W), track and field (outdoor) (M). Member of NAIA.

Intramural and club sports: 15% of students participate. Intramural basketball, tennis, volleyball. Men's club basketball, soccer, tennis. Women's club basketball, tennis.

ADMISSIONS. Academic basis for candidate selection (in order of priority): Secondary school record, class rank, standardized test scores, school's recommendation, essay.

Nonacademic basis for candidate selection: Character and personality are emphasized. Alumni/ae relationship is important. Extracurricular participation and particular talent or ability are considered.

Requirements: Graduation from secondary school is required; GED is accepted. 15 units and the following program of study are required: 4 units of English, 2 units of math, 2 units of science including 1 unit of lab, 1 unit of social studies, 1 unit of history, 4 units of academic electives. Rank in top two-thirds of secondary school class, minimum 2.0 GPA, and evidence of community citizenship recommended. ACT is required; SAT I may be substituted. Campus visit and interview recommended. Off-campus interviews available with an admissions representative.

Procedure: Take SAT I or ACT by December of 12th year. Visit college for interview by July 31 of 12th year. Application deadline is June 1. Notification of admission on rolling basis. $25 reservation fee, nonrefundable. $75 refundable room deposit. Freshmen accepted for all terms.

Special programs: Admission may be deferred one semester. Credit and/or placement may be granted through CEEB Advanced Placement exams for scores of 3 or higher. Credit and/or placement may be granted through CLEP general and subject exams. Early decision program. Deadline for applying for early decision is November 15. Early entrance/early admission program. Concurrent enrollment program.

Transfer students: Transfer students accepted for all terms. In fall 1993, 7% of all new students were transfers into all classes. 118 transfer applications were received, 38 were accepted. Application deadline is June 1 for fall; November 15 for spring. Minimum 2.0 GPA required. Lowest course grade accepted is "C." Maximum number of transferable credits is 90 semester hours. At least 36 semester hours must be completed at the university to receive degree.

Admissions contact: Wendell C. Webster, Director of Admissions. 800 367-8568.

FINANCIAL AID. Available aid: Pell grants, SEOG, state grants, school scholarships and grants, private scholarships, ROTC scholarships, academic merit scholarships, and United Negro College Fund. Perkins Loans (NDSL), PLUS, and Stafford Loans (GSL). Tuition Management Systems and deferred payment plan.

Financial aid statistics: In 1993-94, 95% of all undergraduate aid applicants received aid.

Supporting data/closing dates: FAFSA/FAF: Priority filing date is April 30; deadline is June 1. School's own aid application: Priority filing date is April 30; deadline is June 1. State aid form: Priority filing date is April 30; deadline is June 1. Income tax forms: Priority filing date is April 30; deadline is June 1. Notification of awards on rolling basis.

Financial aid contact: Patricia A. Copely, Director of Financial Aid. 800 367-8565.

STUDENT EMPLOYMENT. Federal Work-Study Program. 86% of full-time undergraduates work on campus during school year. Students may expect to earn an average of $2,000 during school year. Off-campus part-time employment opportunities rated "good."

COMPUTER FACILITIES. Students may access NCR minicomputer/mainframe systems, Internet. Client/LAN operating systems include Apple/Macintosh, DOS, UNIX/XENIX/AIX, Microsoft. Computer facilities are available to all students.

Fees: None.

Hours: 8 AM-10 PM (M-F); 10 AM-5 PM (Sa-Su).

Wiley College

Marshall, TX 75670   **903 927-3300**

Undergraduate profile. 99% Black, 1% White. 80% are state residents; 20% are transfers. Average age of undergraduates is 18.

Enrollment. Undergraduates: 250 men, 250 women (full-time). Freshman class: 323 applicants, 310 accepted, 181 enrolled.

Faculty. 27 full-time; 10 part-time. 65% of faculty holds doctoral degree. Student/faculty ratio: 15 to 1.

Test score averages/ranges. Average SAT I scores: 450 verbal, 400 math. Average ACT scores: 12 composite.

1995-96 Costs. Tuition: $3,663. Room: $1,318. Board: $1,554. Fees, books, misc. academic expenses (school's estimate): $496.

PROFILE. Wiley, founded in 1873, is a church-affiliated, historically Black college. Its 63-acre campus is located in Marshall, in northeastern Texas, 38 miles west of Shreveport, La.

Accreditation: SACS.

Religious orientation: Wiley College is affiliated with the United Methodist Church; one semester of religion required. Attendance is mandatory for chapel, assemblies, and convocations each week.

Library: Collections totaling over 80,000 volumes.

STUDENT BODY. Freshman profile: 99% of freshmen come from public schools.

Undergraduate achievement: 75% of entering class graduates. 15% of students who complete a degree program go on to graudate study within five years.

Foreign students: 20 students are from out of the country. Three countries represented in all.

PROGRAMS OF STUDY. Degrees: B.A., B.S.

Majors: Biology, Business/Economics, Business Education, Chemistry, Communications, Computer Science, Elementary Education, English, History, Hotel/Restaurant Management, Mathematics, Music, Nursing Home Administration, Office Administration, Physical Education, Physics, Religion/Philosophy, Social Science, Sociology.

Distribution of degrees: The majors with the highest enrollment are computer science and hotel/restaurant management; mathematics and religion/philosophy have the lowest.

Requirements: General education requirement.

Academic regulations: Minimum 2.0 GPA required for graduation.

Special: Minors offered in most majors and in accounting and business administration. Associate degrees offered. Dual degrees. Independent study. Accelerated study. Pass/fail grading option. Preprofessional programs in law, medicine, dentistry, and nursing. Teacher certification in early childhood, elementary, and secondary education.

Honors: Honors program.

Academic Assistance: Nonremedial tutoring.

STUDENT LIFE. Housing: All students must live on campus unless living within a 50-mile radius. Women's and men's dorms. School-owned/operated apartments. 70% of students live in college housing.

Services and counseling/handicapped student services: Placement services. Health service. Birth control and personal counseling. Career and academic guidance services. Religious counseling.

Campus organizations: Undergraduate student government. Student newspaper (Wildcat Prowler, published twice/year). Yearbook. Radio station. NAACP. Four fraternities, no chapter houses; three sororities, no chapter houses. 50% of men join a fraternity. 60% of women join a sorority.

Religious organizations: Oxford Club, interdenominational group.

ATHLETICS. Physical education requirements: Two semesters of physical education required.

Intercollegiate competition: Member of NCAA Division III.

ADMISSIONS. Academic basis for candidate selection (in order of priority): Class rank, standardized test scores, secondary school record, school's recommendation.

Nonacademic basis for candidate selection: Character and personality are emphasized. Particular talent or ability is considered.

Requirements: Graduation from secondary school is required; GED is accepted. The following program of study is recommended: 3 units of English, 3 units of math, 2 units of science, 1 unit of foreign language, 2 units of social studies, 1 unit of history. Minimum 2.0 GPA required. Audition required of music program applicants. Basic Studies Lab for applicants not normally admissible. SAT I or ACT is required. Admissions interview recommended. Off-campus interviews available with admissions and alumni representatives.

Procedure: Take SAT I or ACT by January 15 of 12th year. Visit college for interview by March 1 of 12th year. Application deadline is March 1. Notification of admission on rolling basis. Reply is required by May 1. $300 refundable tuition deposit. $50 nonrefundable room deposit. Freshmen accepted for all terms.

Special programs: Admission may be deferred. Early decision program. Early entrance/early admission program. Concurrent enrollment program.

Transfer students: Transfer students accepted for all terms. Application deadline is rolling for fall; rolling for spring. Minimum 2.0 GPA required. Lowest course grade accepted is "C." At least 30 semester hours must be completed at the college to receive degree.

STUDENT EMPLOYMENT. Federal Work-Study Program. 80% of full-time undergraduates work on campus during school year. Students may expect to earn an average of $1,200 during school year. Freshmen are discouraged from working during their first term. Off-campus part-time employment opportunities rated "good."

FINANCIAL AID. Available aid: Pell grants, SEOG, state scholarships and grants, school scholarships, private scholarships and grants, academic merit scholarships, and United Negro College Fund. Perkins Loans (NDSL), Stafford Loans (GSL), and private loans. Deferred payment plan.
Supporting data/closing dates: FAFSA. FAF: Accepted on rolling basis. Income tax forms: Accepted on rolling basis. Notification of awards on rolling basis.
Financial aid contact: Rachel Else, Director of Financial Aid. 903 927-3217.
COMPUTER FACILITIES. 50 IBM/IBM-compatible and Apple/Macintosh microcomputers. Computer facilities are available to all students.
Fees: None.
Hours: 8 AM-10 PM.

Winston-Salem State University

Winston-Salem, NC 27110   910 750-2000

Undergraduate profile. 78% Black, .7% Asian-American, .4% Hispanic, .1% Native American, 20.7% White, .1% Other. 93% are state residents; 51% are transfers. Average age of undergraduates is 25.

Enrollment. Freshman class: 1,167 applicants, 738 accepted, 345 enrolled.

Faculty. 152 full-time, 26 part-time; 108 Black, 58 White, 12 Other. 70% of faculty holds doctoral degree. Student/faculty ratio: 15 to 1.

Test score averages/ranges. Average SAT I scores: 375 verbal, 426 math. Average ACT scores: 17 composite.

1995-96 Costs. Tuition: $628 (state residents), $6,360 (out-of-state). Room & board: $3,048. Fees, books, misc. academic expenses (school's estimate): $1,164.

PROFILE. Winston-Salem State, founded in 1892, is a public, comprehensive university. Its 81-acre campus is located in Winston-Salem.

Accreditation: SACS. Professionally accredited by the National Council for Accreditation of Teacher Education, the National League for Nursing.
Religious orientation: Winston-Salem State University is nonsectarian; no religious requirements.
Library: Collections totaling 162,358 volumes, 1,125 periodical subscriptions, and 98,185 microform items.
Special facilities/museums: Art gallery.
Athletic facilities: Gymnasium, swimming pool, basketball and tennis courts, track.
STUDENT BODY. Freshman profile: 1% of freshmen who took SAT I scored 600 or over on verbal, 1% scored 600 or over on math; 3% scored 500 or over on verbal, 8% scored 500 or over on math; 18% scored 400 or over on verbal, 37% scored 400 or over on math; 59% scored 300 or over on verbal, 63% scored 300 or over on math. 95% of accepted applicants took SAT I.
Undergraduate achievement: 70% of fall 1993 freshmen returned for fall 1994 term. 17% of entering class graduates.
Foreign students: Countries represented include African countries, Bangladesh, China, Nigeria, Pakistan, and the West Indies.
PROGRAMS OF STUDY. Degrees: B.A., B.S.
Majors: Accounting, Applied Science, Art, Biology, Business Administration, Chemistry, Commercial Music, Computer/Information Sciences, Economics, Elementary Education, English, History, Information Systems Management, Mass Communication, Mathematics, Medical Technology, Middle Grades Education, Music Education, Nursing, Physical Education, Physical Therapy, Political Science/Government, Psychology, Sociology, Spanish, Special Education, Sports Management, Therapeutic Recreation, Urban Affairs.
Distribution of degrees: The majors with the highest enrollments are business administration, nursing, and accounting; chemistry, urban affairs, and Spanish have the lowest.
Requirements: General education requirement.
Academic regulations: Freshmen must maintain minimum 1.5 GPA; seniors, 2.0 GPA.

Special: Minors offered in some majors and in Black studies, dramatic arts, environmental sciences, French, housing management, Romance languages, sacred music, and social welfare. Certificate program in computer programming. Courses offered in geography, mass communications, philosophy, physics, and religion. Double majors. Dual degrees. Independent study. Internships. Cooperative education programs. Fourth year B.A. or B.S. in Project Strengthen (health-related science programs) allows seniors to spend year in cooperating dental, medical, or graduate school. Member of U of North Carolina Consortium. Teacher certification in early childhood, elementary, secondary, and special education. ROTC.

Honors: Phi Beta Kappa. Honors program.

Academic Assistance: Nonremedial tutoring.

STUDENT LIFE. Housing: Students may live on or off campus. Coed, women's, and men's dorms. 35% of students live in college housing.

Social atmosphere: Favorite student gathering spots include the Hauser Student Union and Gaines Gym. Sororities, the National Broadcasting Society, and the Student Government Association influence campus life. Popular events include the Mr. Ram Pageant , the coronation of Miss Winston-Salem State, Homecoming Week, Greek Week, and football and basketball games. The News Argus reports, "Most social events take place on campus. Winston-Salem Greeks often co-sponsor events with the Greeks at Wake Forest U. We have many diverse cultural programs throughout the year."

Services and counseling/handicapped student services: Placement services. Health service. Counseling services for military and older students. Career and academic guidance services. Physically disabled student services. Tutors.

Campus organizations: Undergraduate student government. Student newspaper (News Argus, published once/month). Yearbook. Radio station. Band, stage band, University Singers, male octet, choir, music fraternity, Drama Guild, charm club, Circle K, Ram Beautification Club, departmental groups, 70 organizations in all. Six fraternities, no chapter houses; eight sororities, no chapter houses. 30% of men join a fraternity. 25% of women join a sorority.

Religious organizations: Several religious groups.

ATHLETICS. Physical education requirements: Four semesters of physical education required.

Intercollegiate competition: Basketball (M,W), cheerleading (M,W), cross-country (M,W), football (M), softball (W), tennis (M,W), track and field (outdoor) (M,W), volleyball (W). Member of CIAA, NCAA Division II.

Intramural and club sports: Intramural basketball, flag football, swimming, volleyball.

ADMISSIONS. Academic basis for candidate selection (in order of priority): Secondary school record, class rank, standardized test scores, school's recommendation, essay.

Nonacademic basis for candidate selection: Character and personality are important. Extracurricular participation, particular talent or ability, and alumni/ae relationship are considered.

Requirements: Graduation from secondary school is required; GED is accepted. The following program of study is required: 4 units of English, 3 units of math, 3 units of science including 1 unit of lab, 2 units of social studies, 12 units of academic electives. 2 units of foreign language recommended. Minimum combined SAT I score of 725, rank in top half of secondary school class, and minimum 2.0 GPA recommended. Algebra I and II, geometry, and 2 units of foreign language required of business, English, history, and science program applicants. Minimum SAT I verbal score of 390, grade 11 reading level, completion of university core curriculum with minimum 2.6 GPA, and application by second semester of sophomore year required of nursing program applicants. Audition required of music program applicants. Supplemental Education Program for applicants not normally admissible. Applicants with academic deficiencies are required to take noncredit remedial courses prior to sophomore year. SAT I is required; ACT may be substituted. Campus visit recommended.

Procedure: Take SAT I or ACT by January of 12th year. Notification of admission on rolling basis. $75 nonrefundable room deposit. Freshmen accepted for all terms.

Special programs: Admission may be deferred one year. Credit and/or placement may be granted through CEEB Advanced Placement exams for scores of 3 or higher. Credit and/or placement may be granted through CLEP general and subject exams. Credit and placement may be granted through challenge exams. Early entrance/early admission program. Concurrent enrollment program.

Transfer students: Transfer students accepted for all terms. In fall 1994, 51% of all new students were transfers into all classes. 832 transfer applications were received, 765 were accepted. Application deadline is rolling for fall; rolling for spring. Minimum 2.0 GPA required. Lowest course grade accepted is "C." Maximum number of transferable credits is 64 semester hours from a two-year school and 96 semester hours from a four-year school. At least 30 semester hours must be completed at the university to receive degree.

Admissions contact: Van Wilson, Director of Admissions. 910 750-2070.

FINANCIAL AID. Available aid: Pell grants, SEOG, Federal Nursing Student Scholarships, state scholarships and grants, school scholarships and grants, private scholarships and grants, ROTC scholarships, academic merit scholarships, and athletic scholarships. Perkins Loans (NDSL), PLUS, Stafford Loans (GSL), state loans, school loans, and private loans. Tuition Plan Inc.

Financial aid statistics: 10% of aid is not need-based. In 1993-94, 89% of all undergraduate aid applicants received aid; 81% of freshman aid applicants. Average amounts of aid awarded freshmen: Scholarships and grants, $500.

Supporting data/closing dates: FAFSA/FAF: Priority filing date is April 15. School's own aid application: Priority filing date is April 15. Notification of awards begins May 15.

Financial aid contact: Theodore Hindsman, Director of Financial Aid. 910 750-3280.

STUDENT EMPLOYMENT. Federal Work-Study Program. Institutional employment. 29% of full-time undergraduates work on campus during school year. Students may expect to earn an average of $600 during school year. Off-campus part-time employment opportunities rated "good."

COMPUTER FACILITIES. 57 IBM/IBM-compatible and Apple/Macintosh microcomputers; all are networked. Students may access Digital minicomputer/mainframe systems, BITNET. Computer facilities are available to all students.

Fees: $20 computer fee per course.

Hours: 8 AM-11 PM (M-Th); 8 AM-5 PM (F-Sa); 1-6 PM (Su).

GRADUATE CAREER DATA. Companies and businesses that hire graduates: Wachovia Bank, IBM.

PROMINENT ALUMNI/AE. Timmy Newsome, professional football player; Earl "The Pearl" Monroe, professional basketball player; Selma Burke, sculptor.

Xavier University of Louisiana

New Orleans, LA 70125 504 486-7411

Undergraduate profile. 95% Black, 2% Asian-American, 2% White, 1% Foreign. 63% are state residents. Average age of undergraduates is 22.

Enrollment. Undergraduates: 889 men, 1,956 women (full-time). Freshman class: 2,518 applicants, 2,160 accepted, 676 enrolled. Graduate enrollment: 56 men, 213 women.

Faculty. 164 full-time, 32 part-time; 51 Black, 95 White, 18 Other. 74% of faculty holds highest degree in specific field. Student/faculty ratio: 15 to 1.

Test score averages/ranges. Average SAT I scores: 433 verbal, 471 math. Average ACT scores: 21 English, 20 math, 21 composite. Range of ACT scores of middle 50%: 19-21 composite.

1995-96 Costs. Tuition: $7,300. Room & board: $4,300. Fees, books, misc. academic expenses (school's estimate): $700.

PROFILE. Xavier, founded in 1925, is a church-affiliated, liberal arts university. Its 29-acre, urban campus is located in New Orleans.

Accreditation: SACS. Professionally accredited by the American Council on Pharmaceutical Education, the National Association of Schools of Music.

Religious orientation: Xavier University of Louisiana is affiliated with the Roman Catholic Church; two semesters of theology required.

Library: Collections totaling over 113,000 volumes, 1,200 periodical subscriptions, and 70,000 microform items.

Athletic facilities: Gymnasium, tennis courts, swimming pool.

STUDENT BODY. Freshman profile: 1% of freshmen who took SAT I scored 600 or over on verbal, 7% scored 600 or over on math; 23% scored 500 or over on verbal, 38% scored 500 or over on math; 59% scored 400 or over on verbal, 76% scored 400 or over on math; 93% scored 300 or over on verbal, 97% scored 300 or over on math. 42% of accepted applicants took SAT I; 82% took ACT. 74% of freshmen come from public schools.

Undergraduate achievement: 82% of fall 1993 freshmen returned for fall 1994 term. 33% of entering class graduates. 37% of students who complete a degree program immediately go on to graduate study.

Foreign students: 80 students are from out of the country. Countries represented include the Bahamas, Ghana, India, Nigeria, South Africa, and Vietnam.

PROGRAMS OF STUDY. Degrees: B.A., B.Mus., B.S.

Majors: Accounting, Art, Art Education, Biochemistry, Biology, Biology Education, Business Administration, Chemistry, Chemistry Education, Computer Information Systems, Computer Science, Dual Major in Literature, Early Childhood Education, Economics, Elementary Education, English, English Education, French, German, Health/Physical Education, History, Mass Communications, Mathematics, Mathematics Education, Microbiology, Music, Music Education, Music Performance, Pharmacy, Philosophy, Physics, Political Science, Psychology, Social Studies Education, Sociology, Spanish, Special Education, Speech Pathology, Speech Pathology Education, Statistics, Theology.

Distribution of degrees: The majors with the highest enrollments are biology/premedicine, psychology, and chemistry/premedicine; languages, philosophy, and art have the lowest.

Requirements: General education requirement.

Academic regulations: Minimum 2.0 GPA must be maintained.

Special: Minors offered in most majors and in analytical research, languages, and public administration. Double majors. Dual degrees. Independent study. Accelerated study. Internships. Cooperative education programs. Graduate school at which qualified undergraduates may take graduate-level courses. Preprofessional programs in law, medicine, veterinary science, pharmacy, dentistry, theology, and optometry. 3-1 medical and dental programs with Louisiana State U Medical Sch and other medical schools. Statistics/biometrics program with Louisiana State U Medical Sch. 3-2 engineering programs with Georgia Tech, Morgan State U, Southern U, Tulane U, U of Detroit, U of Maryland, U of New Orleans, and U of Wisconsin. 3-2 M.B.A. program with Tulane U. 3-3 law program. Member of New Orleans Consortium. Exchange program with St. Michael's Coll and Notre Dame U. Teacher certification in early childhood, elementary, special education, and vo-tech education. Certification in specific subject areas. ROTC, NROTC, and AFROTC at Tulane U.

Honors: Honors program. Honor societies.

Academic Assistance: Remedial reading, writing, math, and study skills. Nonremedial tutoring.

STUDENT LIFE. Housing: Students may live on or off campus. Women's and men's dorms. 28% of students live in college housing.

Services and counseling/handicapped student services: Placement services. Health service. Counseling services for veteran and older students. Birth control, personal, and psychological counseling. Career and academic guidance services. Religious counseling. Learning disabled services.

Campus organizations: Undergraduate student government. Student newspaper (Xavier Herald, published twice/month). Yearbook. TV station. NAACP, African-Americans with Responsibility to Enlighten (AWARE), National Association of Black Accountants, National Organization of Black Chemists, National Society of Black Engineers. University Chorus, jazz and symphonic bands, Big Brothers/Big Sisters, MAX, Panhellenic Council, dormitory councils, 59 organizations in all. Two fraternities, no chapter houses; four sororities, no chapter houses. 5% of men join a fraternity. 20% of women join a sorority.

Religious organizations: Peer Ministers, Campus Ministry, Legion of Mary, Christian Life Community, Retreat Team, Bible study and prayer groups.

Foreign student organizations: International Student Club.

ATHLETICS. Physical education requirements: One semester of physical education required. **Intercollegiate competition:** 6% of students participate. Basketball (M,W), cheerleading (M,W). Member of Gulf Coast Athletic Conference, NAIA.

Intramural and club sports: 20% of students participate. Intramural archery, flag football, pool, softball, table tennis, tennis, track, volleyball. Men's club basketball, flag football. Women's club volleyball.

ADMISSIONS. Academic basis for candidate selection (in order of priority): Secondary school record, standardized test scores, class rank, school's recommendation, essay.

Nonacademic basis for candidate selection: Character and personality are important. Extracurricular participation and particular talent or ability are considered.

Requirements: Graduation from secondary school is required; GED is accepted. 18 units and the following program of study are required: 4 units of English, 2 units of math, 1 unit of lab science, 1 unit of social studies, 10 units of academic electives. Additional units of math, social studies, and foreign language recommended. Minimum composite ACT score of 16 and minimum 2.0 GPA required. Portfolio required of art program applicants. Audition required of music program applicants. Limited admission consideration for applicants not meeting standard requirements. SAT I or ACT is required. Campus visit and interview recommended. No off-campus interviews.

Procedure: Take SAT I or ACT by January of 12th year. Suggest filing application by October. Application deadline is March 1. Notification of admission by April 1. Reply is required by May 1. $100 room deposit, refundable until one month before start of semester. Freshmen accepted for all terms.

Special programs: Admission may be deferred one year. Credit and/or placement may be granted through CEEB Advanced Placement exams for scores of 3 or higher. Credit and/or placement may be granted through CLEP subject exams. Credit and placement may be granted through challenge exams. Early decision program. In fall 1994, 400 applied for early decision and 400 were accepted. Deadline for applying for early decision is March 1. Concurrent enrollment program.

Transfer students: Transfer students accepted for all terms. In fall 1994, 444 transfer applications were received, 256 were accepted. Application deadline is June 15 for fall; December 1 for spring. Minimum 2.0 GPA required. Lowest course grade accepted is "C." Maximum number of transferable credits is 62 semester hours from a two-year school and 98 semester hours from a four-year school. At least 30 semester hours must be completed at the university to receive degree.

Admissions contact: Winston D. Brown, M.A., Director of Admissions. 504 483-7388.

FINANCIAL AID. Available aid: Pell grants, SEOG, state scholarships and grants, school scholarships, private scholarships and grants, ROTC scholarships, academic merit scholarships, athletic scholarships, and United Negro College Fund. Perkins Loans (NDSL), PLUS, Stafford Loans (GSL), Health Professions Loans, state loans, private loans, and unsubsidized Stafford Loans. Deferred payment plan and family tuition reduction.

Financial aid statistics: 41% of aid is not need-based. In 1994-95, 97% of all undergraduate aid applicants received aid; 97% of freshman aid applicants. Average amounts of aid awarded freshmen: Scholarships and grants, $2,251; loans, $3,003.

Supporting data/closing dates: FAFSA/FAF: Priority filing date is May 1; accepted on rolling basis. School's own aid application: Priority filing date is May 1; accepted on rolling basis. Notification of awards begins June 1.

Financial aid contact: Mildred Higgins, Director of Financial Aid. 504 483-3517.

STUDENT EMPLOYMENT. Federal Work-Study Program. Institutional employment. 18% of full-time undergraduates work on campus during school year. Off-campus part-time employment opportunities rated "fair."

COMPUTER FACILITIES. 136 IBM/IBM-compatible and Apple/Macintosh microcomputers; 86 are networked. Students may access AT&T, Hewlett-Packard, IBM, NCR minicomputer/mainframe systems. Client/LAN operating systems include Apple/Macintosh, DOS, UNIX/XENIX/AIX, X-windows, Microsoft, Novell. Computer facilities are available to all students.

Fees: Computer fee is included in tuition/fees.

Hours: 8:30 AM-9:45 PM.

GRADUATE CAREER DATA. Graduate school percentages: 2% enter law school. 18% enter medical school. 1% enter graduate business programs. 16% enter graduate arts and sciences programs. Highest graduate school enrollments: Clark Atlanta U, Creighton U, Howard U, Louisiana State U, Meharry Medical Coll, Texas Southern U, Tulane U, U of Minnesota, U of Mississippi, Northwestern U, Xavier U. Companies and businesses that hire graduates: AT&T, Champion International, Delta Airlines, Footlocker, local schools and banks, government.

PROMINENT ALUMNI/AE. Dr. Claude H. Organ, Jr., chairperson, American Board of Surgery; Ernst Morial, former mayor of New Orleans; Annabell Bernard, soprano; Dr. Milton Gordon, president, California State U at Fullerton; Mary Nunson Runge, first Black president, American Pharmaceutical Association; Gen. Bernard Randolph, U.S. Air Force (retired); John T. Scott, sculptor.

Further Listings

NAFEO* Members Not Fully Listed

Allen University
Columbia, SC 29204
(803) 376-5701
Private (African Methodist Episcopal).
Enrollment: 306.
Tuition (1995-96): $4,380.

Atlanta Metropolitan College
1630 Stewart Avenue, SW
Atlanta, GA 30310
(404) 756-4441
Public (state), junior.
Enrollment: 1,475.

Bishop State Community College
351 North Broad Street
Mobile, AL 36603-5898
(334) 690-6416
Public (state).
Enrollment: 4,640.

Clinton Junior College
1029 Crawford Road
Rock Hill, SC 29730
(803) 327-7402
Private (African Methodist Episcopal Zion), two-year.

Coahoma Community College
3240 Friars Point Road
Clarksdale, MS 38614
(601) 627-2571
Public (district), junior.
Enrollment: 915.

Compton Community College
1111 East Artesia Boulevard
Compton, CA 90221
(310) 637-2660
Public (district), junior.
Enrollment: 5,200.

Concordia College
Selma, AL 36701
(205) 874-5700
Private (Lutheran).
Enrollment: 348.
Tuition (1995-96): $4,360.

Denmark Technical College
P.O. Box 327
Denmark, SC 29042-0327
(803) 793-3301
Public (state), two-year.
Enrollment:780.

Drew University of Medicine & Science
1621 East 120th Street
Los Angeles, CA 90059
(213) 563-4800
Private.
Enrollment: 625.

Fiorello H. LaGuardia Community College
31-10 Thomson Avenue
Long Island City, NY 11101
(718) 482-5050
Public (local/state).
Enrollment: 10,450.

Hinds Community College
P.O. Box 458
Raymond, MS 39154
(601) 857-5261
Public (district), junior.
Enrollment: 7,663.

J.F. Drake State Technical College
3421 Meridian Street, North
Huntsville, AL 35811
(205) 539-8161
Public (state).
Enrollment: 576.

*National Association for Equal Opportunity in Higher Education

Lawson State Community College
3060 Wilson Road, SW
Birmingham, AL 35221
(205) 929-6301
Public (state).
Enrollment: 1,954.

Lewis College of Business
17370 Meyers Road
Detroit, MI 48235
(313) 862-6300
Private, business.
Enrollment: 279.

Mary Holmes College
Highway 50 West, P.O. Box 1257
West Point, MS 39773
(601) 494-6820
Private (United Presbyterian), two-year.
Enrollment: 403.

Meharry Medical College
1005 D.B. Todd Boulevard
Nashville, TN 37208
(615) 327-6000
Private, professional.
Enrollment: 697.

Morehouse School of Medicine
720 Westview Drive, SW
Atlanta, GA 30310-1495
(404) 752-1500
Private, professional.
Enrollment: 153.

Shorter College
604 Locust
North Little Rock, AR 72114
(501) 374-6305
Private (African Methodist Episcopal),
two-year.
Enrollment: 157.

Simmons University Bible College
1811 Dumesnil Street
Louisville, KY 40210
(502) 776-1443
Private (Baptist).
Enrollment: 125.

Southern University in Shreveport
3050 Martin Luther King, Jr. Drive
Shreveport, LA 71107
(318) 674-3300
Public (state), junior.
Enrollment: 1,082.

Trenholm State Technical College
1225 Air Base Boulevard
P.O. Box 9039
Montgomery, AL 36108
Public (state).
Enrollment 2,909.

Wayne County Community College
1001 West Fort Street
Detroit, MI 48226
(313) 496-2500
Public (state), two-year.

Indexes

General Index

Key to the General Index—

SAT I/ACT range: 1 is combined SAT I of 1400 or more or composite ACT of 32 or more. 2 is combined SAT I of between 1300 and 1400 or composite ACT of 30 or 31. 3 is combined SAT I of between 1200 and 1299 or composite ACT of 28 or 29. 4 is combined SAT I of between 1100 and 1199 or composite ACT of 26 or 27. 5 is combined SAT I of between 1000 and 1099 or composite ACT of 24 or 25. 6 is combined SAT I of between 900 and 999 or composite ACT of 22 or 23. 7 is combined SAT I of between 800 and 899 or composite ACT of 20 or 21. 8 is combined SAT I of between 700 and 799 or composite ACT of 18 or 19. 9 is combined SAT I of less than 700 or composite ACT of less than 19.

Tuition: 1 is over $10,000; 2 is between $7,000 and $9,999; 3 is between $4,000 and $6,999; 4 is less than $4,000; 5 is no tuition for state residents; 6 is no tuition for any student.

Enrollment: 1 is over 20,000 students, 2 is between 12,000 and 19,999, 3 is between 4,000 and 11,999, 4 is less than 4,000.

Religious affiliation: AM is African Methodist Episcopal, AD is Adventist, AG is Assemblies of God, B is Baptist, CC is Church of Christ, CM is Christian and Missionary Alliance, CS is Christian Science, CG is Church of God, CN is Church of the Nazarene, C is Congregational, DC is Disciples of Christ, EP is Episcopal, J is Jewish, L is Lutheran, MN is Mennonite, MT is Methodist, MV is Moravian, MM is Mormon, P is Presbyterian, Q is Quaker (Society of Friends), R is Reformed, RC is Roman Catholic, S is Swedenborgian, W is Wesleyan, OC is other Christian, ND is nondenominational.

Phi Beta Kappa: (*) indicates participation in Phi Beta Kappa.

Military training: A is Army ROTC, AF is Air Force ROTC, N is Navy ROTC.

	SAT/ACT	Tuition	Enrollment	Religious affiliation	Military training	Phi Beta Kappa
Alabama						
Alabama A&M U	9	4	4		A	
Alabama St U	9	4	3		A, AF	
Concordia Coll	N/A	3	N/A			
Miles Coll	9	3	4	MT	A, AF	
Oakwood Coll	9	3	4	AD		
Selma U	N/A	3	4	B	A	
Stillman Coll	9	3	4	P	A	
Talladega Coll	9	3	4	C	A	
Tuskegee U	7	2	4		A, AF	
Arkansas						
Arkansas Baptist Coll	N/A	4	4	B		
Philander Smith Coll	N/A	4	4	MT	A	
U of Arkansas, Pine Bluff	9	4	4		A	
Delaware						
Delaware St U	N/A	4	4		A, AF	
District of Columbia						
Howard U	7	2	3		A, AF	*
U of the District of Columbia	N/A	4	4		A, AF, N	
Florida						
Bethune-Cookman Coll	8	3	4	MT	A, AF	

	SAT/ACT	Tuition	Enrollment	Religious affiliation	Military training	Phi Beta Kappa
Edward Waters Coll	N/A	3	4	AM	A	
Florida A&M U	7	4	3		A, AF, N	
Florida Memorial Coll	4	3	4	B		
Georgia						
Albany St Coll	8	4	4		A	
Clark Atlanta U	7	2	4	MT	A, N	
Fort Valley St Coll	N/A	4	N/A		A	
Morehouse Coll	5	2	4		A, AF, N	*
Morris Brown Coll	9	2	4	AM	A, AF, N	
Paine Coll	9	3	4	MT	A	
Savannah St Coll	8	4	4		A, N	
Spelman Coll	5	2	4		A, AF, N	
Illinois						
Chicago St U	9	4	3		A, AF	*
Indiana						
Martin U	N/A	3	4			
Kentucky						
Kentucky St U	8	4	4		A, AF	
Louisiana						
Dillard U	8	2	4	ID	A, AF	
Grambling St U	9	4	3		A, AF	*
Southern U & A&M Coll	9	4	3		A, N	
Southern U at New Orleans	N/A	4	4		A	
Xavier U of Louisiana	7	2	4	RC	A, AF, N	
Maryland						
Bowie St U	8	4	4		A, AF	*
Coppin St Coll	8	3	4		A	
Morgan St U	7	4	3		A	
Sojourner-Douglass Coll	N/A	3	4			
U of Maryland, Eastern Shore	8	4	4		A	
Michigan						
Marygrove Coll	N/A	2	4	RC		

	SAT/ACT	Tuition	Enrollment	Religious affiliation	Military training	Phi Beta Kappa
Mississippi						
Alcorn St U	8	4	4		A	
Jackson St U	9	4	3		A	*
Mississippi Valley St U	9	4	4		A, AF	
Rust Coll	9	3	4	MT		
Tougaloo Coll	8	3	4	C	A	
Missouri						
Harris-Stowe St Coll	N/A	4	4		A, AF	
Lincoln U	8	4	4		A	
New York						
CUNY, Medgar Evers Coll	N/A	4	4			
CUNY, New York City Tech	N/A	4	3		A, AF	
CUNY, York Coll	8	4	3			
North Carolina						
Barber-Scotia Coll	9	3	4	P	A, AF	
Bennett Coll	8	1	4	MT	A, AF	
Elizabeth City St U	8	4	4		A	
Fayetteville St U	7	4	4		AF	
Johnson C. Smith U	8	2	4		A, AF	*
Livingstone Coll	9	2	4	AM	A	
North Carolina A&T St U	7	4	3		A, AF	
North Carolina Central U	8	4	4		A, AF	
St. Augustine's Coll	7	3	4	EP	A, AF	
Shaw U	9	3	4	B	A, AF	
Winston-Salem St U	7	4	N/A		A	*
Ohio						
Central St U	N/A	4	4		A, AF	
Wilberforce U	8	3	4	AM	A, AF	
Oklahoma						
Langston U	9	3	4		A	
Pennsylvania						
Cheyney U of Pennsylvania	N/A	4	4		A	
Lincoln U	N/A	2	4		A, AF	

	SAT/ACT	Tuition	Enrollment	Religious affiliation	Military training	Phi Beta Kappa
South Carolina						
Allen U	N/A	3	N/A		A	
Benedict Coll	N/A	3	4	B	A, AF	
Claflin Coll	8	3	4	MT	A, AF	
Morris Coll	N/A	3	4	B	A	
South Carolina St U	8	4	4		A, AF	
Voorhees Coll	9	3	4	EP	A	
Tennessee						
Fisk U	N/A	3	N/A	ND	A, AF, N	*
Knoxville Coll	N/A	3	4	P	A	
Lane Coll	9	3	4	MT		
LeMoyne-Owen Coll	N/A	3	4	ID	A, AF, N	
Tennessee St	7	4	3		A, AF, N	*
Texas						
Huston-Tillotson Coll	9	3	4	ID		
Jarvis Christian Coll	9	3	4	DC		*
Paul Quinn Coll	N/A	4	4	AM		
Prairie View A&M U	8	4	3		A, N	
Southwestern Christian Coll	N/A	2	4	CC		
Texas Coll	9	3	4	OC		
Texas Southern U	N/A	4	3			
Wiley Coll	8	4	4	MT		
Virgin Islands						
U of the Virgin Islands	N/A	4	4			
Virginia						
Hampton U	6	2	3		A, N	*
Norfolk St U	N/A	4	3		A, N	
St. Paul's Coll	9	3	4	EP	A	
Virginia St U	9	4	4		A	*
Virginia Union U	8	2	4	B		
West Virginia						
Bluefield St Coll	8	4	4			
West Virginia St Coll	8	4	3		A	

Index of Colleges and Universities

BOOKS FOR COLLEGE-BOUND STUDENTS

COLLEGE ENTRANCE

ACT: American College Testing Program
ACT Cram Course
ACT English Workbook
ACT Math Workbook
ACT SuperCourse
AP American History
AP Biology
AP Chemistry
AP English Composition and Literature
AP European History
AP Mathematics
AP United States Government and Politics
Nursing School Entrance Examinations
PCAT: Pharmacy College Admissions Test
Preparation for the CLEP: College-Level Examination Program
Preparation for the SAT and PSAT: Scholastic Assessment Test
SAT Cram Course
SAT Math Workbook
SAT SuperCourse
SAT Verbal Workbook
SAT II Math Level IC • Level IIC
SAT II SuperCourse
SAT II Writing
TOEFL: Test of English as a Foreign Language
TOEFL Grammar Workbook
TOEFL Reading Comprehension and Vocabulary Workbook
TOEFL Skills for Top Scores
TOEFL SuperCourse

COLLEGE GUIDES

College Admissions: A Crash Course for Panicked Parents
College Applications and Essays

College Scholarships and Financial Aid
College Survival
Ivy League Programs at State School Prices
Lovejoy's College Guide
Lovejoy's College Guide for the Learning Disabled
The Performing Arts Major's College Guide
The Right College
The Transfer Student's Guide to Changing Colleges
Women's Colleges

STUDY AIDS

Associated Press Guide to News Writing
Business Letter Writing
Essential English Composition for College-Bound Students
Essential Math for College-Bound Students
Essential Vocabulary for College-Bound Students
How to Interpret Poetry
How to Read and Write about Fiction
How to Solve Algebra Word Problems
How to Write Book Reports
How to Write Poetry
How to Write Research Papers
How to Write Short Stories
How to Write Themes and Essays
How to Write a Thesis
Monarch Notes Quick Course: William Shakespeare–Eight Plays
Monarch Notes Quick Course: Classics of American Literature
1001 Ideas for English Papers
1001 Ideas for Science Projects
Reading Lists for College-Bound Students
10,000 Ideas for Term Papers, Projects, Reports, and Speeches
Triple Your Reading Speed
Webster's New World™ Power Vocabulary
Webster's New World™ Student Writing Handbook
Writing Great Screenplays for Film and TV

AVAILABLE AT BOOKSTORES EVERYWHERE

MACMILLAN • USA